REEDS
MARINA
& WAYPOINT GUIDE

CW00342214

EDITOR: Lucinda Roch

The source directory for all sail & power boat owners

© Nautical Data 2003

Nautical Data Ltd, The Book Barn
Westbourne, Hampshire PO10 8RS
Tel: 01243 389352
Fax: 01243 379136
e-mail: info@nauticaldata.com

Cover photo: Courtesy of
Discovery Yachts

Section 1

The Marinas, Services and Waypoints Section has been fully updated for the 2004 season. These useful pages provide chartlets and facility details of over 170 marinas around the shores of the UK and Ireland, including the Channel Islands.
Add to this the regionally organised suppliers and services section plus a host of waypoints with associated waycharts and you have the perfect complement to any *Reeds Almanac*.

Section 2

The Marine Supplies & Services section lists more than 500 services which all owners will require from time to time.
It provides a quick and easy reference to manufacturers and retailers of equipment, services and supplies both nationally and locally at coastal and other locations around the British Isles, together with emergency services.

Advertisement Sales
Enquiries about advertising space should be addressed to:
**MS Publications, 2nd Floor
Ewer House, 44-46 Crouch Street
Colchester, Essex, CO3 3HH
Tel: +44(0)1206 506223**
Fax: +44 (0)1206 500228

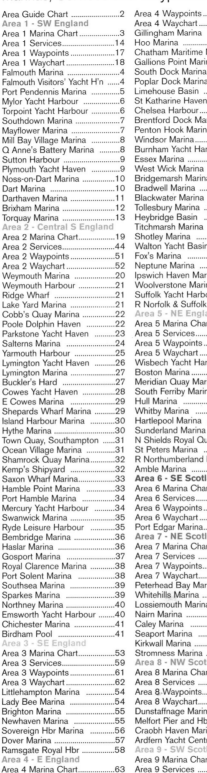

Section 1

Marinas, Services and Waypoints

Section 2

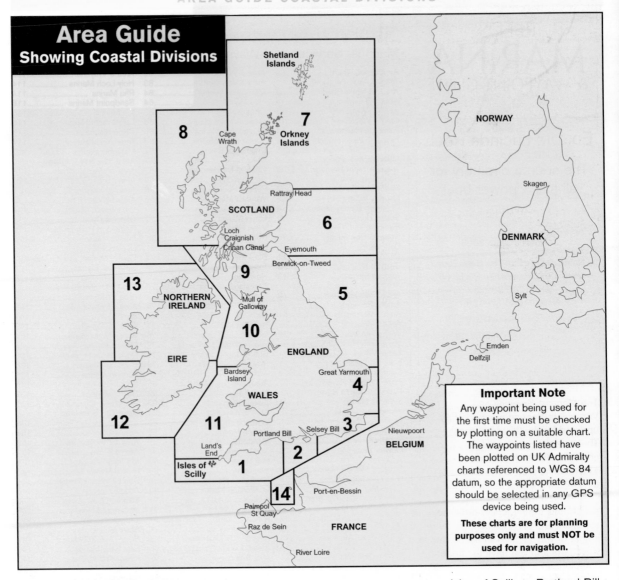

Area Guide
Showing Coastal Divisions

Shetland Islands

7 Orkney Islands

Cape Wrath

8

Rattray Head

SCOTLAND

6

Loch Craignish
Crinan Canal
Eyemouth
Berwick-on-Tweed

13

NORTHERN IRELAND

9

Mull of Galloway

5

10

EIRE

ENGLAND

Bardsey Island

Great Yarmouth

4

WALES

12

11

Portland Bill   Selsey Bill   **3**

Land's End

Nieuwpoort

BELGIUM

Isles of Scilly

1

2

14

Port-en-Bessin

Paimpol St Quay

Raz de Sein

FRANCE

River Loire

NORWAY

Skagen

DENMARK

Sylt

Emden
Delfzijl

Important Note
Any waypoint being used for the first time must be checked by plotting on a suitable chart. The waypoints listed have been plotted on UK Admiralty charts referenced to WGS 84 datum, so the appropriate datum should be selected in any GPS device being used.

These charts are for planning purposes only and must NOT be used for navigation.

Area 1 ......**South West England**	....	Isles of Scilly to Portland Bill
Area 2 ......**Central Southern England**	....	Portland Bill to Selsey Bill
Area 3 ......**South East England**	....	Selsey Bill to North Foreland
Area 4 ......**East England**	....	North Foreland to Great Yarmouth
Area 5 ......**North East England**	....	Great Yarmouth to Berwick-upon-Tweed
Area 6 ......**South East Scotland**	....	Eyemouth to Rattray Head
Area 7 ......**North East Scotland**	....	Rattray Head to Cape Wrath including Orkney & Shetland Is
Area 8 ......**North West Scotland**	....	Cape Wrath to Crinan Canal
Area 9 ......**South West Scotland**	....	Crinan Canal to Mull of Galloway
Area 10 ....**North West England**	....	Isle of Man & N Wales, Mull of Galloway to Bardsey Is
Area 11 ....**South Wales & Bristol Channel**	....	Bardsey Island to Land's End
Area 12 ....**South Ireland**	....	Malahide, south to Liscanor Bay
Area 13 ....**North Ireland**	....	Lambay Island, north to Liscanor Bay
Area 14 ....**Channel Islands**	....	Guernsey, Jersey & Alderney

SOUTH WEST ENGLAND - Isles of Scilly to Portland Bill

Marinecall® WEATHER AT SEA REEDS
WEATHER FORECASTS BY FAX & TELEPHONE

Coastal/Inshore	2-day by Fax	5-day by Phone
Bristol	09061 502 121	09066 526 243
South West	09061 502 120	09066 526 242
Mid Channel	09061 502 119	09066 526 241
Channel Islands	-	09066 526 250
National (3-5 day)	09061 502 109	09066 526 234

Offshore	2-5 day by Fax	2-5 day by Phone
English Channel	09061 502 161	09066 526 251
Southern North Sea	09061 502 162	09066 526 252
Irish Sea	09061 502 163	09066 526 253
Biscay	09061 502 164	09066 526 254

09066 CALLS COST 60P PER MIN. 09061 CALLS COST £1.50 PER MIN.

Key to Marina Plans symbols

🔥	Calor Gas	P	Parking
🛒	Chandler	✗	Pub/Restaurant
♿	Disabled facilities	⚓	Pump out
⚡	Electrical supply		Rigging service
⚡	Electrical repairs		Sail repairs
	Engine repairs	✗	Shipwright
✚	First Aid	🛒	Shop/Supermarket
	Fresh Water		Showers
	Fuel - Diesel		Slipway
	Fuel - Petrol	WC	Toilets
	Hardstanding/boatyard	⊘	Telephone
	Laundry facilities		Trolleys
	Lift-out facilities	Ⓥ	Visitors berths

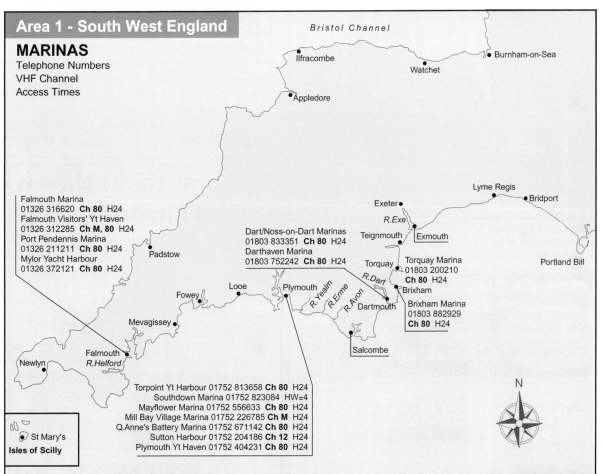

Area 1 - South West England

MARINAS
Telephone Numbers
VHF Channel
Access Times

Bristol Channel

Ilfracombe
Watchet
Burnham-on-Sea
Appledore

Falmouth Marina
01326 316620 **Ch 80** H24
Falmouth Visitors' Yt Haven
01326 312285 **Ch M, 80** H24
Port Pendennis Marina
01326 211211 **Ch 80** H24
Mylor Yacht Harbour
01326 372121 **Ch 80** H24

Padstow

Dart/Noss-on-Dart Marinas
01803 833351 **Ch 80** H24
Darthaven Marina
01803 752242 **Ch 80** H24

Lyme Regis
Bridport

Exeter
R.Exe
Teignmouth
Exmouth

Torquay
R.Dart
Torquay Marina
01803 200210
Ch 80 H24

Portland Bill

Fowey
Looe
Plymouth
R.Yealm
R.Erme
R.Avon
Dartmouth
Brixham
Brixham Marina
01803 882929
Ch 80 H24

Mevagissey

Salcombe

Newlyn
Falmouth
R.Helford

Torpoint Yt Harbour 01752 813658 **Ch 80** H24
Southdown Marina 01752 823084 HW±4
Mayflower Marina 01752 556633 **Ch 80** H24
Mill Bay Village Marina 01752 226785 **Ch M** H24
Q.Anne's Battery Marina 01752 671142 **Ch 80** H24
Sutton Harbour 01752 204186 **Ch 12** H24
Plymouth Yt Haven 01752 404231 **Ch 80** H24

St Mary's
Isles of Scilly

N

WEST COUNTRY CRUISING COMPANION

First published in 1988 as West Country Cruising, Mark Fishwick's definitive sailing guide for the ever attractive coastline of Dorset, Devon, Cornwall and the Isles of Scilly combines a skilful blend of pilotage and cruising information, enhanced with full colour photography, including many additional aerial views, and a wealth of absorbing local history and general interest.

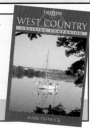

NAUTICAL DATA ORDER HOTLINE: 01243 389898   *Price £19.95*

FALMOUTH MARINA

Falmouth Marina
North Parade, Falmouth, Cornwall, TR11 2TD
Tel: 01326 316620 Fax: 01326 313939
email: falmouth@premiermarinas.com
www.premiermarinas.com

VHF	Ch 80, M
ACCESS	H24

Falmouth Marina lies tucked away in sheltered waters at the southern end of the Fal Estuary. Welcoming to both visiting and residential yachts, its comprehensive facilities include a restaurant, convenience store and hairdresser, while just a 15-minute walk away is Falmouth's town centre where you will find no shortage of shops and eating places. Comprising more than 70 sq miles of navigable water, the Fal Estuary is an intriguing cruising area full of hidden creeks and inlets.

FACILITIES AT A GLANCE

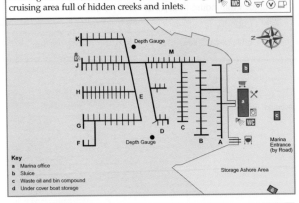

Key
a Marina office
b Sluice
c Waste oil and bin compound
d Under cover boat storage

FALMOUTH VISITORS' YACHT HAVEN

Falmouth Visitors Yacht Haven
44 Arwenack Street
Tel: 01326 312285 Fax: 01326 211352
email: yh@falmouthport.co.uk

VHF	Ch 12
ACCESS	H24

Run by Falmouth Harbour Commissioners (FHC), Falmouth Visitors' Yacht Haven has become increasingly popular since its opening in 1982, enjoying close proximity to the amenities and entertainments of Falmouth town centre. Sheltered by a breakwater, the Haven caters for 100 boats and offers petrol and diesel supplies as well as good shower and laundry facilities.

Falmouth Harbour is considered by some to be the cruising capital of Cornwall and its deep water combined with easily navigable entrance – even in the severest conditions – makes it a favoured destination for visiting yachtsmen.

FACILITIES AT A GLANCE

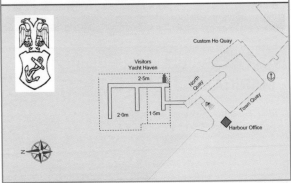

PORT PENDENNIS MARINA

Port Pendennis Marina
Challenger Quay, Falmouth, Cornwall, TR11 3YL
Tel: 01326 211211 Fax: 01326 311116
www.portpendennis.com

VHF | Ch 80
ACCESS | H24

Easily identified by the tower of the National Maritime Museum, Port Pendennis Marina is a convenient arrival or departure point for trans-Atlantic or Mediterranean voyages. Lying adjacent to the town centre, Port Pendennis is divided into an outer marina, with full tidal access, and inner marina, accessible three hours either side of HW. Among its impressive array of marine services is Pendennis Shipyard, one of Britain's most prestigious yacht builders, while other amenities on site include car hire, tennis courts and a yachtsman's lounge, from where you can send faxes or e-mails.

FACILITIES AT A GLANCE

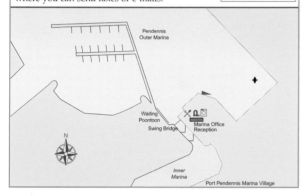

MYLOR YACHT HARBOUR

Mylor Yacht Harbour Marina
Mylor, Falmouth, Cornwall, TR11 5UR
Tel: 01326 372121 Fax: 01326 372120
email: enquiries@mylor.com

VHF Ch 80, M
ACCESS H24

Situated on the western shore of Carrick Roads
in the beautiful Fal Estuary, Mylor Yacht
Harbour has been improved and expanded in
recent years, now comprising two substantial
breakwaters, three inner pontoons and
approximately 250 moorings. With 24 hour
access, good shelter and excellent facilities, it
ranks among the most popular marinas on the
SW Coast of England.

Formerly the Navy's smallest dockyard,
established in 1805, Mylor is today a thriving
yachting centre as well as home to the world's
only remaining sailing oyster fishing fleet. With
Falmouth just 10 mins away, local attractions include
the Eden Project in St Austell and the National
Maritime Museum next to Pendennis Marina.

FACILITIES AT A GLANCE

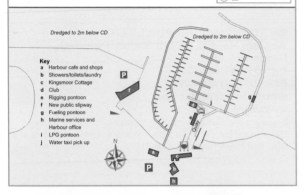

Key
a Harbour cafe and shops
b Showers/toilets/laundry
c Kingsmoor Cottage
d Club
e Rigging pontoon
f New public slipway
g Fueling pontoon
h Marine services and
   Harbour office
i LPG pontoon
j Water taxi pick up

Dredged to 2m below CD

TORPOINT YACHT HARBOUR

Torpoint Yacht Harbour
Marine Drive, Torpoint, Cornwall, PL11 2EH
Tel: 01752 813658 Fax: 01752 813658
email: tyhmarina@hotmail.com

VHF Ch 80
ACCESS H24

Torpoint Yacht Harbour is situated on the western bank of the
River Tamar, virtually opposite the well-established shipyard,
Devonport Management Ltd (DML). It lies within the old
Ballast Pound, built in 1783 to protect and load the barges that
ferried rock ballast out to ships that were light on cargo.

Enclosed within four 20ft-thick walls, the Yacht Harbour is
dredged to 2m and comprises 80 pontoon berths that are
accessible at all states of the tide. There are also drying berths
alongside the quay walls which can be reached approximately
three hours either side of high water.

Just a few minutes walk from the Yacht Harbour, adjacent to
which is the welcoming Torpoint Mosquito
Sailing Club, is Torpoint's town centre, where
there are enough shops and restaurants to suit
most yachtsmen's needs.

FACILITIES AT A GLANCE

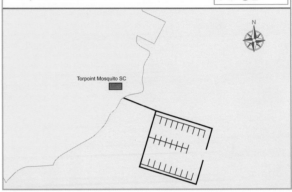

Torpoint Mosquito SC

SOUTHDOWN MARINA

Southdown Marina
Southdown Quay, Millbrook, Cornwall, PL10 1HG
Tel: 01752 823084 Fax: 01752 823084
www.southdownmarina.co.uk

VHF
ACCESS HW±4

Set in peaceful, rural surroundings, Southdown Marina lies in a picturesque inlet on the western bank of the River Tamar, some quarter of a mile from its mouth in Plymouth Sound. It is situated in the shallow inlet of Millbrooke Lake, which stretches westward for a mile or so to the small village of Millbrook.

Ideally suited for yachts that can take the ground, the marina is accessible four hours either side of high water and dries out at low tide onto soft mud. Its boatyard sits on a site which in the 1700s was occupied by the King's Brewhouse to provide ale for the Navy: over 20,000 gallons a week were allegedly ferried across the water to the fleet at Devonport.

The River Tamar and its numerous creeks provide a safe cruising ground in all weathers. Alternatively Plymouth affords a convenient stopover if heading slightly further afield to Dartmouth, Falmouth, Salcombe and the Scilly Isles.

FACILITIES AT A GLANCE

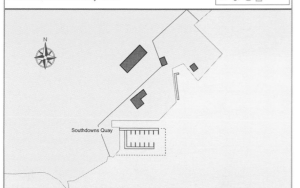

Southdowns Quay

MAYFLOWER MARINA

Mayflower International Marina
Ocean Quay, Richmond Walk, Plymouth, PL1 4LS
Tel: 01752 556633 Fax: 01752 606896
email: mayflower@mayflower.co.uk

VHF Ch 80
ACCESS H24

Sitting on the famous Plymouth Hoe, with the Devon coast to the left and the Cornish coast to the right, Mayflower Marina is a friendly, well-run marina, exemplified by its Five Gold Anchor award. Facilities include 24 hour access to fuel, gas and a launderette, full repair and maintenance services as well as an on site bar and brasserie. The marina is located only a short distance from Plymouth's town centre, where there are regular train services to and from several major towns and cities.

FACILITIES AT A GLANCE

Key
a Marina office, surveyors office
b Brokerage, charter office, chandlery
c Cafe
d Bar
e Brasserie
f Berth holders toilets and showers
g Harbour Master's office
h Riggers shop
i Engineers shop
j Picnic/BBQ area
k Tourist information booth

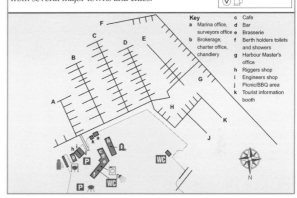

WEATHER FORECASTS BY FAX & TELEPHONE

Coastal/Inshore	2-day by Fax	5-day by Phone
Bristol	09061 502 121	09066 526 243
South West	09061 502 120	09066 526 242
Mid Channel	09061 502 119	09066 526 241
Channel Islands	-	09066 526 250

MILL BAY VILLAGE MARINA

Mill Bay Village Marina
Great Western Road
Mill Bay Docks, Plymouth, Devon, PL1 3TG
Tel: 01752 226785 Fax: 01752 226785

| VHF | Ch M, 80 |
| ACCESS | H24 |

Just west of Plymouth Hoe lies Millbay Docks, encompassing the RoRo terminal from where ferries ply to and from Roscoff and Santander. The entrance to Mill Bay Village Marina, accessible at all states of the tide, can be found on the starboard side of the docks. Offering few facilities for visiting yachtsmen, it is primarily geared up for resident berth holders, although berthing can be made available subject to prior arrangement.

Nearby is the city of Plymouth, where the main shopping precinct is situated around the Royal Parade. Flattened during WWII, this area was rebuilt in a modern, unimaginative way, contrasting sharply with the picturesque, historic Barbican from where the Pilgrim Fathers reputedly boarded the *Mayflower* to sail to the New World in 1620. The latter's ancient streets are full of bars and restaurants, while other attractions include the Mayflower Visitor Centre, the Elizabethan House and Garden and the Plymouth Gin Distillery.

FACILITIES AT A GLANCE

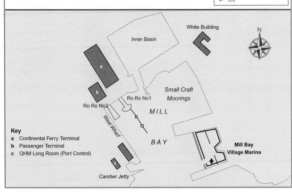

Key
a   Continental Ferry Terminal
b   Passenger Terminal
c   QHM Long Room (Port Control)

QUEEN ANNE'S BATTERY MARINA

Queen Anne's Battery
Plymouth, PL4 0LP
Tel: 01752 671142 Fax: 01752 266297
www.marinas.co.uk email: qab@mdlmarinas.co.uk

| VHF | Ch 80 |
| ACCESS | H24 |

At the centre of Plymouth lies Queen Anne's Battery, comprising 260 resident berths as well as a visitor's basin with alongside pontoon berthing. All berths are well protected by a breakwater and double wavescreen.

As Plymouth Sound frequently provides the starting point for many prestigious international yacht races as well as the finish of the Fastnet Race, the marina is often crowded with racers during the height of the season and its vibrant atmosphere can at times resemble a mini 'Cowes'.

FACILITIES AT A GLANCE

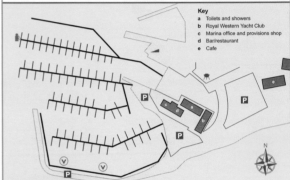

Key
a   Toilets and showers
b   Royal Western Yacht Club
c   Marina office and provisions shop
d   Bar/restaurant
e   Cafe

SUTTON HARBOUR

Sutton Harbour
North Quay House, Sutton Harbour, Plymouth, PL4 0RA
Tel: 01752 204186 Fax: 01752 205403
www.sutton-harbour.co.uk

VHF	Ch 12
ACCESS	H24

Boasting a superb location alongside Plymouth's famous Barbican centre, Sutton Harbour lies just north of Queen Anne's Battery Marina. The harbour can be entered 24 hours a day via a lock which is marked by green and red chevrons. Affording good shelter in 3.5m of water, it offers a comprehensive range of marine services, including a fuel berth that opens from 0800 to 1830.

Situated within a minute's walk from the marina is a Tourist Information Centre, providing all the necessary details of how best to explore the surrounding Devon countryside.

FACILITIES AT A GLANCE

Key
a Fish market
b National Marine Aquarium
c Customs House
d The Cove
e Marina office
f Lock tower

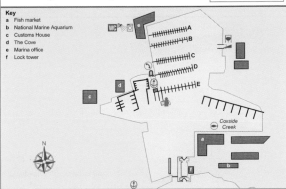

PLYMOUTH YACHT HAVEN

Plymouth Yacht Haven Ltd
Shaw Way, Mount Batten, Plymouth, PL9 9XH
Tel: 01752 404231 Fax: 01752 484177
www.yacthavens.com email: plymouth@yacthavens.com

VHF	Ch M, 80
ACCESS	H24

Situated in Clovelly Bay at the mouth of the Cattewater, Plymouth Yacht Haven offers good protection from the prevailing winds and is within close proximity to Plymouth Sound from where you can enjoy a day's sail to Fowey, Salcombe, Torquay or Dartmouth. Boasting 450 berths, the marina has the capacity to accommodate vessels up to 45m in length and 7m in draught.

Within easy access are several coastal walks, a golf course and a fitness centre with heated swimming pool. A water taxi is also on hand to take yachtsmen across the water to the historic Barbican, incorporating a plethora of shops, restaurants and bars amongst its attractive cobbled streets.

FACILITIES AT A GLANCE

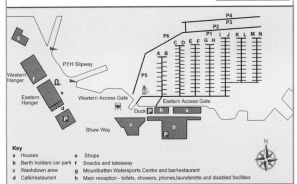

Key
a Houses
b Berth holders car park
c Washdown area
d Café/restaurant
e Shops
f Snacks and takeaway
g Mountbatten Watersports Centre and bar/restaurant
h Main reception - toilets, showers, phones, launderette and disabled facilities

NOSS-ON-DART MARINA

Noss-on-Dart Marina
Noss Quay, Dartmouth, Devon, TQ6 0EA
Tel: 01803 833351 Fax: 01803 835150
email: marinas@dartmarina.com
www.dartmarina.com

VHF Ch 80
ACCESS H24

Upstream of Dartmouth on the east shore of the River Dart is Noss-on-Dart Marina. Enjoying a peaceful rural setting, this marina is well suited to those who prefer a quieter atmosphere. Besides 180 fully serviced berths, 50 fore-and-aft moorings in the middle reaches of the river are also run by the marina, with mooring holders entitled to use all the facilities available to berth holders. During summer, a passenger ferry service runs regularly between Noss-on-Dart and Dartmouth, while a grocery service to your boat can be provided on request.

FACILITIES AT A GLANCE

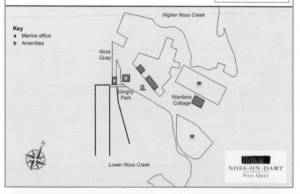

Key
a Marina office
b Amenities

Higher Noss Creek
Noss Quay
Dinghy Park
Wardens Cottage
Lower Noss Creek

NOSS-ON-DART
Noss Quay

DART MARINA

Dart Marina
Sandquay Road, Dartmouth
Devon, TQ6 9PH
Tel: 01803 833351 Fax: 01803 835150
email: marinas@dartmarina.com www.dartmarina.com

VHF Ch 80
ACCESS H24

Located within easy walking distance of the historic town of Dartmouth, the Dart Marina's Five Gold Anchors award bears testament to the high standard of service on offer. The marina boasts 110 fully equipped pontoon berths, all of which come with electricity, fresh water and a television terminal.

DART MARINA
Dartmouth

A popular destination with visiting yachtsmen, the River Dart provides a perfect base from which to go off cruising, whether it be exploring the local bays and creeks of the West Country or heading further afield to Brittany and the Channel Islands.

FACILITIES AT A GLANCE

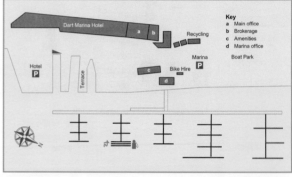

Key
a Main office
b Brokerage
c Amenities
d Marina office

Dart Marina Hotel
Recycling
Hotel
Terrace
Marina
Bike Hire
Boat Park

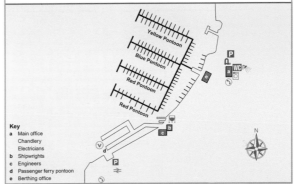
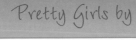

BRIXHAM MARINA

**Brixham Marina
Berry Head Road, Brixham
Devon, TQ5 9BW
Tel: 01803 882929 Fax: 01803 882737
www.marinas.co.uk**

VHF	Ch 80
ACCESS	H24

Home to one of Britain's largest fishing fleets, Brixham Harbour is located on the southern shore of Tor Bay, which is well sheltered from westerly winds and where tidal streams are weak. Brixham Marina, housed in a separate basin to the work boats, provides easy access in all weather conditions and at all states of the tide. Established in 1989, it has become increasingly popular with locals and visitors alike, enjoying

an idyllic setting right on the town's quayside.

Local attractions include a walk out to Berry Head Nature Reserve and a visit to the replica of Sir Francis Drake's ship, the *Golden Hind.*

FACILITIES AT A GLANCE

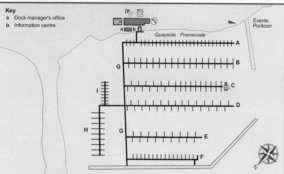

Key
a Dock manager's office
b Information centre

TORQUAY MARINA

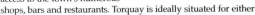

Torquay Marina
Torquay, Devon, TQ2 5EQ
Tel: 01803 200210 Fax: 01803 200225
www.marinas.co.uk

| VHF | Ch 80 |
| ACCESS | H24 |

Tucked away in the north east corner of Tor Bay, Torquay Marina is well sheltered from the prevailing SW'ly winds, providing safe entry in all conditions and at any state of the tide. Located in the centre of Torquay, the marina enjoys easy access to the town's numerous shops, bars and restaurants. Torquay is ideally situated for either exploring Tor Bay itself, with its many delightful anchorages, or else for heading further west to experience several other scenic harbours such as Dartmouth and Salcombe. It also provides a good starting point for crossing to Brittany, Normandy or the Channel Islands.

FACILITIES AT A GLANCE

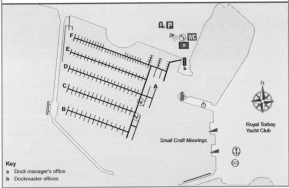

Key
a Dock manager's office
b Dockmaster offices

Addicott Electrics Ltd Teignmouth
01626 774087

Advanced Blast Cleaning Paint
Tavistock
Removal of paint and antifouling; Steel
keels blasted and primed   01822 617192

Alsop, J Salcombe
Sailmaker   01548 843702

Aries Vane Gear Spares Penryn
Kits and spare parts for Aries self-steering
gears   01326 377467

Atlantic Spars Ltd Brixham
Rigging, spars, furling systems
01803 843322

Atlantis Marine Power Ltd Plymouth
Electrics and electronics   01752 225679

Ayers Marine Survey Frybridge
01548 830496

Axe YC Axemouth   01297 20043

Baltic Wharf Boatyard Totnes
01803 867922

Barbican Yacht Agency Ltd Plymouth
Comprehensive yacht service from
surveys and acquisitions to maintenance
and management   01752 228855

Blagdon, A Plymouth
Boatyard   01752 561830

Blagdon & Sons, AS Plymouth
Engine repairs   01752 228155

Boating World Saltash
Chandler   01752 851679

Boatshop Chandlery Brixham
01803 882055

Boatshop Chandlery Noss
01803 833772

Boatshop Chandlery Galmpton
01803 845886

Bosun's Locker Teignmouth
Chandlery   01626 779721

Bowman Yachts Penryn
High performance yachts 01326 376107

Bridger Marine, John Exeter
Chandler; mail order service
01392 216420

Bridport HM   01308 423222

Bridport Police   01308 422266

Brigantine Teignmouth
Yacht chandlers; electronics; engines
01626 872400

Brixham Chandlers Brixham
01803 882055

Brixham HM   01803 853321

Brixham Marina Brixham01803 882929

Brixham Police   0990 777444

Brixham Yacht Supplies Ltd Brixham
01803 882290

Brixham YC Brixham   01803 853332

Buchanan, Keith St Mary's
Sail repairs; canvas products; rigging
01720 422037

CAB Special Batteries Plymouth
Battery manufacturer & supplier
01752 313304

Calibra Sails Dartmouth
01803 833094

Carne (Sales) Ltd, David Falmouth
Boat sales   01326 318314

Carne (Sales) Ltd, David Penryn
Boat sales   01326 374177

Cellar Marine Porthallow
Marine engineering   01326 280214

Challenger Marine Penryn
Engineers, outboards, chandlery,
shipwright, repairs, storage
01326 377222

Charlestown HM   01726 67526

Chris Humphrey Teignmouth
Boatyard, marine engineering
01626 772324

Clarke Designs LLP, Owen
DartmouthYacht design, naval architect,
surveyors   01803 770495

Clean It All Nr Brixham   01803 844564

Coastal Chandlery Torquay
01803 211190

Comet Dinghies Devon   01769 574358

Compass Marine (Dartmouth)
Dartmouth
Fender specialist   01803 835915

Cornish Crabbers Wadebridge
Builder of the 22ft Cornish Crabber & the
Cornish Shrimper   01208 862666

Cornish Cruising Falmouth Marina
Bareboat and skippered charter
01326 211800

Cosalt International Newlyn
Chandlery   01736 363094

Coverack HM   01326 280545

Cox, David Marine Surveyor
01326 340808

Creekside Boatyard (Old Mill Creek)
Dartmouth
Boat repairs; maintenance; storage
01803 832649

Dart Chandlers Dartmouth
01803 833772

Dart Marina Dartmouth   01803 833351

Darthaven Marina Dartmouth
01803 752242

Dartmouth Police   0990 777444

Dartmouth Sailing Dartmouth
Charter, cruises, RYA courses
01803 833399

Dartmouth YC Dartmouth
01803 832305

Dartside Quay Brixham
Mud moorings, boat storage, chandlery,
hoist, marine services   01803 845445

Devtech Plymouth
Electrics and electronics   01752 223388

Dex-Tamar Marine Plymouth
Boat sales; boat repairs; storage; boat
transport; canvas & upholstery
01752 491454

Dixon Chandlery, Peter Exmouth
01395 273248

Dixons Exmouth
Chandlery   01392 273248

Dufour Yachts/Portfolio Marine
Torquay
Performance cruising yachts
01803 380506

East & Co, Robin Kingsbridge
Boatbuilder; repairs; storage
01548 53125

Eland Exeter   01392 255788

Elizabethan Charters (Dartmouth)
Bristol
Charter of Elizabethan 31 from Dartmouth
0117 9615739

Eurospars Ltd Plymouth
Masts and rigging specialist
01752 550550

Exe Leisure Exeter
New & used boats/outboards;
maintenance; repair; rigging; limited
chandlery   01392 879055

Exe SC (River Exe) Exemouth
01395 264607

Falmouth Divers Ltd Penryn
01326 374736

Falmouth HM   01326 312285

Falmouth Marina Falmouth
01326 316620

Falmouth Town SC Falmouth
01326 373915

Falmouth Watersports Association
Falmouth   01326 211223

Falmouth Yacht Haven Falmouth
01326 312285

Fathom Marine Bridport 01308 420988

Flushing SC Falmouth   01326 374043

Forrest Marine Ltd Exeter
Boat transport   01392 833504

Fowey Boatyard Fowey
Boat repairs; maintenance; storage
01726 832194

Fowey Gallants SC Fowey
01726 832335

Fowey Harbour Marine Engineers
Fowey   01726 832806

Fowey HM   01726 832471/2.

Fowey Marine Services Fowey
01726 833236

Fowey Police   0990 777444

Freshwater Boatyard Truro
Boatbuilder; repairs; storage
01326 270443

Gib'Sea Yachts/Portfolio Marine
Torquay
Performance cruising yachts
01803 380506

Golden Black Sailing Cornwall
Skippered and bareboat charters
01209 715757

Green Marine, Jimmy Fore St Beer
Chandler 01297 20744

Green Sailmakers, Paul Plymouth
01752 660317

Gweek Quay Boatyard Helston
Boat repairs; storage; chandler; brokerage
01326 221657

Gul International Ltd Bodmin
Windproof clothing; watersports
equipment 01208 262400

Guy Cotten UK Ltd Liskeard
Clothing 01579 347115

Harbour Marine Plymouth
Boatyard 01752 204690/1

Harns Rigging Totnes
01803 840160

Helford River HM 01326 250749

Helford River SC Helston
01326 231006

Hooper, A Plymouth 01752 830411

Island CC Salcombe 01548 531176

Isles of Scilly Police 01721 422444

Isles of Scilly Steamship Co
St Mary's 01720 422710

Jedynak, A Salcombe
Electronic repairs 01548 843321

Landon Marine Chandlers Truro
01872 272668

Lavis & Son, CH Exmouth
Boatbuilder; repairs; storage
01395 263095

Liberty Yachts Ltd Plymouth
Yacht charter in UK & the Med; brokerage
01752 227911

Lincombe Boat Yard Salcombe
Boat repairs; storage 01548 843580

Lodey Sails Newlyn
Sailmaker 01736 331557

Looe Chandlery West Looe
01503 264355

Looe Divers Hannafore 01503 262727

Looe HM 01503 262839

Looe Police 01503 262233

Looe SC Looe 01503 262559

Lyme Regis HM 01297 442137

Lyme Regis Police 01297 442603

Lyme Regis Power BC Lyme Regis
01297 443788

Lyme Regis SC Lyme Regis
01297 442800

Lympstone SC Exeter 01395 264152

Mainstay Yacht Maintenance
Dartmouth 01803 839076

Marconi Marine Brixham
Marine electronics 01803 851993

Marconi Marine Newlyn
Marine electronics 01736 361320

Marconi Marine Penryn
Marine electronics 01326 378031

Marine & Leisure Europe Ltd Plymouth
Chandler; electronics 01752 268826

Marine Bazaar Plymouth
Chandler 01752 201023

Marine Electronics SW Fowey
01726 833101

Marine Engineering Looe Brixham
01803 844777

Marine Engineering Looe Looe
01503 263009

Marine Instruments Falmouth
Electronics 01326 312414

MarineCo Looe
Chandlery 01503 265444

Mariners Weigh Shaldon
Outboards 01626 873698

**Mashford Brothers Ltd, Cremyll
Shipyard** Plymouth
Boatyard 01752 822232

**Mathew Sail Loft, A (Ocean Blue
Chandlery)** Penzance 01736 364004

Mayflower Chandlery Plymouth
01752 500121

Mayflower International Marina
Plymouth 01752 556633

Mayflower SC Plymouth 01752 662526

Mears HJ Axmouth
Boatbuilder 01297 23344

Mevagissey HM 01726 843305

Mevagissey Police 0990 777444

Mill Bay Village Marina Plymouth
01752 226785

Mitchell Sails Fowey 01726 833731

Mojo Maritime Penzance
Underwater engineer 01736 762771

Moore & Son, J Mevagissey
Traditional boatbuilder & repairs; chandler
01726 842964

Mount Batten Boathouse Plymouth
Engines, chandlery, electronics, tenders
and outboards 01752 482666

Mount's Bay Engineering Newlyn
01736 363014

Mousehole HM 01736 731511

Mullion Cove HM 01326 240222

Multi Composites Ltd Torpoint
builder, refits, spray painters
01752 823513

Mylor Chandlery & Rigging Falmouth
01326 375482

Mylor Yacht Harbour Falmouth
01326 372121

Mylor YC Falmouth 01326 374391

Navionics UK Plymouth
Electronic charts 01752 204735

Network Yacht Brokers Plymouth
Brokers; agents 01752 605377

Newlyn HM 01736 362523

Noss-on-Dart Marina Dartmouth
Chandlery, sails, rigger 01803 834582

Ocean Blue Penzance
Chandlery, sails, rigger 01736 364004

Ocean Marine (Mayflower Marina)
Plymouth 01752 500121

Ocean Sails Plymouth 01752 563666

Ösen Sails Ltd Plymouth
Sail makers, repairs, covers
01752 563666

Outriggers/Upper Deck Marine Fowey
Chandlery 01726 833233

Padstow Harbour Commissioners
01841 532239

Paignton SC Paignton 01803 525817

Pantaenius UK Ltd Plymouth
Marine insurance 01752 223656

Par HM 01726 818337

Pasco's Boatyard Truro 01326 270269

PC Maritime Plymouth
Weatherfax/Navtex software
01752 254205

Pearn and Co, Norman (Looe Boatyard)
Looe
Moorings; repairs; boat sales; storage
01503 262244

Penrose Sailmakers Falmouth
01326 312705

**Penzance Dry Dock and Engineering
Co Ltd** Penzance 01736 363838

Penzance HM 01736 366113

Penzance Marine Services Penzance
Repairs, chandlery 01736 361081

Penzance Police 01736 362395

Penzance SC Penzance 01736 364989

Performance Yachting Plymouth
Sailing and power tuition; yacht delivery
01752 565023

Perry Marine, Rob Axminster
01297 631314

Philip Leisure Group Dartmouth
Marina; river moorings; hotel; ferry;
storage 01803 833351

Plym YC Plymouth 01752 404991

Plymouth Composite Construction
Plymouth
Hull and GRP repair 01752 787048

Plymouth Marine Electronics Plymouth
01752 227711

Plymouth Police 01752 701188

Plymouth Sailing School
01752 667170

Plymouth Yacht Haven Plymouth
01752 404231

Ponsharden Boatyard Penryn
01326 372215
Boat repairs; storage

Port Navas YC Falmouth 01326 340065

Port of Falmouth Sailing Association
Falmouth 01326 372927

Port Pendennis Marina Falmouth
01326 211211

Porthleven HM 01326 574207

Portway Yacht Charters Falmouth
01326 212320

Portway Yacht Charters Plymouth
01752 606999

Premium Liferaft Services Dartmouth
Hire/sales of liferafts and safety
equipment 01803 833094

Premium Liferaft Services Falmouth
As above 01326 374646

Premium Liferaft Services Plymouth
As above 01752 667170

Premium Liferaft Services Salcombe
As above 01548 842777

Pump International Ltd Cornwall
Hand pump specialist 01209 831937

Quba Sails Salcombe
Sailcloth clothing; corporate/team clothing
01548 844026

Quayside Marine Salcombe
Chandlery 01548 844300

Queen Anne's Battery Marina
Plymouth 01752 671142

Rat Island Sailboat Company (Yard)
St Mary's 01720 423399

Ravenspring Ltd Totnes
Drysuit and thermal ranges
01803 867092

Reddish Marine Salcombe
Marine engineering 01548 844094

Reed's Nautical Bradford-on-Avon
Mail order of nautical books, charts and
prints 01225 868821

Restronguet SC Falmouth
01326 374536

Retreat Boatyard Ltd Exeter
01392 874720/875934

Ribeye Dartmouth
RIBs and inflatables 01803 832060

River Dart HM 01803 832337

River Exe Dockmaster 01392 274306

River Yealm HM 01752 872533

River Yealm Police 0990 777444

RNSA (Plymouth) Plymouth
01752 55123/83

Royal Cornwall YC (RCYC) Falmouth
01326 312126

Royal Dart YC Dartmouth
01803 752496

Royal Fowey YC Fowey 01726 833573

Royal Plymouth Corinthian YC
Plymouth 01752 664327

Royal Torbay YC Torquay
01803 292006

Royal Western YC Plymouth
01752 660077

Rustler Yachts Ltd Penryn
High performance yachts 01326 376107

Sailaway St Anthony
Chandlery, repairs 01326 231357

Sails & Canvas Exeter 01392 877527

Salcombe Boatstore Salcombe
Chandlery, rigger 01548 843708

Salcombe HM 01548 843791

Salcombe Police 01548 842107

Salcombe YC Salcombe 01548 842593

Saltash SC Saltash 01752 845988

Scillonian Sailing and BC St Mary's
01720 277229

Sea Chest Nautical Bookshop
Plymouth 01752 222012

Sea-Com Electronics Penzance
01736 369695

Seafit Marine Services Falmouth
Repairs and services 01326 313713

Seaware Ltd Penryn
Chandler 01326 377948

Shipmates Chandlery Dartmouth
01803 839292

Shipmates Chandlery Salcombe
01548 844555

Sleeman & Hawken Ltd Shaldon
Diesel centre 01626 872750

SM International Plymouth
Electrics & electronics 01752 662129

South Devon Sailing School
Newton Abbot 01626 52352

South West Marine Plumbing
Brixham 01803 859048

South West Sails Penryn
01326 375291

Southcoasting Navigators Devon
Sailing tuition; yacht delivery; aids to
navigation 01626 335626

Southdown Marina Millbrook
01752 823084

St Mary's HM 01720 422768

St Mawes SC St Mawes 01326 270686

Starcross Fishing & CC (River Exe)
Starcross 01626 891996

Starcross YC Exeter 01626 890470

Starey Marine Salcombe
Marine engineering 01548 843655

Starlight Yachts Penryn
High performance sailing yachts
01326 376107

Sutton Harbour Marina Plymouth
01752 204186

SW Nets Newlyn
Chandlery 01736 360254

Tamar River SC Plymouth
01752 362741

Teign Corinthian YC Teignmouth
01626 772734

Teign Diving Centre Teignmouth
01626 773965

Teignmouth HM 01626 773165

Teignmouth Police 01626 772433

The Foc'sle Exeter
Chandler 01392 874105

Tiflex Liskeard
Decking; adhesives 01579 320808

Toms and Son Ltd, C Fowey
Boatbuilders and repairs 01726 870232

Topsham SC Topsham 01392 877524

Torbay Boating Centre Paignton
01803 558760

Torpoint Mosquito SC – Plymouth
Plymouth 01752 812508

Torpoint Yacht Harbour Plymouth
01752 813658

Torquay Chandlers Torquay
01803 211854

Torquay HM 01803 292429

Torquay Marina Torquay 01803 200210

Torquay Police 0990 777444

Trouts Boatyard (River Exe) Topsham
Boat repairs; maintenance 01392 873044

UK Customs Nationwide
0845 0109000

Upper Deck Marine Fowey
01726 832287

Victoria Marine Exmouth
Outboard maintenance 01392 265044

Weir Quay Boatyard Bere Alston
01822 840474

Western Marine Power Ltd Plymouth
Marine engineers 01752 408804

Westways of Plymouth Plymouth
Brokerage 01752 670770

Wharram Designs, James Truro
Catamaran designer 01872 864792

Winters Marine Ltd Salcombe
Boatyard; storage; chandlery
01548 843580

Wright, M Manaccan
Marine engineering 01326 231502

Yacht Parts (Plymouth) Plymouth
Chandler 01752 252489

Yealm YC Newton Ferrers 01752 8722

39 North Kingskerwell
Charter management; Mediterranean
holidays 07071 393939

Waypoint Guide Area 1 – South West England - Isles of Scilly to Portland Bill

1

34	**Portland Bill** - 5M S of	50°25'·85N	02°27'·38W
43	**Guernsey SW** - 1·8M W Les Hanois	49°26'·10N	02°45'·08W
60	**Roches Douvres Light** - 2·5M NE	49°08'·18N	02°46'·70W
	St Malo - 1·3M NW Grande Jardin Lt Bn	48°41'·04N	02°06'·48W
	Cherbourg - 0·5M N of W ent	49°40'·86N	01°39'·57W
97	**Bridport** - 1M S of entrance	50°41'·53N	02°45'·79W
98	**Lyme Regis** - 1M SSE on Ldg Lts	50°42'·83N	02°54'·89W
99	**River Exe** - 0·3M S of E Exe Lt By	50°35'·70N	03°22'·37W
100	**Teignmouth** - 1M E of Bar	50°32'·33N	03°27'·87W
101	**Torbay** - 1·7M NE of Berry Hd	50°25'·13N	03°27'·01W
102	**Dartmouth** - 2M 150° from ent	50°18'·28N	03°31'·67W
103	**Start Point** - 2M S of	50°11'·33N	03°38'·54W
104	**Salcombe** - 1·5M S of bar	50°11'·65N	03°46'·67W
105	**Bolt Tail** - 1·3M SW of R Avon	50°15'·55N	03°54'·25W
106	**River Erme** - 1·5M SSW of Battisborough Island	50°16'·77N	03°58'·52W
107	**River Yealm** -1·2M SW of Yealm Hd	50°17'·48N	04°05'·77W
108	**Plymouth** - 0·9M S of W end of brkwtr	50°19'·17N	04°09'·57W
109	**Rame Head** - 0·2M S of	50°18'·17N	04°13'·39W
110	**Eddystone** - 1M S of	50°09'·84N	04°15'·92W
111	**Looe** - 1·5M SE of entrance	50°20'·26N	04°24'·80W
112	**Polperro** - 0·7M S of	50°19'·04N	04°30'·87W
113	**Fowey** - 1·5M SSW of ent	50°18'·23N	04°39'·57W
114	**Charlestown** - 1M SE of	50°19'·03N	04°44'·17W
115	**Mevagissey** - 0·8M E of	50°16'·17N	04°45'·65W
116	**Gwineas ECM** - 0·2M E of	50°14'·43N	04°45'·07W
117	**Dodman Point** - 1·3M SSE of	50°11'·90N	04°47'·00W
118	**Falmouth** - 0·8M S of St Anthony Hd	50°07'·67N	05°00'·97W
119	**Helford River** -1M E of ent	50°05'·74N	05°04'·06W
120	**Manacles** - 0·2M E of	50°02'·84N	05°01'·56W
121	**Coverack** - 1M E of	50°01'·34N	05°04'·36W
122	**Black Head** - 0·7M SE of	49°59'·73N	05°05'·36W
123	**Lizard** - 3M S of	49°54'·59N	05°12'·17W
124	**Porth Mellin** - 2M W of	50°00'·90N	05°18'·78W
125	**Porthleven** - 0·4M SW of	50°04'·54N	05°19'·76W
126	**Mountamopus SCM** - 0·2M S	50°04'·44N	05°26'·26W
127	**Penzance** - 1·5M SE of and for Mousehole	50°06'·04N	05°30'·06W
128	**Tater Du Light** -1·5M ESE	50°02'·54N	05°32'·67W
129	**Runnel Stone Light Buoy** - 0·3M S	50°00'·88N	05°40'·37W
130	**Wolf Rock** - 2M S of	49°54'·68N	05°48'·56W
131	**St Mary's, Scilly** - 2M E of St Mary's Sound	49°54'·04N	06°15'·06W
	Treguier - 4·1M N of Pointe de Chateau	48°56'·24N	03°14'·36W
	Roscoff - 6M NNE of ent	48°49'·14N	03°54'·36W
	Ushant Creac'h Light - 3·5M NW	48°30'·04N	05°11'·36W

Distance Table - South West England

Approximate distances in nautical miles are by the most direct route while avoiding dangers and allowing for Traffic Separation Schemes

		1	2	3	4	5	6	7	8	9	10	11	12	13	14	15	16	17	18	19	20
1.	Milford Haven	1																			
2.	Lundy Island	28	2																		
3.	Padstow	67	40	3																	
4.	Longships	100	80	47	4																
5.	Scilly (Crow Sound)	120	102	69	22	5															
6.	Penzance	115	95	62	15	35	6														
7.	Lizard Point	123	103	72	23	42	16	7													
8.	Falmouth	139	119	88	39	60	32	16	8												
9.	Mevagissey	152	132	99	52	69	46	28	17	9											
10.	Fowey	157	137	106	57	76	49	34	22	7	10										
11.	Looe	163	143	110	63	80	57	39	29	16	11	11									
12.	Plymouth (bkwtr)	170	150	117	70	92	64	49	39	25	22	11	12								
13.	R Yealm (ent)	172	152	119	72	89	66	49	39	28	23	16	4	13							
14.	Salcombe	181	161	128	81	102	74	59	50	40	36	29	22	17	14						
15.	Start Point	186	166	135	86	103	80	63	55	45	40	33	24	22	7	15					
16.	Dartmouth	195	175	142	95	116	88	72	63	54	48	42	35	31	14	9	16				
17.	Torbay	201	181	150	101	118	96	78	70	62	55	50	39	38	24	15	11	17			
18.	Exmouth	213	193	162	113	131	107	90	82	73	67	61	51	49	33	27	24	12	18		
19.	Lyme Regis	226	206	173	126	144	120	104	96	86	81	74	63	62	48	41	35	30	21	19	
20.	Portland Bill	235	215	184	135	151	128	112	104	93	89	81	73	70	55	49	45	42	36	22	20

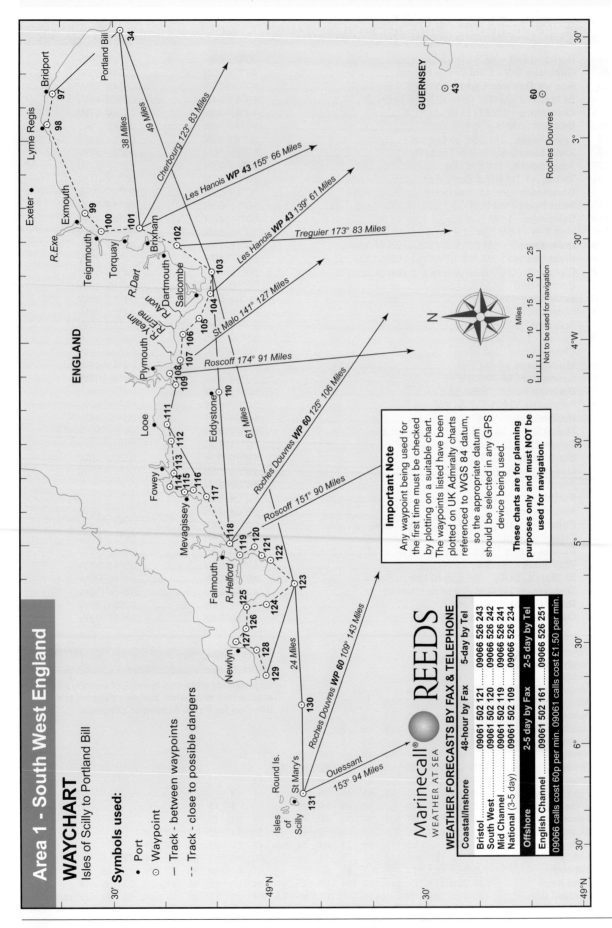

Area 1 - South West England

WAYCHART
Isles of Scilly to Portland Bill

Symbols used:
- ● Port
- ⊙ Waypoint
- — Track - between waypoints
- -- Track - close to possible dangers

Important Note

Any waypoint being used for the first time must be checked by plotting on a suitable chart. The waypoints listed have been plotted on UK Admiralty charts referenced to WGS 84 datum, so the appropriate datum should be selected in any GPS device being used.

These charts are for planning purposes only and must NOT be used for navigation.

Marinecall ● **REEDS**
WEATHER AT SEA

WEATHER FORECASTS BY FAX & TELEPHONE

Coastal/Inshore	48-hour by Fax	5-day by Tel
Bristol	09061 502 121	09066 526 243
South West	09061 502 120	09066 526 242
Mid Channel	09061 502 119	09066 526 241
National (3-5 day)	09061 502 109	09066 526 234

Offshore	2-5 day by Fax	2-5 day by Tel
English Channel	09061 502 161	09066 526 251

09066 calls cost 60p per min. 09061 calls cost £1.50 per min.

Marinecall® REEDS
WEATHER AT SEA
WEATHER FORECASTS BY FAX & TELEPHONE

Coastal/Inshore	2-day by Fax	5-day by Phone
South West	09061 502 120	09066 526 242
Mid Channel	09061 502 119	09066 526 241
Channel East	09061 502 118	09066 526 240
Channel Islands	-	09066 526 250
National (3-5 day)	09061 502 109	09066 526 234

Offshore	2-5 day by Fax	2-5 day by Phone
English Channel	09061 502 161	09066 526 251
Southern North Sea	09061 502 162	09066 526 252
Irish Sea	09061 502 163	09066 526 253
Biscay	09061 502 164	09066 526 254

09066 CALLS COST 60P PER MIN. 09061 CALLS COST £1.50 PER MIN.

Key to Marina Plans symbols

Calor Gas		P	Parking
Chandler			Pub/Restaurant
Disabled facilities			Pump out
Electrical supply			Rigging service
Electrical repairs			Sail repairs
Engine repairs			Shipwright
First Aid			Shop/Supermarket
Fresh Water			Showers
Fuel - Diesel			Slipway
Fuel - Petrol		WC	Toilets
Hardstanding/boatyard			Telephone
Laundry facilities			Trolleys
Lift-out facilities		V	Visitors berths

Area 2 - Central Southern England

MARINAS
Telephone Numbers
VHF Channel
Access Times

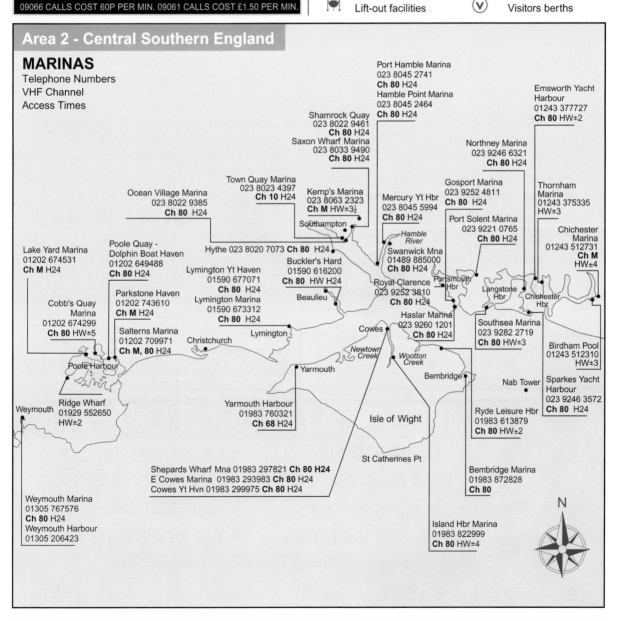

Port Hamble Marina 023 8045 2741 **Ch 80** H24
Hamble Point Marina 023 8045 2464 **Ch 80** H24
Emsworth Yacht Harbour 01243 377727 **Ch 80** HW±2
Shamrock Quay 023 8022 9461 **Ch 80** H24
Saxon Wharf Marina 023 8033 9490 **Ch 80** H24
Northney Marina 023 9246 6321 **Ch 80** H24
Town Quay Marina 023 8023 4397 **Ch 10** H24
Kemp's Marina 023 8063 2323 **Ch M** HW±3½
Gosport Marina 023 9252 4811 **Ch 80** H24
Thornham Marina 01243 375335 HW±3
Ocean Village Marina 023 8022 9385 **Ch 80** H24
Mercury Yt Hbr 023 8045 5994 **Ch 80** H24
Port Solent Marina 023 9221 0765 **Ch 80** H24
Chichester Marina 01243 512731 **Ch M** HW±4
Southampton
Hamble River
Lake Yard Marina 01202 674531 **Ch M** H24
Poole Quay - Dolphin Boat Haven 01202 649488 **Ch 80** H24
Hythe 023 8020 7073 **Ch 80** H24
Buckler's Hard 01590 616200 **Ch 80** HW H24
Swanwick Mna 01489 885000 **Ch 80** H24
Portsmouth Hbr
Langstone Hbr
Chichester Hbr
Cobb's Quay Marina 01202 674299 **Ch 80** HW±5
Lymington Yt Haven 01590 677071 **Ch 80** H24
Parkstone Haven 01202 743610 **Ch M** H24
Lymington Marina 01590 673312 **Ch 80** H24
Beaulieu
Royal Clarence 023 9252 3810 **Ch 80** H24
Haslar Marina 023 9260 1201 **Ch 80** H24
Southsea Marina 023 9282 2719 **Ch 80** HW±3
Birdham Pool 01243 512310 HW±3
Salterns Marina 01202 709971 **Ch M, 80** H24
Christchurch
Lymington
Cowes
Newtown Creek
Wootton Creek
Bembridge
Nab Tower
Sparkes Yacht Harbour 023 9246 3572 **Ch 80** H24
Poole Harbour
Weymouth
Ridge Wharf 01929 552650 HW±2
Yarmouth
Yarmouth Harbour 01983 760321 **Ch 68** H24
Isle of Wight
Ryde Leisure Hbr 01983 613879 **Ch 80** HW±2
St Catherines Pt
Shepards Wharf Mna 01983 297821 **Ch 80 H24**
E Cowes Marina 01983 293983 **Ch 80** H24
Cowes Yt Hvn 01983 299975 **Ch 80** H24
Bembridge Marina 01983 872828 **Ch 80**
Weymouth Marina 01305 767576 **Ch 80** H24
Weymouth Harbour 01305 206423
Island Hbr Marina 01983 822999 **Ch 80** HW±4
N

WEYMOUTH MARINA

Weymouth Marina
70 Commercial Road, Dorset, DT4 8NA
Tel: 01305 767576 Fax: 01305 767575
www.weymouth-marina.co.uk
email: sales@weymouth-marina.co.uk

VHF	Ch 80
ACCESS	H24

With more than 280 permanent and visitors' berths, Weymouth is a modern, purpose-built marina ideally situated for yachtsmen cruising between the West Country and the Solent. It is also conveniently placed for sailing to France or the Channel Islands. Accessed via the town's historic lifting bridge, which during the height of the summer opens each hour between 0800 – 2100, the marina is dredged to 2.5m below chart datum. It provides easy access to the town centre, with its abundance of shops, pubs and restaurants, as well as to the traditional seafront where an impressive sandy beach is overlooked by an esplanade of hotels.

FACILITIES AT A GLANCE

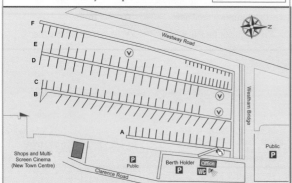

PREMIUM LIFERAFT SERVICES
WEYMOUTH
Tel: (01305) 821040
Freephone: 0800 243673
e-mail: info@liferafts.com
www.liferafts.com
Hire and sales of DoT and RORC approved liferafts and safety equipment.

DEAN & REDDYHOFF LTD - WEYMOUTH MARINA
70 Commercial Rd, Weymouth, Dorset DT4 8NA
Tel: (01305) 767576
Fax: (01305) 767575
e-mail: sales@weymouth-marina.co.uk
www.weymouth-marina.co.uk
Located in the centre of town only minutes from local pubs & restaurants, the marina has proven a great success with berth holders and visitors alike. Weymouth's recent regeneration programme has been a complete success, making Weymouth a must visit port, whilst cruising the South Coast.

THE CHANNEL CRUISING COMPANION
NEW FOR 2003
ORDER YOURS TODAY
CALL THE
NAUTICAL DATA ORDER HOTLINE:
+44 (0)1243 389898

WEYMOUTH HARBOUR

Weymouth & Portland Borough Council
North Quay, Weymouth, Dorset, DT4 8TA
Tel: 01305 206423 Fax: 01305 767927

VHF	Ch 12, 16
ACCESS	H24

Weymouth Harbour, which lies to the NE of Portland in the protected waters of Weymouth Bay, benefits from deep water at all states of the tide. If wishing to moor up in the old Georgian outer harbour, you should contact the harbour authority, which also controls several municipal pontoons above the bridge. In recent years the facilities have been significantly improved and now include electricity and fresh water on both quays, as well as free showers and a coin-operated launderette. Visiting yachtsmen are very welcome both at the Royal Dorset Yacht Club, situated on Customs House Quay in the inner harbour, and the Weymouth Sailing Club, on the south pier of the outer harbour.

FACILITIES AT A GLANCE

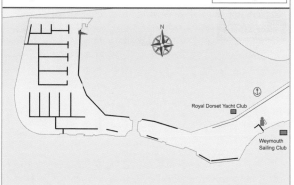

Royal Dorset Yacht Club

Weymouth Sailing Club

RIDGE WHARF YACHT CENTRE

Ridge Wharf Yacht Centre
Ridge, Wareham, Dorset, BH20 5BG
Tel: 01929 552650 Fax: 01929 554434

VHF	
ACCESS	HW±2

On the south bank of the River Frome, which acts as the boundary to the North of the Isle of Purbeck, is Ridge Wharf Yacht Centre. Access for a 1.5m draught is between one and two hours either side of HW, with berths drying out to soft mud. The Yacht Centre cannot be contacted on VHF, so it is best to phone up ahead of time to inquire about berthing availability.

A trip upstream to the ancient market town of Wareham is well worth while, although owners of deep-draughted yachts may prefer to go by dinghy. Tucked between the Rivers Frome and Trent, it is packed full of cafés, restaurants and shops.

FACILITIES AT A GLANCE

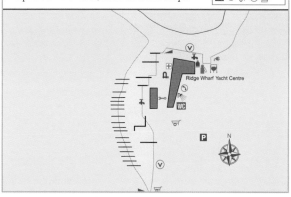

Ridge Wharf Yacht Centre

LAKE YARD MARINA

Lake Yard Marina
Lake Drive, Hamworthy, Poole, Dorset BH15 4DT
Tel: 01202 674531 Fax: 01202 677518
Email: yard@bostonwhaler.co.uk www.lakeyard.co.uk

VHF	Ch M
ACCESS	H24

Lake Yard is situated towards the NW end of Poole Harbour, just beyond the SHM No 73. The entrance can be easily identified by 2FR (vert) and 2FG (vert) lights. Enjoying 24 hour access, the marina has no designated visitors' berths, but will accommodate visiting yachtsmen if resident berth holders are away. Its on site facilities include full maintenance and repair services as well as hard standing and a 50 ton boat hoist, although for the nearest fuel go to Corralls (Tel 01202 674551), opposite the Town Quay. Lake Yard's Waterfront Club, offering spectacular views across the harbour, opens seven days a week for lunchtime and evening meals.

FACILITIES AT A GLANCE

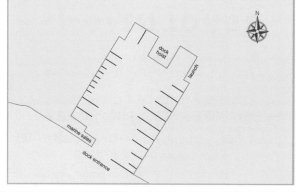

dock hoist

launch

marine sales

dock entrance

COBB'S QUAY MARINA

Cobb's Quay
Hamworthy, Poole, Dorset, BH15 4EL
Tel: 01202 674299 Fax: 01202 665217
Email: a.osman@mdlmarinas.co.uk www.marinas.co.uk

VHF	Ch 80
ACCESS	HW±5

Lying on the west side of Holes Bay in Poole Harbour, Cobb's Quay is accessed via the lifting bridge at Poole Quay. With fully serviced pontoons for yachts up to 25m LOA, the marina can be entered five hours either side of high water and is normally able to accommodate visiting yachts. On site is Cobb's Quay Yacht Club, which welcomes visitors to its bar and restaurant.

Poole is one of the largest natural harbours in the world and is considered by many to be among the finest. Its N side incorporates several modern marinas in close proximity to a multitude of shops and restaurants, while its S side boasts tranquil anchorages set within unspoilt nature reserves.

FACILITIES AT A GLANCE

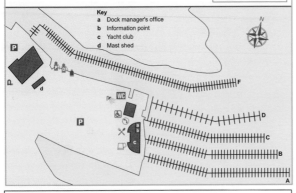

Key
a Dock manager's office
b Information point
c Yacht club
d Mast shed

POOLE DOLPHIN HAVEN

Dolphin Haven
20 Newquay Road, Hamworthy, Poole, Dorset, BH15 4AF
Tel: 01202 649488 Fax: 01202 649488
email: harbourmaster@phc.com

VHF	Ch 80
ACCESS	H24

Once inside Poole Harbour entrance, small yachts heading for Dolphin Haven should use the Boat Channel running parallel south of the dredged Middle Ship Channel, which is primarily used by ferries sailing to and from the Hamworthy terminal. The marina, benefiting from deep water at all states of the tide, is then

accessed via the Little Channel and can be easily identified by its large breakwater. Although 100 berths are designated entirely to visitors, due to its central location, the marina can get very crowded in season so it is best to reserve a berth ahead of time. A stone's throw away is Poole Quay where, besides a multitude of bars and restaurants, there are several places of interest, including the well-known Poole Pottery and the Waterfront Museum in Old High Street.

FACILITIES AT A GLANCE

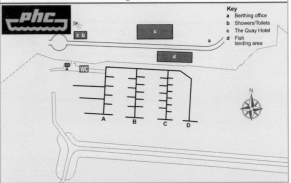

Key
a Berthing office
b Showers/Toilets
c The Quay Hotel
d Fish landing area

PARKSTONE YACHT HAVEN

Parkstone Yacht Club
Pearce Avenue, Parkstone, Poole, Dorset, BH14 8EH
Tel: 01202 743610 Fax: 01202 738824
email: haven@parkstoneyc.co.uk

VHF	Ch M, 80
ACCESS	H24

Situated on the north side of Poole Harbour between Salterns Marina and Dolphin Boat Haven, Parkstone Yacht Haven can be entered at all states of the tides. Its approach channel has been dredged to 2.5m and is clearly marked by buoys. Run by the Parkstone Yacht Club, the Haven provides 200 deep water berths for members and eight visitors' berths, although it will accommodate more visiting yachtsmen when resident berth holders are away. With a busy sailing programme for over 2,500 members, the Yacht Club plays host to a variety of events including Poole Week, which is held towards the end of August.

FACILITIES AT A GLANCE

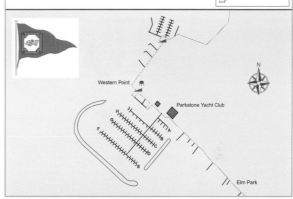

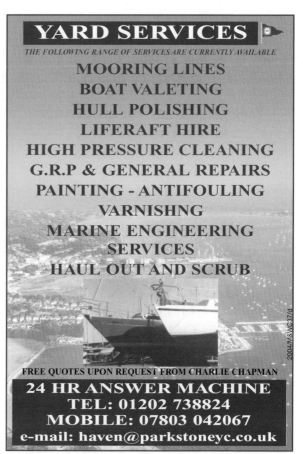

SALTERNS MARINA

Salterns Marina
40 Salterns Way, Lilliput, Poole
Dorset, BH14 8JR
Tel: 01202 709971 Fax: 01202 700398
email: marina@salterns.co.uk www.salterns.co.uk

VHF	Ch M, 80
ACCESS	H24

Holding both the Blue Flag and Five Gold Anchor awards, Salterns Marina provides a service which is second to none. Located off the North Channel, it is approached from the No 31 SHM and benefits from deep water at all states of the tide. Facilities include 220 alongside pontoon berths as well as 75 swinging moorings with a free launch service. However, with very few designated visitors' berths, it is best to contact the marina ahead of time for availability. Fuel, diesel and gas can all be obtained 24 hours a day and the well-stocked chandlery, incorporating a coffee shop, stays open seven days a week.

FACILITIES AT A GLANCE

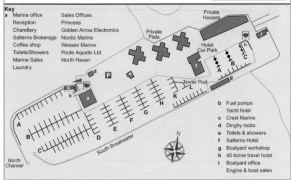

Key

a   Marina office
    Reception
    Chandlery
    Salterns Brokerage
    Coffee shop
    Toilets/Showers
    Marine Sales
    Laundry

Sales Offices:
Princess
Golden Arrow Electronics
Nordic Marine
Wessex Marine
Poole Aquatic Ltd
North Haven

b   Fuel pumps
    Yacht hoist
c   Crest Marine
d   Dinghy racks
e   Toilets & showers
f   Salterns Hotel
g   Boatyard workshop
h   45 tonne travel hoist
i   Boatyard office
    Engine & boat sales

2

Yarmouth

Situated in a marvellous setting at the mouth of the western Yar estuary, the port is a vibrant community with a range of amenities to suit all ages and interests. It is rich is maritime history, with narrow streets full or intriguing small shops, pubs and tea rooms.

Sailing on the River Yar

The Harbour has excellent facilities for visiting yachtsmen. Accessible at all states of the tide, it boasts a modern and well appointed harbour building on the Quay providing quality shower and laundry.

For yachting needs, a number of specialist marine businesses are located nearby whilst for general day to day requirements, the town offers plenty for both the browser and serious shopper.

- ◆ Launderette
- ◆ Disabled Access and facilities
- ◆ Showers
- ◆ Conference/training/hospitality room. Capacity up to 50 people
- ◆ Fuel

Telephone: +44 (0) 1983 760321
Fax: +44 (0) 1983 761192
E-mail: info@yar-iow-harbour.demon.co.uk
www.yarmouth-harbour.co.uk

2004/M&WC36/d

YARMOUTH HARBOUR

Yarmouth Harbour
Yarmouth, Isle of Wight, PO41 0NT
Tel: 01983 760321 Fax: 01983 761192
www.yarmouth-harbour.co.uk

| VHF | Ch 68 |
| ACCESS | H24 |

The most western harbour on the Isle of Wight, Yarmouth is not only a convenient passage stopover but has become a very desirable destination in its own right, with virtually all weather and tidal access, although strong N to NE'ly winds can produce a considerable swell. The HM launch patrols the harbour entrance and will direct visiting yachtsmen to a pontoon berth or pile. With the exception of the town quay, the way ashore is by dinghy or water taxi (VHF Ch 15). The pretty harbour and town offer plenty of fine restaurants and amenities as well as being within easy reach of many of the Isle of Wight tourist attractions. One of its primary features is the castle, constructed in 1547 by order of Henry VIII.

FACILITIES AT A GLANCE

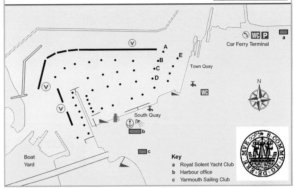

Key
a Royal Solent Yacht Club
b Harbour office
c Yarmouth Sailing Club

LYMINGTON YACHT HAVEN

Lymington Yacht Haven
King's Saltern Road, Lymington, S041 3QD
Tel: 01590 677071 Fax: 01590 678186
www.yachthavens.com email: lymington@yachthavens.com

VHF	Ch 80
ACCESS	H24

The attractive old market town of Lymington lies at the western end of the Solent, just three miles from the Needles Channel. Despite the numerous ferries plying to and from the Isle of Wight, the river is well sheltered and navigable at all states of the tide, proving a popular destination with visiting yachtsmen.

Lymington Yacht Haven is the first of the two marinas from seaward, situated on the port hand side. Offering easy access to the Solent, it is a good 15-minute walk from the town centre and is therefore often quieter than the nearby Lymington Marina.

FACILITIES AT A GLANCE

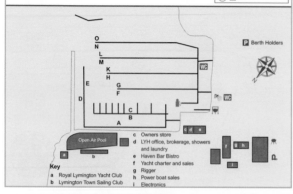

Key
a Royal Lymington Yacht Club
b Lymington Town Sailing Club

c Owners store
d LYH office, brokerage, showers and laundry
e Haven Bar Bistro
f Yacht charter and sales
g Rigger
h Power boat sales
i Electronics

P Berth Holders

LYMINGTON CRUISING SCHOOL
24 Waterloo Road, Lymington, Hampshire SO41 9DB
Tel: (01590) 677478
Fax: (01590) 689210
e-mail: lymingtoncruisin@aol.com
www.lymingtoncruising.co.uk
All RYA practical and shorebased courses including: Yachtmaster preparation, Coastal Skipper, Day Skipper, Competant Crew, SRC and First Aid. Relaxed, friendly, caring service. Courses structured to suit the individuals needs. Adventure and fun but safety paramount.

2

LYMINGTON MARINA

Lymington Marina Ltd
The Shipyard, Lymington, Hampshire, SO41 3YL
Tel: 01590 673312 Fax: 01590 679811
www.berthon.co.uk email: marina@berthon.co.uk

| VHF | Ch 80 |
| ACCESS | H24 |

Situated approximately half a mile up river of Lymington Yacht Haven, on the port hand side, is Lymington Marina. Easily accessible at all states of the tide, it offers between 60 to 70 visitors' berths, although its close proximity to the town centre and first rate services mean that it can get very crowded in summer.

Besides the numerous attractions and activities to be found in the town itself, Lymington also benefits from having the New Forest, with its wild ponies and picturesque scenery, literally on its doorstep. Alternatively, the Solent Way footpath provides an invigorating walk to and from Hurst Castle.

FACILITIES AT A GLANCE

Key
a Dockmaster's office
b Berthon International
c Yacht maintenance & repair
d Yeoman Marine
e Building refit shed
f Hood Sailmakers
g Anchor House
h Seaforth House

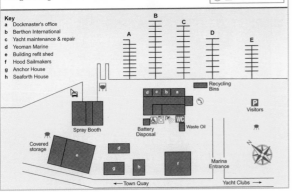

BUCKLER'S HARD MARINA

Buckler's Hard
Beaulieu, Brockenhurst, Hampshire, SO42 7XB
Tel: 01590 616200 Fax: 01590 616211
www.bucklershard.co.uk

| VHF | |
| ACCESS | H24 |

Meandering through the New Forest, the Beaulieu River is considered by many to be one of the most attractive harbours on the mainland side of the Solent. A few miles upstream from the mouth of the river lies Buckler's Hard, an historic 18th century village where shipwrights skilfully constructed warships for Nelson's fleet.

The marina, which offers deep water at all states of the tide (although note that the river's entrance bar can only be crossed approximately two hours either side of LW), is manned 24 hours a day. It's comprehensive facilities range from boat and rigging repairs to a fuel pump and chandlery.

FACILITIES AT A GLANCE

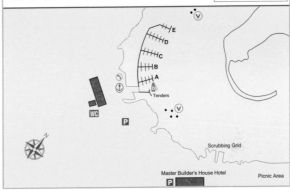

COWES YACHT HAVEN

Cowes Yacht Haven
Vectis Yard, Cowes, Isle of Wight, PO31 7BD
Tel: 01983 299975 Fax: 01983 200332
www.cowesyachthaven.com
email: info@cowesyachthaven.demon.co.uk

| VHF | Ch 80 |
| ACCESS | H24 |

Situated virtually at the centre of the Solent, Cowes is best known as Britain's premier yachting centre and offers all types of facilities to yachtsmen. Cowes Yacht Haven, operating 24 hours a day, has very few permanent moorings and is dedicated to catering for visitors and events. At peak times it can become very crowded and for occasions such as Skandia Life Cowes Week and Hoya Round the Island Race you need to book up in advance.

FACILITIES AT A GLANCE

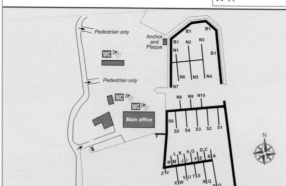

COWES YACHT HAVEN
Vectis Yard, High Street, Cowes, Isle of Wight PO31 7BD
Tel: (01983) 299975
Fax: (01983) 200332
e-mail: info@cowesyachthaven.com
www.cowesyachthaven.com
Marina and yachting event centre.

AQUA TOGS/SHIPMATES GROUP
115 High Street, Cowes, Isle of Wight PO31 7AX
Tel: (01983) 295071 Fax: (01983) 290169
e-mail: sales@chandlery.co.uk
www.chandlery.co.uk
Leading suppliers of brand name technical marine clothing, leisurewear, safety kit and footwear, specialist chandleries in Cowes and Dartmouth, book and chart agents, mail order available. Branches in Cowes, Lymington, Dartmouth, Salcombe, Seaview and Ryde.

EAST COWES MARINA

East Cowes Marina
Britannia Way, East Cowes, Isle of Wight, PO32 6UB
Tel: 01983 293983 Fax: 01983 299276
www.eastcowesmarina.co.uk

| VHF | Ch 80 |
| ACCESS | H24 |

Accommodating around 200 residential yachts and 150 visiting boats, East Cowes Marina is situated in a relaxed semi-rural setting about half a mile above the chain ferry on the Medina River. The on site marine services range from riggers and chandlers to cranage and repair and also include excellent ablution facilities as well as an on site restaurant. Although the chandlery stocks essential items, the nearest convenience store is in East Cowes, which is about a 15-minute walk away. Several water taxis provide a return service to Cowes, ensuring a quick and easy way of getting to the town centre.

FACILITIES AT A GLANCE

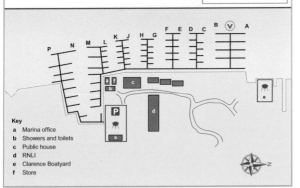

Key
a Marina office
b Showers and toilets
c Public house
d RNLI
e Clarence Boatyard
f Store

SHEPARDS WHARF MARINA

Shepards Wharf Boatyard
Medina Road, Cowes, Isle of Wight, PO31 7HT
Tel: 01983 297821 Fax: 01983 294814
www.shephards.co.uk

| VHF | Ch 80 |
| ACCESS | H24 |

A cable upstream of Cowes Yacht Haven, still on the starboard side, is Shepards Wharf. Incorporating several visitor pontoon berths, its facilities include water as well as full boatyard services ranging from a chandler and sailmaker to a 20-ton boat hoist. Fuel can be obtained from Lallows Boatyard (Tel 01983 292111) or Cowes Yacht Haven. For berthing availability, visiting yachtsmen should contact Cowes Harbour Control on VHF Ch 69 or Tel 01983 293952.

Shepards Wharf is within easy walking distance of Cowes town centre, where among the restaurants to be highly recommended are the Red Duster and Murrays Seafoods on the High Street and Tonino's on Shooters Hill. Also worth visiting are the Maritime Museum, exhibiting the Uffa Fox boats *Avenger* and *Coweslip*, and the Sir Max Aitken Museum. Sir Max contributed enormously to ocean yacht racing and the museum is dedicated to his collection of nautical instruments, paintings and maritime artefacts.

FACILITIES AT A GLANCE

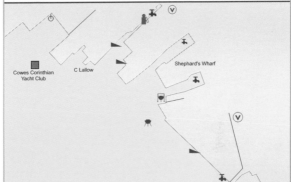

Cowes Corinthian Yacht Club
C Lallow
Shephard's Wharf

ISLAND HARBOUR MARINA

Island Harbour Marina
Mill Lane, Binfield, Newport, Isle of Wight, PO30 2LA
Tel: 01983 822999 Fax: 01983 526020
email: pafharbour@aol.com

VHF	Ch 80
ACCESS	HW±4

Situated in beautiful rolling farmland about half a mile south of Folly Inn, Island Harbour Marina provides around 200 visitors' berths. Protected by a lock that is operated daily from 0700 – 2100 during the summer and from 0800 – 1730 during the winter, the marina is accessible for about four hours either side of HW for draughts of 1.5m.

Due to its remote setting, the marina's on site restaurant also sells essential provisions and newspapers. A half hour walk along the river brings you to Newport, the capital and county town of the Isle of Wight.

FACILITIES AT A GLANCE

Key
a Control tower
b Bin store
c Chandlery
d Restaurant

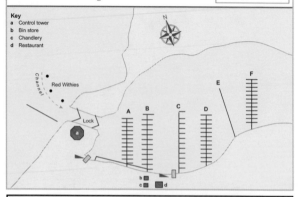

HYTHE MARINA

Hythe Marina
Shamrock Way, Hythe, Southampton, SO45 6DY
Tel: 023 8020 7073 Fax: 023 8084 2424
www.marinas.co.uk email: dwilson@mdlmarinas.co.uk

VHF	Ch 80
ACCESS	H24

Situated on the western shores of Southampton Water, Hythe Marina Village is approached by a dredged channel leading to a lock basin. The lock gates are controlled 24 hours a day throughout the year, with a waiting pontoon to the south of the approach basin.

Hythe Marina Village incorporates full marine services as well as on site restaurants and shops. Forming an integral part of the New Forest Waterside, Hythe is the perfect base from which to explore Hampshire's pretty inland villages and towns, or alternatively you can catch the ferry to Southampton's Town Quay.

FACILITIES AT A GLANCE

Key
a Boathouse
b Lock building
c Waste oil

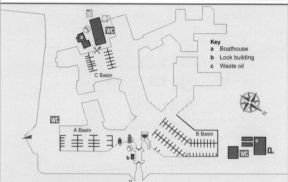

TOWN QUAY MARINA

Town Quay Management Office
Town Quay, Southampton, SO14 2AQ
Tel: 023 8023 4397 Fax: 023 8023 5302
www.marina-info.com

VHF | Ch 10
ACCESS | H24

Town Quay lies above the cruise liner dock on the starboard side of the River Test. Enjoying close proximity to the city centre, it proves extremely popular with  locals. Visitors' berths can therefore be quite scarce so it is definitely advisable for visiting yachtsmen to contact the marina ahead of time to find out about availability. When approaching Town Quay, which is accessible at all states of the tide, beware of the fast ferries shuttling frequently between Southampton and the Isle of Wight.

Town Quay is the nearest marina to the Southampton International Boat Show, which takes place at the Mayflower Park from around the second to third week in September. Reputed to be Europe's most impressive on-water show, it is well worth a visit.

FACILITIES AT A GLANCE

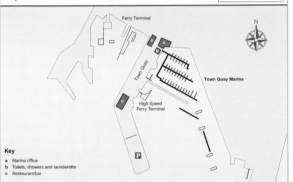

Key
a Marina office
b Toilets, showers and launderette
c Restaurant/bar

OCEAN VILLAGE MARINA

Ocean Village Marina
2 Channel Way, Southampton, SO14 3TG
Tel: 023 8022 9385 Fax: 023 8023 3515
www.marinas.co.uk email: oceanvillage@mdlmarinas.co.uk

VHF | Ch 80
ACCESS | H24

The entrance to Ocean Village Marina lies on the port side of the River Itchen, just before the Itchen Bridge. With the capacity to accommodate large yachts and tall ships, the marina, accessible 24 hours a day, is renowned for hosting the starts of the Volvo and BT Global  Challenge races. Situated at the heart of a waterside development incorporating shops, cinemas, restaurants and housing as well as The Royal Southampton Yacht Club, Ocean Village offers a vibrant atmosphere along with high quality service.

FACILITIES AT A GLANCE

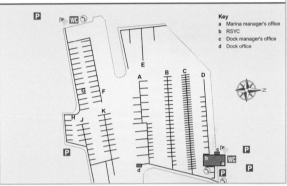

Key
a Marina manager's office
b RSYC
c Dock manager's office
d Dock office

SHAMROCK QUAY MARINA

Shamrock Quay Marina
William Street, Northam, Southampton, Hants, SO14 5QL
Tel: 023 8022 9461 Fax: 023 8021 3808
email: r.fogerty@mdlmarinas.co.uk

VHF	Ch 80
ACCESS	H24

Shamrock Quay, lying upstream of the Itchen Bridge on the port hand side, offers excellent facilities to yachtsmen. It also benefits from being accessible 24 hours a day, although the inside berths can get quite shallow at LWS. Note that it is best to arrive at slack water as the cross tide can be tricky when close quarter manoeuvring.

The city centre is about two miles away, where among the numerous attractions are the Maritime Museum at Town Quay, the Medieval Merchant's House in French Street and the Southampton City Art Gallery in the Civic Centre.

FACILITIES AT A GLANCE

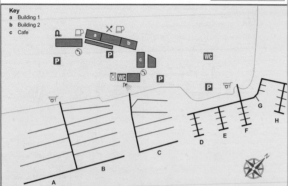

Key
a Building 1
b Building 2
c Cafe

KEMP'S SHIPYARD

Kemp's Shipyard Ltd
Quayside Road, Southampton, SO18 1BZ
Tel: 023 80 632323 Fax: 023 80 226002
enquiries@kempsquay.com

VHF	Ch M
ACCESS	HW±3.5

At the head of the River Itchen on the starboard side is Kemp's Marina, a family-run business with a friendly, old-fashioned feel. Accessible only 3½ hrs either side of HW, it has a limited number of deep water

berths, the rest being half tide, drying out to soft mud. Its restricted access is, however, reflected in the lower prices.

Although situated on the outskirts of Southampton, a short bus or taxi ride will soon get you to the city centre. Besides a nearby BP Garage selling bread and milk, the closest supermarkets can be found in Bitterne Shopping Centre, which is five minutes away by bus.

FACILITIES AT A GLANCE

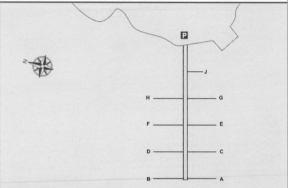

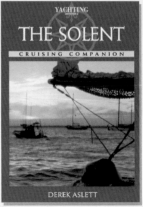

SAXON WHARF MARINA

Saxon Wharf Marina
Lower York Street, Northam
Southampton, SO14 5QF
Tel: 023 8033 9490 Fax: 023 8033 5215
www.marinas.co.uk email: saxonwharf@mdlmarinas.co.uk

VHF Ch 80
ACCESS H24

Saxon Wharf is a relatively new development which is situated towards the top of the River Itchen at the head of Southampton Water. Equipped with 50-metre marina berths and heavy duty pontoons, it is intended to accommodate superyachts and larger vessels. Boasting a 200-ton boat hoist, a 500-ton slipway and several marine specialists, including Southampton Yacht Services, it is the ideal place for the refit and restoration of big boats, whether it be a quick liftout or a large scale project. Located close to Southampton city centre and airport, Saxon Wharf is easily accessible by road, rail or air.

FACILITIES AT A GLANCE

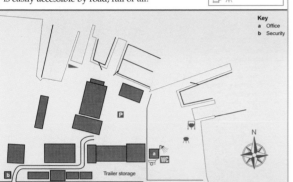

Key
a Office
b Security

N

Trailer storage

HAMBLE POINT MARINA

Hamble Point Marina
School Lane, Hamble, Southampton, SO31 4NB
Tel: 023 8045 2464 Fax: 023 8045 6440
email: hamblepoint@mdlmarinas.co.uk

VHF Ch 80
ACCESS H24

Situated virtually opposite Warsash, this is the first marina you will come to on the western bank of the River Hamble. Accommodating yachts up to 20m in length, it offers easy access to the Solent. As with all the berths in the Hamble, be careful when manoeuvring at certain states of the tide and if possible try to avoid berthing when the tide is ebbing strongly. Boasting extensive facilities, the marina is within a 15-minute walk of Hamble Village, where services include a plethora of pubs and restaurants as well as a post office, bank and general store.

FACILITIES AT A GLANCE

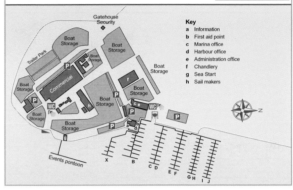

Gatehouse Security

Key
a Information
b First aid point
c Marina office
d Harbour office
e Administration office
f Chandlery
g Sea Start
h Sail makers

PORT HAMBLE MARINA

Port Hamble Marina
Satchell Lane, Hamble, Southampton, SO31 4QD
Tel: 023 8045 2741 Fax: 023 8045 5206
www.marinas.co.uk

VHF Ch 80
ACCESS H24

On the west bank of the River Hamble, Port Hamble is the closest marina to the picturesque Hamble Village, therefore proving extremely popular with visiting yachtsmen. However, with no dedicated places for visitors, berthing availability is often scarce in the summer and it is best to contact the marina ahead of time.

Besides exploring the River Hamble, renowned for its maritime history which began as far back as the ninth century when King Alfred's men sank as many as 20 Viking long ships at Bursledon, other nearby places of interest include the 13th century Netley Abbey, allegedly haunted by Blind Peter the monk, and the Royal Victoria Country Park.

FACILITIES AT A GLANCE

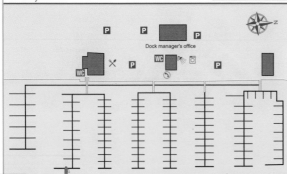

MERCURY YACHT HARBOUR

Mercury Yacht Harbour
Satchell Lane, Hamble, Southampton, SO31 4HQ
Tel: 023 8045 5994 Fax: 023 8045 7369
www.marinas.co.uk email: mercury@mdlmarinas.co.uk

VHF Ch 80
ACCESS H24

Mercury Yacht Harbour is the third marina from seaward on the western bank of the River Hamble, tucked away in a picturesque, wooded site adjacent to Badnam Creek. Enjoying deep water at all states of the tide, it accommodates yachts up to 24m LOA and boasts an extensive array of facilities.

Hamble Village is at least a 20-minute walk away, although the on site chandlery does stock a small amount of essential items, and for a good meal you need look no further than the Oyster Quay bar and restaurant whose balcony offers striking views of the water.

FACILITIES AT A GLANCE

Key
a Toilets
b Launderette
c Chandlery
d Restaurant and bar
e Brokerage
f Dockmaster,
   marina manager's office
g Waste disposal
h Recycling area

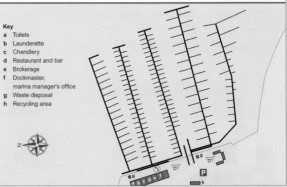

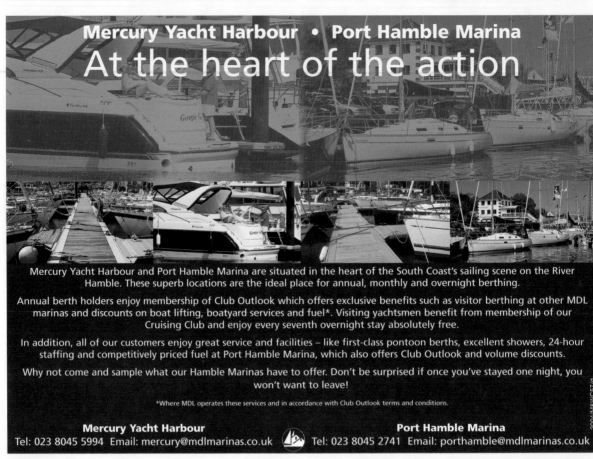

Mercury Yacht Harbour • Port Hamble Marina
At the heart of the action

Mercury Yacht Harbour and Port Hamble Marina are situated in the heart of the South Coast's sailing scene on the River Hamble. These superb locations are the ideal place for annual, monthly and overnight berthing.

Annual berth holders enjoy membership of Club Outlook which offers exclusive benefits such as visitor berthing at other MDL marinas and discounts on boat lifting, boatyard services and fuel*. Visiting yachtsmen benefit from membership of our Cruising Club and enjoy every seventh overnight stay absolutely free.

In addition, all of our customers enjoy great service and facilities – like first-class pontoon berths, excellent showers, 24-hour staffing and competitively priced fuel at Port Hamble Marina, which also offers Club Outlook and volume discounts.

Why not come and sample what our Hamble Marinas have to offer. Don't be surprised if once you've stayed one night, you won't want to leave!

*Where MDL operates these services and in accordance with Club Outlook terms and conditions.

Mercury Yacht Harbour
Tel: 023 8045 5994 Email: mercury@mdlmarinas.co.uk

Port Hamble Marina
Tel: 023 8045 2741 Email: porthamble@mdlmarinas.co.uk

2004/M&WC57/d

SWANWICK MARINA

Swanwick Marina
Swanwick, Southampton, Hampshire, SO31 1ZL
Tel: 01489 885000 Fax: 01489 885509
www.moody.co.uk email: sales@moody.co.uk

VHF Ch 80
ACCESS H24

Situated on the east bank of the River Hamble next to Bursledon Bridge, Swanwick Marina is accessible at all states of the tide and can accommodate yachts up to 20m LOA.

The marina's fully-licensed bar and bistro, the Doghouse, overlooking the river, is open for breakfast, lunch and dinner during the summer. Alternatively, just a short row or walk away is the celebrated Jolly Sailor pub in Bursledon on the west bank, made famous for being the local watering hole in the British television series *Howard's Way*.

FACILITIES AT A GLANCE

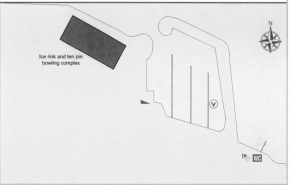

Key
a Marina office
b Pub/restaurant
c Chandlery
d Moody offices

RYDE LEISURE HARBOUR

Ryde Harbour
The Esplanade, Ryde, Isle of Wight, PO33 1JA
Tel: 01983 613879 Fax: 01983 613879
www.rydeharbour.com email: rydeharbour@amserve.net

VHF Ch 80
ACCESS HW±2

Known as the 'gateway to the Island', Ryde, with its elegant houses and abundant shops, is among the Isle of Wight's most popular resorts. Its well-protected harbour is conveniently close to the exceptional beaches as well as to the town's restaurants and amusements.

Drying to 2.5m and therefore only accessible to yachts that can take the ground, the harbour accommodates 90 resident boats as well as up to 75 visiting yachts.

Ideal for family cruising, Ryde offers a wealth of activities, ranging from ten pin bowling and ice skating to crazy golf and tennis.

FACILITIES AT A GLANCE

Ice rink and ten pin bowling complex

BEMBRIDGE MARINA

Bembridge Marina
Harbour Office, St Helens Quay, Ryde
Isle of Wight, PO33 1YS
Tel: 01983 872828 Fax: 01983 872922
email: bembridge@leisureharbours.co.uk
www.leisureharbour.co.uk

VHF	Ch 80
ACCESS	HW±2.5

Bembridge is a compact, pretty harbour whose entrance, although restricted by the tides (recommended entry for a 1.5m draught is 2½hrs before HW), is well sheltered in all but north north easterly gales. Offering excellent sailing clubs, beautiful beaches and fine restaurants, this Isle of Wight port is a first class haven with plenty of charm. With approximately 100 new visitors' berths on the Duver Marina pontoons, the marina at St Helen's Quay, at the western end of the harbour, is now allocated to annual berth holders only.

FACILITIES AT A GLANCE

Key
a Marina office
b Brading Haven YC

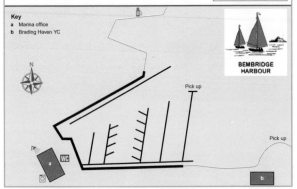

HASLAR MARINA

Haslar Marina
Haslar Road, Gosport, Hampshire, PO12 1NU
Tel: 023 9260 1201 Fax: 023 9260 2201
www.haslarmarina.co.uk

VHF	Ch 80
ACCESS	H24

This modern, purpose-built marina lies to port on the western side of Portsmouth Harbour entrance and is easily recognised by its prominent lightship incorporating a bar and restaurant. Accessible at all states of the tide, Haslar's extensive facilities do not however include fuel, the nearest being at the Camper and Nicholsons jetty only a fuel cables north.

Within close proximity is the town of Gosport where the Royal Navy Submarine Museum and the Museum of Naval Firepower 'Explosion' are well worth a visit.

FACILITIES AT A GLANCE

Key
a Admin. offices,
   security, toilets,
   showers, weather,
   soft drinks machine
b Rubbish skips,
   security gate
c Bistro/bar and
   independent operators,
   trolleys
d Security, car park
e Superloo: toilets,
   showers, trolleys
f Bar, restaurant, toilets,
   public telephone,
   shower, laundry
g The Millennium
   Timespace
h Public slipway

GOSPORT MARINA

Gosport Marina Ltd
Mumby Road, Gosport, Hampshire, PO12 1AH
Tel: 023 9252 4811 Fax: 023 9258 9541
email: peter@gosport-marina.com
www.cnmarinas.com

VHF	Ch M, 80
ACCESS	H24

A few cables north of Haslar Marina, again on the port hand side, lies Gosport Marina. Boasting 150 fully-serviced visitors' berths, its extensive range of facilities incorporates a fuel barge on its southern breakwater as well as shower and laundry amenities. Numerous boatyard and engineering specialists are also located in and around the premises, including the legendary Camper & Nicholsons yard.

Within easy reach of the marina is Gosport town centre, offering a cosmopolitan selection of restaurants along with several supermarkets and shops.

FACILITIES AT A GLANCE

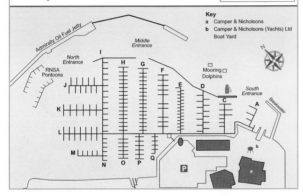

Key
a Camper & Nicholsons
b Camper & Nicholsons (Yachts) Ltd
   Boat Yard

ROYAL CLARENCE MARINA

Royal Clarence Marina, Royal Clarence Yard
Weevil Lane, Gosport, Hampshire PO12 1AX
Tel: 023 9252 3810 Fax: 023 9252 3980
email: enquiries@royalclarencemarina.co.uk
www.royalclarencemarina.co.uk

VHF Ch 80
ACCESS H24

Royal Clarence Marina
benefits from a unique setting
within a deep-water basin in
front of the Royal Navy's
former victualling yard. Only
10 minutes from the entrance
to Portsmouth Harbour, it
forms part of a £100 million
redevelopment scheme which,

anticipated to be completed in 2005, will incorporate residential homes,
waterfront bars and restaurants as well as shopping
outlets. Among its facilities are fully serviced finger
pontoon berths up to 18m in length, while over
200m of alongside berthing will accommodate
Yacht Club rallies and other maritime events.

FACILITIES AT A GLANCE

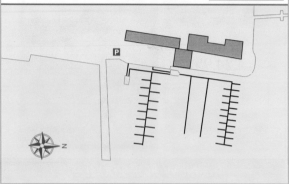

PORT SOLENT MARINA

Port Solent Marina
South Lockside, Portsmouth, PO6 4TJ
Tel: 023 9221 0765 Fax: 023 9232 4241
www.premiermarinas.com
email: kirstvs@premiermarinas.com

VHF Ch 80
ACCESS H24

Port Solent Marina is
located to the north east of
Portsmouth Harbour, not
far from the historic
Portchester Castle.
Accessible via a 24-hour
lock, this purpose built

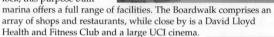

marina offers a full range of facilities. The Boardwalk comprises an
array of shops and restaurants, while close by is a David Lloyd
Health and Fitness Club and a large UCI cinema.

No visit to Portsmouth Harbour is complete
without a trip to the Historic Dockyard, home to
Henry VIII's *Mary Rose*, Nelson's HMS *Victory*
and the first iron battleship, HMS *Warrior*, built
in 1860.

FACILITIES AT A GLANCE

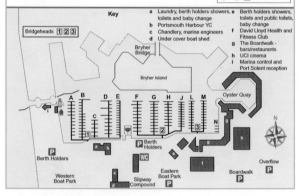

Key

a Laundry, berth holders showers,
   toilets and baby change
b Portsmouth Harbour YC
c Chandlery, marine engineers
d Under cover boat shed
e Berth holders showers,
   toilets and baby change
   Berth holders showers,
   toilets and public toilets,
   baby change
f David Lloyd Health and
   Fitness Club
g The Boardwalk -
   bars/restaurants
h UCI cinema
i Marina control and
   Port Solent reception

2

SOUTHSEA MARINA

Southsea Marina
Fort Cumberland Road, PO4 9RJ
Tel: 02392 822719 Fax: 02392 822220
email: southsea@premiermarinas.com
www.premiermarinas.com

VHF	Ch 80
ACCESS	HW±3

Southsea Marina is located on the western shore of Langstone Harbour, an expansive tidal bay situated between Hayling Island and Portsmouth. Its channel is clearly marked by five starboard and nine port hand marks. The entrance is operated by a tidal gate which closes at around half tide when the depth is about 1.6m. The marina has a small shop and restaurant on site, otherwise the nearest town is Southsea where its castle and the Royal Marines Museum are among the numerous local attractions.

FACILITIES AT A GLANCE

SPARKES MARINA

Sparkes Marina
Wittering Road, Hayling Island, Hampshire, PO11 9SR
Tel: 02392 463572 Fax: 02392 465741
email: info@sparkes.co.uk www.sparkes.co.uk

VHF	Ch 80
ACCESS	H24

Just inside the entrance to Chichester Harbour, on the eastern shores of Hayling Island, lies Sparkes Marina and Boatyard. Its approach channel has been dredged to 2m MLW and can be identified by an unlit ECM. One of two marinas in Chichester to have full tidal access, its facilities include a wide range of marine services as well as a well-stocked chandlery and first class restaurant. Within close proximity are a newsagent, farm shop and various takeaways, while a taxi ride away are Capers and Jaspers, two restaurants on Hayling Island renowned for their top quality cuisine.

FACILITIES AT A GLANCE

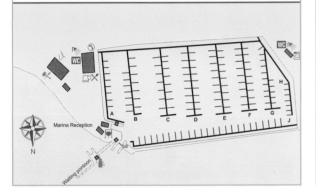

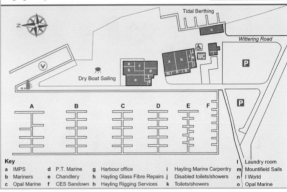

Key

a IMPS	d P.T. Marine	g Harbour office	i Hayling Marine Carpentry	l Laundry room
b Mariners	e Chandlery	h Hayling Glass Fibre Repairs	j Disabled toilets/showers	m Mountifield Sails
c Opal Marine	f CES Sandown	h Hayling Rigging Services	k Toilets/showers	n I World
				o Opal Marine

NORTHNEY MARINA

Northney Marina
Northney Road, Hayling Island, Hampshire, PO11 0NH
Tel: 023 9246 6321 Fax: 023 9246 1467
www.marinas.co.uk email: msmith@mdlmarinas.co.uk

VHF	Ch 80
ACCESS	H24

One of two marinas in Chichester Harbour to be accessible at all states of the tide, Northney Marina is on the northern shore of Hayling Island in the well marked Sweare Deep Channel, which branches off to port almost at the end of the Emsworth Channel. With a new facilities block having recently been completed, the marina now incorporates a very basic grocery store as well as improved ablution facilities. Bicycles are also available for hire, providing a simple means of exploring Hayling Island and its award-winning sandy beaches.

FACILITIES AT A GLANCE

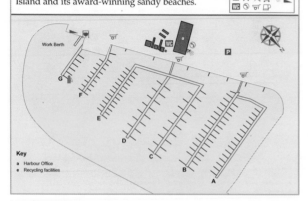

Key
a Harbour Office
e Recycling facilities

EMSWORTH YACHT HARBOUR

Emsworth Yacht Harbour
Thorney Road, Emsworth, Hants, PO10 8BP
Tel: 01243 377727 Fax: 01243 373432
email: info@emsworth-marina.co.uk
www.emsworth-marina.co.uk

VHF	Ch 80
ACCESS	HW±2

Accessible about one and a half to two hours either side of high water, Emsworth Yacht Harbour is a sheltered site, offering good facilities to yachtsmen.

Created in 1964 from a log pond, the marina is within easy walking distance of the pretty little town of Emsworth, which boasts at least 10 pubs, several high quality restaurants and two well-stocked convenience stores.

FACILITIES AT A GLANCE

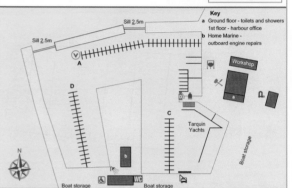

Key
a Ground floor - toilets and showers
   1st floor - harbour office
b Home Marine -
   outboard engine repairs

A complete boatbuilding, refit and repair service operating from new fully fitted joinery and electrical workshops in the Teal Building at Northney Marina

Antifouling
Battery monitoring systems
Boat Refits
Boat Repairs
Boatbuilding
Charting Systems
Electrical inspections with detailed reports
Electrical repairs & rewiring
Electronic installations
Full electronics interfacing to G.P.S., Auto-pilot, Plotter, Radar, Echo sounder, VHF, etc.

Authorised installer of Vetus equipment

All projects undertaken - Large or small

Call in at our workshops any day of the week.

Corporate contact numbers;
Unit B, The Teal Building
Northney Marina, Hayling Island
Hampshire PO11 0NH
Tel: 023 9246 9246
Fax: 023 9246 1246

Westerly & Storebo specialists

G.R.P. work
Joinery
Marine plumbing
Paint spraying
Painting and varnishing
Polishing
Shipwright work
Shore power
Sign writing
Valeting
Wood machining

SIDE-POWER

Specific contact numbers;
Northney Yacht Services
Peter Thomas
078 5099 1499

European Yacht Services
Barrie Hooper
078 0129 9707

Marine Electrical
Steve Hughes
023 9271 9054

Northney Marine Services

2004/M&WC52/d

CHICHESTER MARINA

Chichester Marina
Birdham, Chichester, West Sussex, PO20 7EJ
Tel: 01243 512731 Fax: 01243 513472
email: chichester@premiermarinas.com
www.premiermarinas.com

VHF	Ch 80
ACCESS	HW±4

Chichester Marina, nestling in an enormous natural harbour, has more than 1,000 berths, making it one of the largest marinas in the UK. Its approach channel can be easily identified by the CM SHM pile but dries to 0.5m, therefore restricting access to around two hours either side of LW if you draw around 1.5m. Besides the wide ranging marine facilities, there are also a restaurant and small convenience store on site. Chichester, which is only about a five minute bus or taxi ride away, has several places of interest, the most notable being the cathedral.

FACILITIES AT A GLANCE

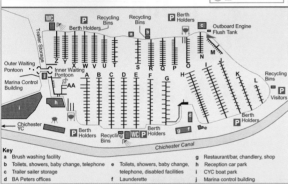

Key
a Brush washing facility
b Toilets, showers, baby change, telephone
c Trailer sailer storage
d BA Peters offices
e Toilets, showers, baby change, telephone, disabled facilities
f Launderette
g Restaurant/bar, chandlery, shop
h Reception car park
i CYC boat park
j Marina control building

BIRDHAM POOL MARINA

Birdham Pool Marina
Birdham Pool, Chichester, Sussex
Tel: 01243 512310 Fax: 01243 513163
email: bpool@petersplc.com

VHF	Ch 80
ACCESS	HW±3

Birdham Pool must be among Britain's most charming and rustic marinas. Only accessible three hours either side of HW via a lock, any visiting yachtsman will not be disappointed by its unique and picturesque setting. To get to Birdham Pool, enter the channel at the Birdham SHM beacon. The channel is marked by green piles that should be left no more than 3m to starboard. There is a wide range of marine facilities on hand, including a small chandlery that opens six days a week.

FACILITIES AT A GLANCE

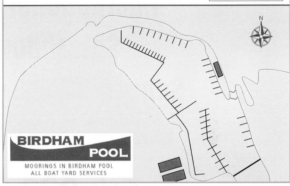

BIRDHAM POOL
MOORINGS IN BIRDHAM POOL
ALL BOAT YARD SERVICES

CRUISING COMPANION SERIES

The Cruising Companion range covers popular cruising grounds in W Europe. With superb quality port plans, full-colour aerial photography, and the latest pilotage and approach information, the Cruising Companion series adds 'what to do' information to the 'how to get there' pilotage, with full coverage of shore-side facilities and places of interest.

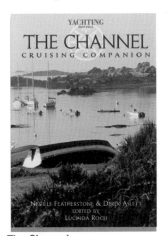

The Channel
£29.95 ISBN: 1 904358 12 8

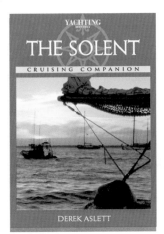

The Solent
£24.95 ISBN: 1 904358 11 X

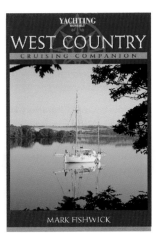

West Country
£19.95 ISBN: 0 333 90454 0

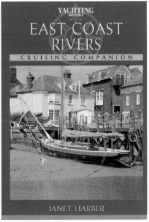

East Coast Rivers
£19.95 ISBN: 0 333 90455 9

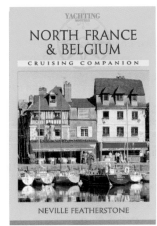

North France & Belgium
£24.95 ISBN: 0 333 98954 6

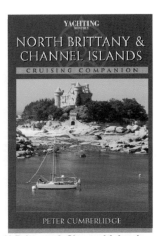

N Brittany & Channel Islands
£24.95 ISBN: 0 333 90452 4

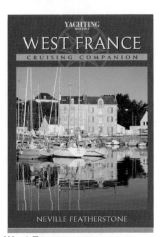

West France
£24.95 ISBN: 0 333 90453 2

North West Spain
£24.95 ISBN: 1 904358 10 1

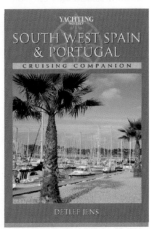

South West Spain & Portugal
£24.95 ISBN: 0 333 90773 6

Available from all good chandlers or direct from:

Nautical Data Limited • The Book Barn • Westbourne • Hampshire PO10 8RS • UK
tel: +44 (0)1243 389352 • fax: +44 (0)1243 379136 • email: sales@nauticaldata.com • web: www.nauticaldata.com

A & V Leisure Portsmouth
Sail repairs   023 9251 0204

Acamar Marine Services/Sirius Yacht Training Christchurch   01202 488030

Admiral Marine Ltd Salisbury
Yacht insurance   01722 416106

Aladdin's Cave Chandlery Ltd
Chichester   01243 773788

Aladdin's Cave Chandlery Ltd (Deacons) Bursledon   023 8040 2182

Aladdin's Cave Chandlery (Camper & Nicholsons) Gosport   023 8040 2182

Aladdin's Cave Chandlery Ltd (Hamble Point) Southampton
                             023 8045 5058

Aladdin's Cave Chandlery Ltd (Mercury) Southampton 023 8045 4849

Aladdin's Cave Chandlery Ltd (Port Hamble) Southampton   023 8045 4858

Aladdin's Cave Chandlery Ltd (Swanwick) Swanwick   01489 575828

Ampair Ringwood
Wind and water powered battery charging systems   01425 480780

Ancasta International Boat Sales
Southampton
Brokerage   023 8045 0000

Andark Diving Southampton
                             01489 581755

Arthurs Chandlery, R Gosport
                             023 9252 6522

Arton, Charles Milford-on-Sea
Canvas goods; upholstery 01590 644682

Arun Sails Chichester   01243 573185

Aqua Togs/Shipmates Group Cowes
Marine clothing supplier   01983 295071

Atkin & Associates Lymington
Sailing & motor yacht surveyors
                             01590 688633

Atkinson Marine Lymington
Electrical and electronic supplier
                             01590 688389

Attrill & Sons, H Bembridge
Repairs; engineer   01983 872319

Auto & Marine Services Botley
Marine engineer   01489 785009

Auto Marine Southsea
Marine engineer   023 9282 5601

Auto Marine Sales Southsea
Chandler   023 9281 2263

AW Marine Haslar Marina, Gosport
Electronic/electrical specialist
                             023 9250 1207

B P S C Marine Services Southampton
Repairs to nautical and survey instruments
                             023 8023 0045

Bainbridge International Southampton
Sail cloth/equipment   01489 776000

Banks Sails, Bruce Southampton
Sailmaker   01489 582444

Barden UK Ltd Fareham
Batteries; chargers; SOLARA solar power
                             01489 570770

Beaulieu River HM   01590 616200

Beaulieu River Police   023 80335444

Beaulieu River SC Brockenhurst
                             01590 616273

Bembridge Boatyard Marine Works
Storage; minor repairs   01983 872911

Bembridge Coast Hotel Bembridge
                             01983 873931

Bembridge HM   01983 872828

Bembridge Marina Bembridge
                             01983 872828

Bembridge Outboards   01983 872817

Bembridge SC Isle of Wight
                             01983 872686

Bengco Engineering Hamble
                             023 8045 7595

Berthon Boat Co Lymington
                             01590 673312

BHG Marine Beaulieu
Stockists of RIBS, Avon Inflatables & Yamaha outboards   0845 644 6645

Birdham Shipyard Ltd Birdham
Yacht repairs; slipping   01243 512310

Birdham Shipyard Chichester
                             01243 512310

Blakes Paints Southampton
Antifouling; osmosis prevention
                             01489 864440

Bluecastle Chandlers Portland
                             01305 822298

Bluewater Horizons Weymouth
Boat repairs; sales; storage; chandler
                             01305 782080

Boat Sales International Ltd
Southampton
UK dealer for Farr yachts 023 8045 7966

BoatScrubber International Haslar
Marina, Gosport
Hull cleaning   023 9251 0567

Boatyard, Parkstone Poole
Boatyard; chandlery   01202 672687

Bosham Quaymaster Nr Chichester
                             01243 573336

Bosham SC Nr Chichester
                             01243 572341

Bosham Sailing School Nr Chichester
                             01243 572555

Brading Haven YC Isle of Wight
                             01983 872289

British Offshore Sailing School
Hamble   023 8045 7733

Brookes & Gatehouse Romsey
Electronics   01794 518448

Buckler's Hard Boat Builders Ltd
Beaulieu
Chandlery, sailmaker, marine engineers
                             01590 616214

Buckler's Hard Marina Beaulieu
                             01590 616200

Bukh Diesel UK Ltd Poole
Marine inboard engines; spares
                             01202 668840

Bussell & Co, WL Weymouth
Chandlers and riggers   01305 785633

Buzzard Marine Isle of Wight
Chandlery, marine engineers
                             01983 760707

C&J Marine Textiles Chichester
Sprayhoods, biminis, cockpit enclosures; sails   01243 785485

Café Mozart Cowes
Waterside restaurant   01983 293681

Calibra Marine International Ltd
Southampton
Anchors; propellers; reefing systems; gangways; hatches; brokerage
                             08702 400358

Camber Berthing Offices Portsmouth
                             023 9229 7395

Camper & Nicholsons Marinas Ltd
Gosport   023 9252 4811

Camper & Nicholsons Yachting
Portsmouth
Boatbuilder; repairs; maintenance
                             023 9258 0221

Carbospars Ltd Hamble
Masts; spars   023 8045 6736

Castle Cove SC Weymouth
                             01305 783708

CC Marine Chichester
Adhesive tapes   01243 672606

CE Proof Hamble
Surveyor   023 8045 3245

C-map Ltd Fareham
Marine electronics; chartware
                             01329 517777

C Q Chandlers Ltd Poole
                             01202 682095

Chatham Clothing Company Ltd
Chippenham
Leisure clothing   01249 460770

Chichester Cruiser and Racing Club
01483 770391

Chichester Chandlery 01243 784572

Chichester Harbour HM 01243 512301

Chichester Marina Chichester
01243 512731

Chichester YC Chichester
01243 512918

Christchurch Boat Shop Christchurch
Chandlery 01202 482751

Christchurch HM 01202 495061

Christchurch Police 01202 486333

Christchurch SC Christchurch
01202 483150

CJR Propulsion Ltd Southampton
Propellers and marine sterngear
023 8063 9366

Clare Lallow Cowes
Boatbuilder; repairs; fuel 01983 292112

Clarence Marine Engineering Gosport
Marine engineers 023 9251 1555

Clark's Boatworks Portland
Repair and maintenance 01305 860265

C-map Ltd Fareham
Marine electronics; chartware
01329 517777

Coastal Leisure Ltd Southampton
Boat sales; brokerage; yacht management
yacht/boat charter 023 8033 2222

Coastal Sea School Weymouth
Training courses; first aid courses
0870 321 3271

Cobb's Quay Marina Poole
01202 674299

Cobnor Activities Centre Trust Nr
Chichester 01243 572791

Comfort Afloat Gosport
Upholstery; covers; matresses
023 9260 2686

Compass Point Chandlery
Southampton 023 8045 2388

Compass Watersports Devizes
Mail order chandlery and clothing supplier
01380 813100

Convoi Exceptionnel Ltd Southampton
International marine haulage and abnormal
load consultants 023 8045 3045

Coombes, AA Bembridge
Boat repairs 01983 872296

Covercare Fareham
Sailmaker; canvas goods 01329 311878

Covercraft Southampton
Canvas goods 023 8033 8286

Cowes Combined Clubs 01983 295744

Cowes Corinthian YC Isle of Wight
01983 296333

Cowes Harbour Water Taxi
07050 344818

Cowes HM 01983 293952

Cowes Yacht Haven Isle of Wight
01983 299975

Cowes Yachting
Marketing organisation for Cowes
01983 280770

C Q Chandlers Ltd Poole
01202 682095

Crane Marine, John Havant
Marine engineer 023 9240 0121

Crewsaver Gosport
Manufactures lifejackets, lifesaving
equipment, sailing clothing, accessories
023 9252 8621

Crusader Sails Poole 01202 670580

Cutler Marine Engineering, John
Emsworth 01243 375014

Darglow Engineering Ltd Wareham
Maxprop propellers 01929 556512

David Greening Yacht Design Ltd
Chichester
Yacht design; surveys; naval architecture
023 9263 1806

Davis Marine, Ron Portland
01305 821175

Davis's Boatyard Poole 01202 674349

Deacon's Boat Yard Hamble
Boatyard; chandlery 023 8040 2253

**Dean & Reddyhoff – East Cowes
Marina** 01983 293983

Dean & Reddyhoff – Haslar Marina
023 9260 1201

**Dean & Reddyhoff – Weymouth
Marina** 01305 767576

Dehler Yachts UK Ltd Hamble
Performance cruising yachts
023 8045 8260

Dell Quay SC Chichester 01243 785080

DG Wroath Cowes Yacht Haven
Electrical engineer 01983 281467

Discovery Yachts Limited Southampton
Cruising yachts 023 8086 5555

Diverse Yacht Services Hamble
Navigation & electronic equipment
023 8045 3399

Dolphin Haven Poole 01202 649488

Dolphin Quay Boatyard Ltd Emsworth
Specialists in wooden boats
01243 373234

Dorset Yacht Company Poole
Repairs 01202 674531

Doyle Sails Southampton
Sailmaker 023 8033 2622

East Cowes Marina Isle of Wight
01983 293983

East Cowes SC Isle of Wight
01983 531687

East Dorset SC Poole 01202 706111

Eastney Cruising Association
Portsmouth 023 9273 4103

Echopilot Marine Electronics Ltd
Ringwood
Electronics 01425 476211

Elephant Boatyard Southampton
023 8040 3268

Eling SC 023 8086 3987

Emark Marine Ltd Emsworth
Marine engineers 01243 375383

Emblem Enterprises East Cowes
Repairs 01983 294243

Emsworth Chandlery Emsworth
01243 375500

Emsworth SC Emsworth 01243 372850

Emsworth Shipyard Emsworth
Boatbuilders; repairs 01243 375211

Emsworth Slipper SC Emsworth
01243 372523

Emsworth Yacht Harbour Emsworth
01243 377727

Epic Ventures Ltd Cowes
01983 291292

Euronav Ltd Portsmouth
Electronics 023 9237 3855

Fairweather Marine Fareham
Boatbuilders; repairs 01329 283500

Fareham Marina Fareham
01329 822445

Fareham Sailing & Motor BC Fareham
01329 233324

Fat Face Havant
Clothing 02392 485555

Fischer Panda UK Ltd Verwood
Manufactures marine generators
01202 820840

Fishbourne Quay Boatyard Ryde
01983 882200

Five Star Sailing Warsash
Sailing tuition 01489 885599

Flew Sailmakers Portchester
Sailmaker 01329 822676

Flexicovers Poole
Canvas goods; boat covers
01202 721309

Foil Sails Lymington
Sailmaker 01590 612052

Force 4 Chandlery Lymington
01590 673698

Force 4 Chandlery Poole
01202 723311

Four Seasons Gosport
Yacht Charter   023 9251 1789

Frederiksen Boat Fittings (UK) Ltd
Gosport
Deck fittings; blocks   023 9252 5377

Furneaux Riddall & Co Ltd Portsmouth
Marine lamps; torches   023 9266 8624

Furuno (UK) Ltd Denmead
Electronics   023 9223 0303

Garmin Romsey
Navigational equipment   01794 519944

Genacis Poole
Dolphin water-cooled diesel generators
01202 624356

Geonav UK Ltd Poole
Navigational equipment   0870 240 4575

Giles Naval Architects, Laurent
Lymington
Yacht designer; naval architect
01590 641777

Go Sail Ltd East Cowes
Sailing School   01983 280220

Golden Arrow Marine Ltd Southampton
Electronics   023 8071 0371

Goodway Sea School Gosport
07887 500710

Gordon, AD Portland
Yacht rigging   01305 821569

Gori Propellers Poole
Stern gear; propellers   01202 621631

Gosport Boat Yard Gosport
Engineer; repairs   023 9258 6216

Gosport CC Gosport   02392 586838

Grand Soleil UK Ltd Hamble
Performance yachts   023 8045 5977

Greenham Regis Marine Electronics
Cowes   01983 293996

Greenham Regis Marine Electronics
Emsworth   01243 378314

Greenham Regis Marine Electronics
Lymington   01590 671144

Greenham Regis Marine Electronics
Southampton   023 8063 6555

Haines Boatyard Chichester
Maintenance; repairs   01243 512228

Hale Marine, Ron Portsmouth
Outboard engine repairs 023 9273 2985

Halsey Lidgard Sailmakers Chichester
01243 545410

Halsey Lidgard Sailmakers Southsea
023 9229 4700

Halyard Salisbury
Noise insulation materials 01722 710922

Hamble Point Marina Southampton
023 8045 2464

Hamble Point Yacht Charters Hamble
023 8045 7110

Hamble River HM   01489 576387

Hamble River Police   023 80335444

Hamble River SC Southampton
023 80452070

Hamble River Taxi Hamble
023 8045 4512/07720 438402

Hamble School of Yachting Ltd
Hamble   023 8045 2688

Hamble Yacht Services Hamble
023 8045 4111

Hampshire Marine Ltd Stubbington
Marine engineer   01329 665561

Hardway Marine Store Gosport
Berthing; engineering; repairs
023 9258 0420

Hardway SC Gosport   02392 581875

Harbour Engineering Itchenor
Marine engineer   01243 513454

Harken UK Lymington
Hardware   01590 689122

Harley Racing Yachts Ltd Cowes
01983 280060

Harvey Design, Ray Barton on Sea
Yacht designer   01425 613492

Harwoods Yacht Chandlers Yarmouth
01983 760258

Haslar Marina Gosport 023 9260 1201

Hayles, Harold Yarmouth
Chandlery, marine engineering
01983 760373

Hayling Ferry SC; Locks SC Hayling
Island   023 8082 9833

Hayling Island SC Hayling Island
023 9246 3768

Hayling Yacht Company Hayling Island
Chandlery, marine engineering
023 9246 3592

Highcliffe SC Christchurch
01425 274874

Hobo Yachting Southampton
RYA tuition   023 8033 4574

Holman Rigging Chichester Marina
Specialist mast and rigging service
01243 514000

Home Marine Emsworth
Outboard engine repairs 01243 266048

Hood Sailmakers Lymington
01590 675011

Hornet SC Gosport   023 9258 0403

Hornsey (Chandlery) Ltd, Chris
Southsea   023 9273 4728

Howells & Son, KJ Poole
Teak joinery   01202 665724

Humphreys Yacht Designs, Rob
Lymington   01590 679344

Hunter & Combes Cowes
Chandlery   01983 299599

Hythe Marina Village Southampton
023 8020 7073

Hythe SC Southampton 023 8084 6563

ICS Electronics Arundel
Electronics – GMDSS/NAVTEX
01903 731101

Index Marine Poole
Electrical equipment   01202 430149

International Barge & Yacht Brokers
Southampton   023 8045 5205

International Coatings Ltd
Southampton
Antifoulings, varnishes, epoxies, cleaners
023 8022 6722

International Yachtmaster Academy
Southampton
RYA sailing tuition   023 8067 8723

Island Chandlers East Cowes Marina
01983 299800

Island Harbour Marina Newport
01983 822999

Island SC Isle of Wight 01983 296621

Itchen Marine Southampton
023 8063 1500

Itchenor SC Chichester 01243 512400

J Boats UK Southampton
High performance yachts 023 8045 5669

Jasper Covers Fareham
Canvas covers   01329 845353

JB Yacht Services Southampton
Canopies, spray hoods, winter covers
01489 572487

JG Technologies Ltd Weymouth
Electrical & electronic equipment
0845 458 9616

**JP Services – Marine Safety &
Training** Tangmere, Chichester
Maritime training   01243 537552

JS Mouldings International Bursledon
GRP repair specialists; bow & stern
thrusters   023 8040 3220

Kelvin Hughes Ltd Southampton
Nautical books; charts; navigational
software   023 8063 4911

2

Kemp Sails Ltd Wareham
01929 554308/554378

Kemps Quay Marina Southampton
023 8063 2323

Kevin Mole Outboards Cowes
01983 289699

Keyhaven Police 01590 615101

Keyhaven YC Keyhaven 01590 642165

Kingfisher Marine Weymouth
Marine equipment, boatbuilding, repairs
and maintenance 01305 766595

Kings Yacht Agency Beaulieu/
Southampton
Yacht brokers (specialising in Nicholson
yachts) 01590 616316/023 8033 1533

Kiss Marine Hythe
Marine services; repairs 023 8084 0100

Knox-Johnson, Paul Southsea
Broker 023 9286 4524

**Krueger Marine & Vehicle Heating
Systems** New Milton
Electrical equipment 01425 619869

Lake Yard Marina Poole 01202 674531

Lallows Brokerage Cowes
01983 282005

Landau UK Ltd Hamble
Electronic & electrical equipment; safety
products 01489 881588

Langstone Harbour HM
023 9246 3419

Langstone SC Havant 023 92484577

Lansdale Pannell Marine Chichester
Outboard engine specialists
01243 512374

Latham's Boatyard Poole
New build; repairs; storage
01202 748029

Levy, Derek Brighton
Surveyor
01273 721095

Lewmar Ltd Havant
Winches, anchoring systems, hardware
023 9247 1841

Lifeline Marine Services Poole
Repairs 01202 669676

Lilliput SC Poole 01202 740319

Locks SC Portsmouth 023 92829833

Lombard Southampton
Marine finance specialists 023 8051 5050

Lucas Sails Portchester
Sail repairs, awnings, boat covers
023 9237 3699

Lymington Cruising School Lymington
01590 677478

Lymington HM 01590 672014

Lymington Marina Lymington
01590 673312

Lymington Town SC Lymington
01590 674514

Lymington Yacht Haven Lymington
01590 677071

Mad Cowes Clothing Co Cowes
01983 293710

Maptech Emsworth
Navigational software, digital charts
01243 389352

Marchwood YC Marchwood
023 8066 6141

Mari Lynch Godalming
Marine art/yacht portraits 01483 201085

Marina Developments Ltd (MDL)
Hamble
Marina group 023 8045 7155

Marine Computing International Ltd
Southampton
On board computer systems
023 8045 8047

Marine Connections Bitterne
023 803 36200

Marine Electronics Weymouth
07970 855775

Marine Gleam Lymington
Marine valeting 0800 074 4672

Marine Maintenance Portsmouth
Engineering; repairs 023 9260 2344

Marine Propulsion Hayling Island
Marine engineers 023 9246 1694

**Marine Superstore Port Solent
Chandlery** Portsmouth 023 92219843

Marine Support & Towage
Cowes, Isle of Wight
Fuel 01983 200716/07860 297633

Marineware Ltd Southampton
Paint, varnish, lacquer 023 8033 0208

Maritime Services International Ltd
Gosport
Marine consultants 023 9252 4490

Maritime Workshop Gosport
Boatbuilders; repairs 023 9252 7805

Mastervolt UK Ltd Romsey
Electrical & battery charging equipment
01794 516443

McGrail, Tony Parkstone
Surveyor 01202 718440

McMurdo Pains Wessex Portsmouth
Electronics; flares; safety equipment
023 9262 3900

Mechanical Services Weymouth
07831 263524

Mengham Marine Hayling Island
Chandlery 023 92464333

Mengham Rythe SC Hayling Island
023 92463337

Mercury Yacht Harbour Southampton
023 8045 5994

Meridian Sailing School and Charter
Southampton 023 8023 4627

Merlin Equipment Ltd Poole
Marine power systems 01202 697979

Mike Reeder School of Seamanship
Lymington
Motorcruising school; yacht delivery
01590 674560

Mitchell's Boatyard Poole
01202 747857

Mobile Marine Electrical Services
Port Solent
Marine engineers 023 9220 1668

Mobile Yacht Maintenance Weymouth
All aspects of yacht maintenance
07900 148806

Moody Service & Construction
Swanwick
Repairs, maintenance, storage
01489 885000

Moody Yachts International Ltd
Swanwick
Cruising yachts 01489 885000

Moonfleet Sailing Poole
Sailing tuition 01202 682269

Mooring Mate Ltd Bournemouth
Products for mooring up 01202 421199

Motortech Marine Engineering
Portsmouth 023 9251 3200

Mountifield Sails Hayling Island
Sailmaker 023 9246 3720

Multihull International Ltd Birdham
Multihull experts 01243 512111

Multihull World Emsworth
Multihull sales 01243 377333

Najad Yachts Hamble
UK dealer for Najad high quality yachts
023 8045 5555

National Federation of Sea Schools, The
Woodlands
Sailing tuition 023 8029 3822

Nauquip Warsash
Hardware 01489 885336

Nauticat UK Ltd Southampton
UK distributor of Nautical motor sailers
023 8045 3900

Navcom Chichester
Electronics 01243 776625

Netley SC Netley 023 80454272

New Dawn Dive Centre Lymington
01590 675656

Newtown Creek HM 01983 525994

Newtown Creek Police 01983 528000

Nick Cox Yacht Chandlery Ltd
Lymington 01590 673489

Nordic Marine Poole
Dealer for Malö Yachts 01202 700089

North Haven YC Poole 01202 708830

North Sails Portsmouth
Sail repairs 01329 231525

Northney Marina Hayling Island
023 9246 6321

Northshore Yachts Chichester
Boatyard; storage; maintenance; repairs
01243 512611

Ocean Rigging Lymington
01590 676292

Ocean Safety Southampton
Safety equipment 023 8072 0800

Ocean Village Marina Southampton
023 8022 9385

Ocean World Ltd Cowes
Marine leisure clothing; crew logos
01983 291744

Ocean Youth Trust South Gosport
Youth Education Charity 0870 241 22 52

Offshore Marine Services Ltd
Bembridge 01983 873125

Old Harbour Dive School Portland
01305 861000

On Deck Sailing Southampton
RYA courses 023 8033 3887

Onward Trading Co Ltd Southampton
Teak deck furniture 023 8063 7810

Opal Marine Gosport
Sail boat distributor 023 9258 3242

Outboard Centre Fareham
Outboard repairs; services 01329 234277

Parker & Kay Sailmakers South
Hamble 023 8045 8213

Parkstone YC (Haven) Ltd
Poole 01202 743610

Pascall Atkey & Sons Ltd Cowes
Chandler 01983 292381

Peculiars Chandler (Haslar Marina)
Gosport 023 9258 8815

Pepe Boatyard Hayling Island
Yacht chandlers; boatbuilders; repairs;
storage; inboard & outboard sales and
servicing 023 9246 1968

Peters & May Southampton
Yacht transport 023 8048 0480

Peters Chandlery Chichester
Chandler; broker 01243 511033

Piplers of Poole Poole
Chandler 01202 673056

Plastimo (UK) Ltd Eastleigh
Safety equipment; compasses; electronics;
reefing & rigging; deck fittings; cookers
023 8026 2211

Poole Canvas Co Ltd Poole
Canvas products 01202 677477

Poole Glassfibre Centre Poole
01202 676612

Poole Harbour Police 01202 223954

Poole HM 01202 440233

Poole YC Poole 01202 672687

Port Hamble Marina Southampton
023 8045 2741

Port Solent Marina Portsmouth
023 9221 0765

Portchester SC Portchester
01329 376375

Portland HM 01305 824044

Portland Police 01305 821205

**Portsmouth Harbour Commercial
Docks HM** 023 9229 7395

Portsmouth Harbour Control
023 9272 3694

Portsmouth Harbour HM
023 9272 3124

Portsmouth Marine Engineering
Fareham
Berthing; storage 01329 232854

Portsmouth Outdoor Centre
Portsmouth
Sailing tuition 023 9266 3873

Portsmouth SC Portsmouth
023 9282 0596

Power Afloat, Elkins Boatyard
Christchurch
Marine engineering 01202 489555

Powersail and Island Chandlers
East Cowes
Chandlery & all boating needs
01983 299800

Premier Marinas Limited Portsmouth
UK marina owner and operator
023 9221 4145

Premium Liferaft Services Lymington
Hire/sale of liferaft and safety equipment
01590 688407

Premium Liferaft Services Poole
Hire/sale of liferaft and safety equipment
01202 743665

Premium Liferaft Services Weymouth
Hire/sale of liferaft and safety equipment
01305 821040

Propeller Revolutions Poole
01202 671226

PT Marine Engineering Hayling Island
Marine engineers 023 9246 9332

PT Yacht Charters Portsmouth
023 9252 1585

Pumpkin Marine Supplies
Northney Marina, Hayling Island
Chandlery 023 9246 8794

Purbeck Marine Poole
Sales/services of Yanmar & Perkins
marine engines 01202 686592

Quay Consultants Ltd West Wittering
Yacht surveyors & consultants
01243 673056

Quay Sails (Poole) Ltd Poole
01202 681128

Quay West Chandlers Poole
01202 742488

Quayside Fuel
Mobile marine fuel delivery service
077 4718 2181/079 7073 7620

R&J Marine Electronics (Poole) Ltd
Poole 01202 680666

R & M Marine Portsmouth
Marine engineers 023 9265 1355

Rampart Yachts Southampton
Boatbuilder; repairs 023 8023 4777

RAF YC 023 80452208

Ratsey & Lapthorn Cowes
Sailmaker 01983 294051

Raymarine Ltd Portsmouth
Electronics 023 9269 3611

Redclyffe YC Poole 01929 557227

Relling One Design Portland
Sailmaker 01305 826555

RHP Marine Cowes
Electrical engineers 01983 290421

Ribs UK Ltd Southampton
Ribs and inflatable boats 023 8022 2262

Richards, Eddie East Cowes
Repairs 01983 299740

Richardson Sails Southampton
023 80403914

Richardsons Boatbuilders Binfield,
Newport 01983 821095

Ridge Wharf Yacht Centre Wareham
Berthing 01929 552650

Rig Shop Poole
Sailmakers, rigging 01202 677717

Rig Shop Southampton
Sailmakers, rigging 023 8033 8341

RK Marine Ltd Hamble
Marine engineer; Volvo Penta dealer
01489 583585

R K Marine Ltd Swanwick
Marine engineer; Volvo Penta dealer
01489 583572

Rockall Sails Chichester 01243 573185

Rossiter Yachts Christchurch
Boatbuilders, repairs & restoration, marine
engineering, storage, fuel 01202 483250

Rotomarine Ltd Bosham
Reefing systems 01243 573131

Royal Motor YC Poole 01202 707227

Royal Corinthian YC (Cowes) Cowes
01983 292608

Royal Dorset YC Weymouth
01305 786258

Royal London YC Isle of Wight
01983 299727

Royal Lymington YC Lymington
01590 672677

Royal National Lifeboat Institution
Poole 01202 663000

**Royal Naval Club and Royal Albert
YC** Portsmouth 023 9282 5924

Royal Naval Sailing Association
Gosport 023 9252 1100

Royal Solent YC Yarmouth
01983 760256

Royal Southampton YC Southampton
023 8022 3352

Royal Southern YC Southampton
023 8045 0300

Royal Victoria YC Fishbourne
01983 882325

Royal Yacht Squadron Isle of Wight
01983 292191

Royal Yachting Association (RYA)
Southampton 0845 345 0400

Ryde HM 01983 613879

Ryde Leisure Harbour Ryde
01983 613879

Sally Water Training East Cowes
01983 299033

Saltern Sail Co West Cowes
01983 280014

Saltern Sail Company Yarmouth
01983 760120

Salterns Brokerage 01202 707222

Salterns Chandlery Poole
01202 701556

Salterns Marina Boatyard & Hotel
Poole 01202 707321

Sandbanks Yacht Company Poole
Repairs 01202 707500

Satcom Distribution Ltd Salisbury
Satellite communications equipment
01722 410800

Saxon Wharf Marina Southampton
023 8033 9490

Scope Event Management Salisbury
Motor yacht charter from Poole
01722 335599

Sea Electric Hamble
Electrical installer 023 8045 6255

Sea 'N' Ski
Waterskiing tuition 023 9234 6153

Sea Start Ltd Southampton
Marine breakdown service 0800 885500

Sea Teach Ltd Emsworth
Chandlery; sails; reefing equipment
01243 375774

Sea Ventures Ltd Lymington
Jeanneau dealer; bare boat charter
01590 672472

Seafever East Grinstead
Powerboat trainer 01342 316293

Seaview YC Isle of Wight 01983 613268

Seaward Marine Ltd Cowes
Motor boat & workboat builders; boat
repairs 01983 280333

Seaway Marine Gosport
Marine engineers 023 9260 2722

Seldén Mast Ltd Southampton
Masts; spars 01489 484000

Shamrock Chandlery Southampton
023 8063 2725

Shamrock Quay Marina Southampton
023 8022 9461

**Shell Bay Marine & Watersports
Centre** Studland Bay
Chandlery 01202 450340

Shepards Wharf Boatyard Ltd Cowes
Boat repairs; maintenance; storage
01983 297821

Sheraton Marine Cabinet Witney
Manufactures teak and mahogany marine
fittings 01993 868275

Ship 'N Shore Hayling Island
Chandler 023 9263 7373

Shore Sailmakers
Swanwick Marina, Southampton
01489 589450

Shorewater Sports Chichester
Wetsuits; watersports equipment
01243 672315

Silverwood Yacht Services Ltd
Portsmouth
Boat repairs; rigging 023 9232 7067

Simrad Ltd Gosport
Marine electronics 01329 245100

Solent Outboards Southampton
Outboard repairs; services
023 8063 3115

Smith, Paul Isle of Wight
Boatcare 01983 754726

Solent Outboards Southampton
Outboard repairs; services
023 8063 3115

Solent Yacht Charter Gosport
Yacht charter; management; boat sales
023 9260 2708

South Coast Marine Christchurch
Chandlery, marine engineering
01202 482695

Southampton HM 023 8033 9733

Southampton Police 023 80845511

Southampton SC Southampton
023 80446575

Southampton Yacht Services Ltd
Southampton
Builders & refitters of luxury yachts
023 803 35266

Southern Cylinder Services Fareham
Subaqua & cylinder testing facilities
01329 221125

Southern Sails Poole 01202 677000

Southern Spar Services Northam
Masts; spars; rigging; reefing gear
023 8033 1714

Southsea Marina Southsea
023 9282 2719

Southwater Marine Hamble
Powerboat sales, service 023 8045 2255

Sowester Simpson-Lawrence Ltd
Poole
Marine equipment; engines; steering &
control systems 01202 667700

SP Systems Newport
Epoxy resins for laminating, bonding,
coating and filling. Structural engineering
of GRP and composite materials
01983 828000

Sparkes Boatyard Hayling Island
023 9246 3572

Sparkes Marina Hayling Island
023 9246 3572

Spinlock Ltd Cowes
Rigging/rope systems 01983 295555

Spinnaker Yacht Chandlery Bembridge
01983 874324

Stephen Jones Yacht Design Warsash
Yacht designer 01489 576439

Stone Pier Yacht Services Warsash
Refit and restoration services
01489 885400

Stone Yacht Services, Adrian
Cowes Yacht Haven
Repairs   01983 297898

Stratton Boatyard, Ken Bembridge
Repairs; engineer   01983 873185

Strickland Marine Engineering, Brian
Chichester   01243 513454

Sunbird Marine Services Fareham
Yacht brokers   01329 842613

Sunsail Portsmouth
Sailing holidays; yacht charter; tuition
                           023 9222 2224

Sunseeker International Marina Poole
                           01202 381111

Swanage Police   01929 422004

Swanage SC Swanage   01929 422987

Swanwick Marina Southampton
                           01489 885000

Swanwick Yacht Surveyors
Southampton   01489 564822

T & G Clothing Stockbridge
                           01264 811000

Tacktick Ltd Emsworth
Electronics   01243 379331

Taplin International Southampton
Electrical equipment   023 8032 2304

Tarquin Boat Co Emsworth
Boatbuilder   01243 375211

Tarquin Marina Emsworth
                           01243 377727

Team Sailing Gosport
Yacht charter; sea school; team training
                           023 9273 5199

Technix Rubber & Plastics Ltd
Southampton
Fendering, adhesives, sealants; flooring
                           023 8063 5523

Temple, Chris Yarmouth
Surveyor   01983 760947

The Gosport Marina Ltd Gosport
                           023 9252 4811

Thorney Island SC Thorney Island
                           01243 371731

Thornham Marina Emsworth
                           01243 375335

Tinley Electronics Lymington
Marine electronics   01590 610071

Toomer & Hayter Ltd Bournemouth
Marine upholstery   01202 515789

Top Yacht Charter Ltd Chichester
Yacht charter; management; sailing
holidays   01243 520950

Town Quay Marina Southampton
                           023 8023 4397

Trade Grade Products Ltd Poole
Adhesives; tapes; mastics; sealants
                           01202 820177

Trafalgar Yachts Fareham
Berthing; chandler; broker (specialising in
Westerly yachts)   01329 822445

Transas Nautic Portsmouth
Marine Electronics   023 9267 4016

Transworld Yachts Hamble
Broker   023 8045 7704

Tudor SC Portsmouth   023 9266 2002

UK Customs Nationwide 0845 0109000

UK McWilliam Cowes
Sailmaker   01983 281100

Upham Marine Electronics, Roger
Chichester   01243 528299

Vasey Marine Engineering, Gordon
Fareham
Repairs   07798 638625

Vetus Den Ouden Ltd Totton,
Southampton
Wholesalers of diesel engines,
generators, propellers, shafts and
much more   023 8086 1033

Victory Marine Services Cowes
Repairs   01983 200226

WB Marine Chichester
Engine and outdrive repair services
                           01243 512857

Warsash Nautical Bookshop
Southampton   01489 572384

Warsash SC Southampton
                           023 8058 3575

Waterside Properties Uk Ltd
Port Solent   023 9220 0022

Watson Marine Ltd, Charles Hamble
Yacht agents & brokers   023 8045 6505

Wessex Resins & Adhesives Ltd
Romsey
Adhesives; epoxy products
                           01794 521111

West Point Marine Services Fareham
Marine engineers   01329 232881

West Solent Boatbuilders Lymington
                           01590 642080

Weston CC Southampton 07905 557298

Weston SC Southampton
                           023 8045 2527

Weymouth HM   01305 206423

Weymouth Marina Weymouth
                           01305 767576

Weymouth Police   01305 250512

Weymouth SC Weymouth
                           01305 785481

Weysure Ltd Weymouth
Commercial/marine brokers
                           07000 939787

Wicor Marine Fareham
Berthing; storage; chandlery; repairs
                           01329 237112

Wilsons Boatyard Portsmouth
Repairs   023 9246 4869

Woodleigh Power Equipment
Horndean
Marine engine manufacturers/suppliers
                           023 9257 1360

Wragg, Chris Lymington
Supplier of furling & reefing systems
                           01590 677052

X-Yachts Hamble
Cruiser/racing yachts   023 8045 6100

XW Rigging Haslar Marina, Gosport
                           023 9251 3553

Yacht & Sports Gear Ltd Chichester
Chandler; yacht equipment
                           01243 784572

Yacht Care Ltd Lymington
Complete boat service from valeting to
deliveries   01590 688856

Yacht Designers & Surveyors
Association Bordon   0845 0900 162

Yacht Solutions Ltd Portsmouth
Repair; painting; rigging repairs;
undercover storage   023 9220 0670

Yachting Instruments Ltd Sturminster
Compasses; ships clocks; barometers;
race timers; watersport clothing
                           01258 817662

Yachtmail Ltd Lymington
Chandlery   01590 672784

Yarmouth Harbour Yarmouth
                           01983 760321

Yarmouth HM   01983 760321

Yarmouth Marine Service
Repairs, refit, storage, pontoon berths
                           01983 760521

Yarmouth Police   01983 528000

Yarmouth SC Yarmouth   01983 760270

Yeoman Romsey
Chartplotters & marine electronics
                           01794 521079

1° West Marine Ltd Portsmouth
Engineering & Rigging   023 9283 8335

407 Racing Lymington
Yacht charter   01590 688407

Waypoint Guide Area 2 – Central Southern England - Portland Bill to Selsey Bill

1	**Nab Tower** - 0·5M NW of	50°40'·41N	00°57'·64W
2	**West Pole Bn** - 0·3M S of	50°45'·41N	00°56'·46W
3	**Langstone Fairway Buoy** - 0·5M S of	50°45'·81N	01°01'·36W
4	**Main Passage** - Dolphin gap off Southsea	50°46'·01N	01°04'·11W
5	**Horse Sand PHM** - Portsmouth approach	50°45'·52N	01°05'·27W
6	**Horse Sand/No Man's Land Forts** - midway	50°44'·73N	01°05'·09W
7	**Gilkicker Point** - 0·3M S of	50°46'·03N	01°08'·49W
8	**Bembridge Tide Gauge**	50°42'·47N	01°05'·00W
9	**Bembridge Ledge ECM**	50°41'·16N	01°02'·78W
10	**West Princessa WCM** - S of Bembridge	50°40'·15N	01°03'·64W
11	**Dunnose Head** - 1M off	50°35'·03N	01°10'·09W
12	**St Catherine's Point** - 1M S of	50°33'·55N	01°17'·89W
13	**Wootton Beacon**	50°44'·54N	01°12'·14W
14	**Peel Bank Buoy** - east Solent	50°45'·49N	01°13'·34W
15	**Old Castle Point** - 0·3M N of	50°46'·35N	01°16'·59W
16	**Cowes entrance**	50°46'·23N	01°17'·95W
17	**Egypt Point** - 0·4M N of	50°46'·42N	01°18'·79W
18	**Hamble Point SCM**	50°50'·15N	01°18'·67W
19	**Beaulieu Spit Beacon** - 0·3M off	50°46'·85N	01°21'·69W
20	**Newtown** - 0·5M NW of entrance	50°43'·90N	01°25'·29W
21	**Yarmouth entrance** - 0·4M NNE of	50°42'·83N	01°29'·96W
22	**Lymington, Jack in the basket** - seaward mark	50°44'·27N	01°30'·57W
23	**Hurst Narrows** - midway	50°42'·23N	01°32'·49W
24	**Keyhaven** - 0·2M E of entrance	50°42'·83N	01°32'·89W
25	**Fairway Buoy** - Needles channel	50°38'·23N	01°38'·99W
26	**Christchurch** - 0·3M E of ent	50°43'·58N	01°43'·53W
27	**Poole No 1 Bar Buoy** - 1M E of	50°39'·32N	01°53'·58W
28	**Swanage** - 0·7M NE of pier	50°37'·03N	01°56'·08W
29	**Anvil Point** - 1·5M SE of	50°34'·33N	01°56'·08W
30	**St Albans Head** - 1·5M S of	50°33'·08N	02°03'·34W
31	**East Shambles** - 1M SE of	50°30'·03N	02°18'·98W
32	**Lulworth Cove** - 0·1M S of ent	50°36'·90N	02°14'·83W
33	**Weymouth** - 1M E of ent	50°36'·63N	02°25'·00W
34	**Portland Bill** - 5M S of	50°25'·76N	02°27'·38W
35	**Alderney - Bray Harbour** - 1M NE of	49°44'·60N	02°10'·63W
37	**Casquets** - 1M W of	49°43'·32N	02°24'·15W
93	**Cap de La Hague** - 2M W of	49°43'·54N	01°59'·45W
	Cherbourg - 0·5M N of W entrance	49°40'·86N	01°39'·57W
103	**Start Point** - 2M S of	50°11'·33N	03°38'·54W
	Le Havre - 0·5M NE of Le Havre LHA	49°32'·00N	00°09'·04W
	St-Vaast-la-Hougue - 3M ENE of entrance	49°36'·34N	01°11'·08W

Distance Table - Central Southern England

Approximate distances in nautical miles are by the most direct route while avoiding dangers and allowing for Traffic Separation Schemes

	1	2	3	4	5	6	7	8	9	10	11	12	13	14	15	16	17	18	19	20
1. Exmouth	1																			
2. Lyme Regis	21	2																		
3. Portland Bill	36	22	3																	
4. Weymouth	46	32	8	4																
5. Swanage	58	44	22	22	5															
6. Poole Hbr ent	65	51	28	26	6	6														
7. Needles Lt Ho	73	58	35	34	14	14	7													
8. Lymington	79	64	42	40	20	24	6	8												
9. Yarmouth (IOW)	77	63	40	39	18	22	4	2	9											
10. Beaulieu R. ent	84	69	46	45	25	29	11	7	7	10										
11. Cowes	86	71	49	46	28	27	14	10	9	2	11									
12. Southampton	93	78	55	54	34	34	20	16	16	9	9	12								
13. R. Hamble (ent)	90	75	53	51	32	34	18	12	13	6	6	5	13							
14. Portsmouth	96	81	58	57	37	35	23	19	19	12	10	18	13	14						
15. Langstone Hbr	98	84	61	59	39	39	25	21	21	14	12	21	18	5	15					
16. Chichester Bar	101	86	63	62	42	42	28	23	24	17	15	23	18	8	5	16				
17. Bembridge	97	81	59	58	38	39	24	18	19	13	10	18	15	5	6	8	17			
18. Nab Tower	102	86	64	63	43	44	29	23	24	18	15	24	19	10	7	6	6	18		
19. St Catherine's Pt	82	68	45	44	25	25	12	19	21	27	15	36	29	20	20	19	17	15	19	
20. Littlehampton	117	102	79	79	60	61	46	44	45	38	36	45	42	31	28	25	28	22	35	20

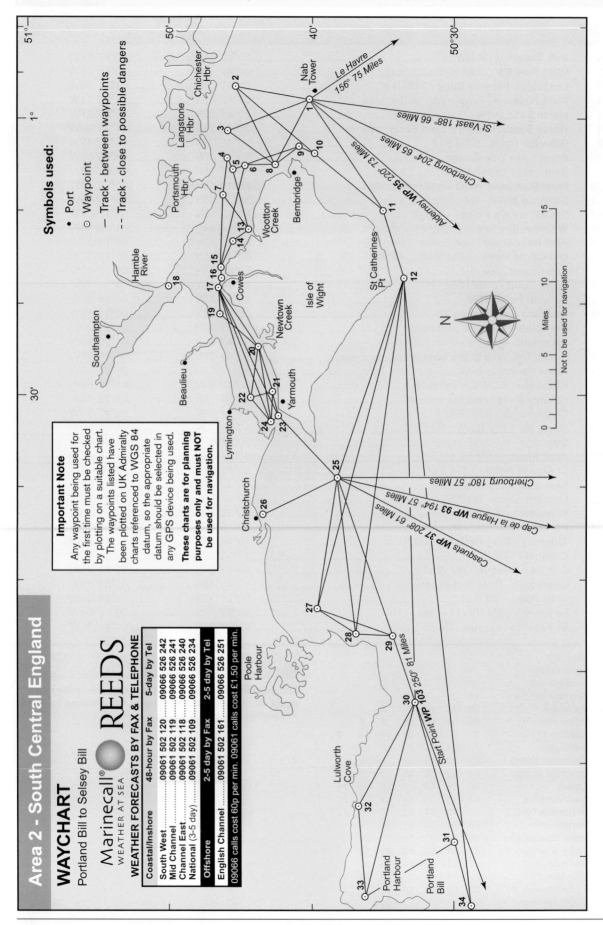

Area 2 - South Central England

WAYCHART
Portland Bill to Selsey Bill

Marinecall® REEDS
WEATHER AT SEA

WEATHER FORECASTS BY FAX & TELEPHONE

Coastal/Inshore	48-hour by Fax	5-day by Tel
South West	09061 502 120	09066 526 242
Mid Channel	09061 502 119	09066 526 241
Channel East	09061 502 118	09066 526 240
National (3-5 day)	09061 502 109	09066 526 234
Offshore	**2-5 day by Fax**	**2-5 day by Tel**
English Channel	09061 502 161	09066 526 251

09066 calls cost 60p per min. 09061 calls cost £1.50 per min.

Important Note

Any waypoint being used for the first time must be checked by plotting on a suitable chart. The waypoints listed have been plotted on UK Admiralty charts referenced to WGS 84 datum, so the appropriate datum should be selected in any GPS device being used.

These charts are for planning purposes only and must NOT be used for navigation.

Symbols used:

- Port
- ⊙ Waypoint
- — Track - between waypoints
- -- Track - close to possible dangers

Not to be used for navigation

Le Havre 156° 75 Miles
St Vaast 188° 66 Miles
Cherbourg 204° 65 Miles
Alderney WP 35 220° 73 Miles
Cherbourg 180° 57 Miles
Cap de la Hague WP 93 194° 57 Miles
Casquets WP 37 208° 61 Miles
Start Point WP 103 250° 81 Miles

Chichester Hbr
Langstone Hbr
Portsmouth Hbr
Hamble River
Southampton
Beaulieu
Wootton Creek
Bembridge
Isle of Wight
St Catherines Pt
Cowes
Newtown Creek
Yarmouth
Lymington
Christchurch
Poole Harbour
Lulworth Cove
Portland Harbour
Portland Bill
Nab Tower

Key to Marina Plans symbols

Calor Gas		P	Parking
Chandler		✕	Pub/Restaurant
Disabled facilities			Pump out
Electrical supply			Rigging service
Electrical repairs			Sail repairs
Engine repairs			Shipwright
First Aid			Shop/Supermarket
Fresh Water			Showers
Fuel - Diesel			Slipway
Fuel - Petrol		WC	Toilets
Hardstanding/boatyard			Telephone
Laundry facilities			Trolleys
Lift-out facilities		Ⓥ	Visitors berths

3

Area 3 - South East England

MARINAS
Telephone Numbers
VHF Channel
Access Times

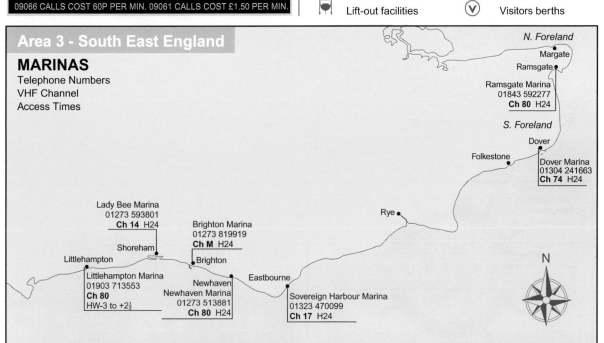

N. Foreland
Margate
Ramsgate
Ramsgate Marina
01843 592277
Ch 80 H24

S. Foreland

Dover
Folkestone
Dover Marina
01304 241663
Ch 74 H24

Lady Bee Marina
01273 593801
Ch 14 H24

Brighton Marina
01273 819919
Ch M H24

Rye

Shoreham

Littlehampton

Brighton

Littlehampton Marina
01903 713553
Ch 80
HW-3 to +2½

Newhaven
Newhaven Marina
01273 513881
Ch 80 H24

Eastbourne

Sovereign Harbour Marina
01323 470099
Ch 17 H24

N

LITTLEHAMPTON MARINA

Littlehampton Marina
Ferry Road, Littlehampton, W Sussex
Tel: 01903 713553 Fax: 01903 732264

VHF	Ch 80
ACCESS	HW-3 to +2.5

A typical English seaside town with funfair, promenade and fine sandy beaches, Littlehampton lies roughly midway between Brighton and Chichester at the mouth of the River Arun. It affords a convenient stopover for yachts either east or west bound, providing you have the right tidal conditions to cross the entrance bar with its charted depth of 0.7m. The marina lies about three cables above Town Quay and Fisherman's Quay, both of which are on the starboard side of the River Arun, and is accessed via a retractable footbridge that opens on request to the HM (note that you should contact him by 1630 the day before you require entry).

FACILITIES AT A GLANCE

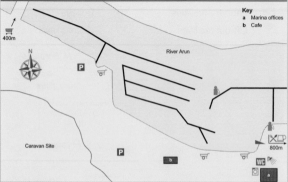

Key
a Marina offices
b Cafe

LADY BEE MARINA

Lady Bee Marina
138-140 Albion Street, Southwick
West Sussex, BN42 4EG
Tel: 01273 593801 Fax: 01273 870349

VHF	Ch 14
ACCESS	H24

Shoreham, only five miles west of Brighton, is one of the South Coast's major commercial ports handling, among other products, steel, grain, tarmac and timber. On first impressions it may seem that Shoreham has little to offer the visiting yachtsman, but once through the lock and into the eastern arm of the River Adur, the quiet Lady Bee Marina, with its Spanish waterside restaurant, can make this harbour an interesting alternative to the lively atmosphere of Brighton Marina. Run by the Harbour Office, the marina meets all the usual requirements, although fuel is available in cans from Southwick garage or from Corral's diesel pump situated in the western arm.

FACILITIES AT A GLANCE

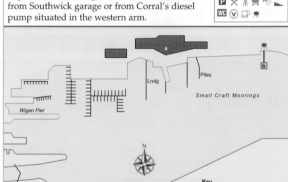

Key
a Sussex Yacht Club
b Riverside Boatyard

BRIGHTON MARINA

Brighton Marina
East Lockside, Brighton, East Sussex, BN2 5HA
Tel: 01273 819919 Fax: 01273 675082
www.premiermarinas.com

VHF Ch M
ACCESS H24

Situated halfway between Portsmouth and Dungeness, Brighton Marina, with its extensive range of shops, restaurants and facilities, is a popular and convenient stopover for east and west-going passagemakers. Note, however, that it is not advisable to attempt entry in strong south to south-easterly winds.

Only half a mile from the marina is the historic city of Brighton itself, renowned for being a cultural centre with a cosmopolitan atmosphere. Among its numerous attractions are the exotic Royal Pavilion, built for King George IV in the 1800s, and the Lanes, with its multitude of antiques shops.

FACILITIES AT A GLANCE

NEWHAVEN MARINA

Newhaven Marina
The Yacht Harbour, Fort Road, Newhaven
East Sussex, BN9 9BY
Tel: 01273 513881 Fax: 01273 510493
email: john.sterling@seacontainers.com

VHF Ch 80
ACCESS H24

Some seven miles from Brighton, Newhaven lies at the mouth of the River Ouse. With its large fishing fleet and regular ferry services to Dieppe, the harbour has over the years become progressively commercial, therefore care is needed to keep clear of large vessels under manoeuvre. The marina lies approximately quarter of a mile from the harbour entrance on the west bank and was recently dredged to allow full tidal access except on LWS. However, as Newhaven is prone to silting up, it is advisable for yachts with a minimum draught of 1.5m to check the depth with the marina first.

FACILITIES AT A GLANCE

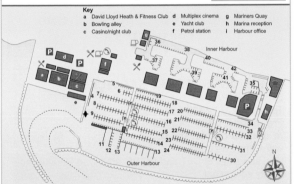

Key
a David Lloyd Heath & Fitness Club
b Bowling alley
c Casino/night club
d Multiplex cinema
e Yacht club
f Petrol station
g Mariners Quay
h Marina reception
i Harbour office

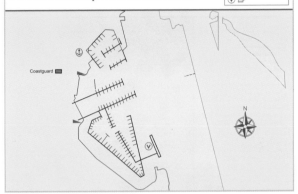

SOVEREIGN HARBOUR MARINA

Sovereign Harbour Marina Ltd
Pevensey Bay Road, Eastbourne
East Sussex, BN23 6JH
Tel: 01323 470099 Fax: 01323 470077
www.sovereignharbour.co.uk

| VHF | Ch 17 |
| ACCESS | H24 |

Opened 10 years ago, Sovereign Harbour is situated a few miles NE of Eastbourne and is accessible at all states of the tide and weather except for in strong NE to SE'ly winds. Entered via a lock at all times of the day or night, the marina is part of one of the largest waterfront complexes in Britain, enjoying close proximity to shops, restaurants and a multiplex cinema. A short bus or taxi ride takes you to Eastbourne, where again you will find an array of shops and eating places to suit all tastes and budgets.

FACILITIES AT A GLANCE

Key
a The Waterfront, shops, restaurants, pubs and offices
b Harbour office - weather information and visitor's information
c Cinema
d Retail park - supermarket and post office
e Restaurant
f Toilets, showers, telephone, launderette and disabled facilities
g 24 hr fuel pontoon (diesel, petrol, LPG, and holding tank pump out)
h Recycling centre
i Boatyard, boatpark, marine engineers, riggers and electricians

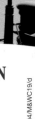

DOVER MARINA

Dover Harbour Board
Harbour House, Dover, Kent, CT17 9TF
Tel: 01304 241663 Fax: 01304 242549
e-mail: andy.cornford@doverport.co.uk

| VHF | Ch 80 |
| ACCESS | H24 |

Nestling under the famous White Cliffs, Dover sits between South Foreland to the NE and Folkestone to the SW. Boasting a maritime history stretching back as far as the Bronze Age, Dover is today one of Britain's busiest commercial ports, with a continuous stream of ferries and cruise liners plying to and from their European destinations. However, over the past years the harbour has made itself more attractive to the cruising yachtsman, with the marina, set well away from the busy ferry terminal, offering three sheltered berthing options in the Tidal Harbour, Granville Dock and Wellington Dock.

FACILITIES AT A GLANCE

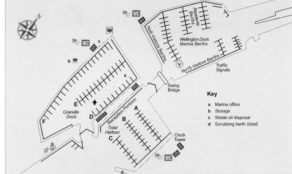

Key
a Marina office
b Storage
c Waste oil disposal
d Scrubbing berth (tidal)

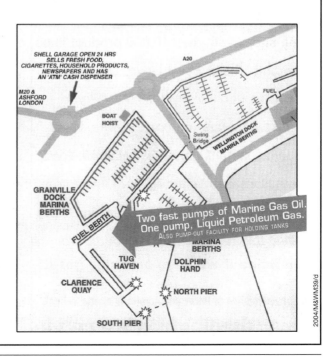

RAMSGATE ROYAL HARBOUR

The Royal Harbour Ramsgate Marina
Harbour Office, Military Road, Ramsgate
Kent, CT11 9LQ
Tel: 01843 592277 Fax: 01843 590941
www.ramsgatemarina.co.uk

| VHF | Ch 80 |
| ACCESS | H24 |

Steeped in maritime history, Ramsgate was awarded 'Royal' status in 1821 by George IV in recognition of the warm welcome he received when sailing from Ramsgate to Hanover with the Royal Squadron. Offering good shelter and modern facilities, the Royal Harbour can be accessed in all conditions except in strong E'ly winds and comprises an inner marina, entered approximately HW±2, a western marina in 3m of water and an eastern marina with a 2m depth. Permission to enter or leave the Royal Harbour must be obtained from Ramsgate Port Control on Ch 14.

FACILITIES AT A GLANCE

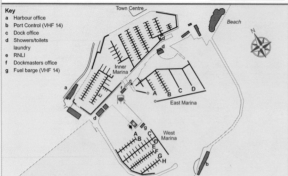

Key
a Harbour office
b Port Control (VHF 14)
c Dock office
d Showers/toilets
  laundry
e RNLI
f Dockmasters office
g Fuel barge (VHF 14)

CRUISING COMPANION SERIES

The Cruising Companion range covers popular cruising grounds in W Europe. With superb quality port plans, full-colour aerial photography, and the latest pilotage and approach information, the Cruising Companion series adds 'what to do' information to the 'how to get there' pilotage, with full coverage of shore-side facilities and places of interest.

THE SOLENT
£24.95
1 904358 11 X

THE CHANNEL
£29.95
1 904358 12 8

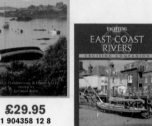

EAST COAST RIVERS
£19.95
0 333 90455 9

NORTH FRANCE & BELGIUM
£24.95
0 333 98954 6

WEST FRANCE
£24.95
0 333 90453 2

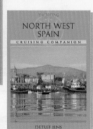

NORTH WEST SPAIN
£24.95
1 904358 10 1

SOUTH WEST SPAIN & PORTUGAL
£24.95
0 333 90773 6

NORTH BRITTANY & CHANNEL ISLANDS
£24.95
0 333 90452 4

WEST COUNTRY
£19.95
0 333 90454 0

A & P Ship Care Ramsgate Ramsgate
Yacht maintenance; refit; repairs
01843 593140

Absolute Marine Littlehampton
On line chandlery   01903 734411

Adec Marine Ltd Croydon
Liferaft service station for the SE. Hire
and sell new rafts & other safety
equipment   020 8686 9717

Adur Boat Sales Lady Bee Marina,
Southwick
Yacht brokers   01273 596680

Arun Aquasports Littlehampton
Chandler   01903 713553

Arun Canvas and Rigging Ltd
Littlehampton   01903 732561

Arun Craft Littlehampton
Marine Engineering   01903 723667

Arun Nautique Littlehampton
Chandler; on-line services 01903 730558

Arun Yacht Club Littlehampton
01903 714533

Aruncraft Chandlers Littlehampton
01903 723667

Ayton, Joy Shoreham
Sail repairs   01273 553173

Barnes Ltd, GP Shoreham
Chandler   01273 591705/596680

Booth Marine Surveys, Graham
Birchington-on-Sea
Authorised for MCA Codes of Practice
01843 843793

Bosun's Locker Ramsgate
01843 597158

Brighton HM   01273 819919

Brighton Marina Boatyard
Brighton   01273 819919

Brighton Marina Brighton
01273 819919

Brighton Marina YC Peacehaven
01273 818711

Brighton Police   01273 606744

Cantell and Son Ltd Newhaven
Shipyard   01273 514118

Chabot, Gary Newhaven
Boatyard   01273 611076

Chippendale Craft Rye
Boatyard   01797 227707

Churcher Marine Worthing
Chandlery   01903 230523

Compass Marine Lancing
Chandlery   01903 761773

**Davis International Watersports,
Mike** Shoreham
Watersports equipment   01273 455892

Davis's Yacht Chandler Littlehampton
01903 722778

Davies Marine Services Ramsgate
Boatyard; repairs; rigging; engineering
01843 586172

Dover HM   01304 240400 Ext 4520

Dover Marina Dover   01304 241663

Dover Police   01304 216084

Dover Police   01304 240055

Dover Yacht Co Dover   01304 201073

Eastbourne HM   01323 470099

Eastbourne Police   01323 722522

Euro Tek Marine, Brighton Marina
Marine electronics   01273 687790

Fathom Diving (Chislehurst)
Chislehurst   020 8289 8237

Felton Marine Engineering
Brighton Marina
Volvo Penta dealer   01273 601779

Felton Marine Engineering
Sovereign Marina, Eastbourne
Volvo Penta dealer   01323 470211

Folkestone HM   01303 715354

Folkestone Police   01303 850055

Folkestone Yacht and Motor BC
Folkestone   01303 251574

Gowen Ocean Sailmakers
West Mersea   01206 384412

Hammond plc George Dover
Marine Gas Oil   01304 206809

Hastings and St Leonards YC Hastings
01424 420656

Haven Knox-Johnston West Malling
Marine insurance   01732 223600

Highway Marine Sandwich
Drying pontoon berths   01304 613925

Hillyard, David Littlehampton
Shipyard; repairs; maintenance
01903 713327

Hooper Marine Littlehampton
Marine engineering   01903 731195

Hughes, Susan Ramsgate
Tailored bedding for yacht berths
01843 596472

Iron Wharf Boatyard Faversham
Moorings, storage, chandlery, brokerage,
fuel   01795 537122

Lady Bee Marina Brighton
01273 593801

Lancing Marine Brighton
Engine sales, spares and services
01273 410025

Langley Marine Services Eastbourne
Boat and engine repairs   01323 470244

Leonard Marine, Peter Newhaven
Boatyard   01273 515987

Littlehampton HM   01903 721215

Littlehampton Marina Littlehampton
01903 713553

Littlehampton Police   01903 731733

Littlehampton Sailing and Motor Club
Littlehampton   01903 715859

Marconi Marine Southampton
Marine electronics   023 8051 1868

**Marine & General Insurance Services
Ltd** Maidstone
Marine insurance   01622 201106

Marinetrack Ltd Shoreham-by-Sea
Electronic safety systems   01273 265425

Marlec Marine Ramsgate
Marine engineering   01843 592176

Marlow Ropes Hailsham
Performance yacht ropes   01323 847234

Muggeridge Ship Chandlers Shoreham
01273 553173

Navigators & General Insurance
Brighton   01273 863400

Newhaven & Seaford SC Seaford
01323 890077

Newhaven HM   01273 612868

Newhaven Marina Ltd Newhaven
01273 513881

Newhaven Police   01273 515801

Newhaven YC Newhaven 01273 589849

Newing, Roy E Canterbury
Boat repairs; basic chandler
01227 860345

Northrop Sails Ramsgate
01843 851665

Norwood Marine Margate
Marine consultants and advisors
01843 835711

Ocean Yachts UK Battle
Yacht sales   0845 1300235

Pace, Andy Newhaven
Marine engineering   01273 516010

Phillips, HJ Rye
Boatyard   01797 223234

Premium Liferaft Services Eastbourne
Hire/sales of liferafts and safety
equipment   01323 723294

ProProtector Ltd Maidstone
Propeller protectors   01622 728738

Ramsgate HM   01843 572100

Ramsgate Police   01843 231055

Ramsgate Royal Harbour Marina
Ramsgate   01843 572100

Riley Marine Dover
Complete marine service   01304 214544

Riverside Yard Shoreham Beach
01273 592456

Royal Cinque Ports YC Dover
01304 206262

Royal Harbour Marina Ramsgate
01843 592277

Royal Temple YC Ramsgate
01843 591766

Rye Harbour Marine Rye
Boatyard   01797 227667

Rye Harbour SC Rye   01797 223136

Rye Police   01797 222112

Saga Boat Insurance Folkestone
01303 771135

Sandrock Marine Rye   01797 222679

Sandwich HM   01304 617197/612162

Sandwich Marina   07974 754558

Sandwich Sailing and Motor Club
01843 585711

Sandwich Town Quay   01304 614967

Sea Cruisers of Rye Rye
Chandlery   01797 222070

Sea Technical Services Ltd Denmead
023 9225 5200

Sea-Lift Ltd Dover   01304 201112

Sharp & Enright DoverShip
Chandler   01304 206295

Shoreham HM   01273 598100

Shoreham Police   01273 454521

Shoreham SC Henfield   01273 453078

Simpson Marine Ltd Newhaven
Chandler   01273 612612

Smith & Gibbs Eastbourne
Chandler   01323 734656

Southern Masts & Rigging Brighton
Chandler   01273 818189

Sovereign Harbour Marina Eastbourne
01323 470099

Sovereign Harbour YC Eastbourne
01323 470888

Strand Shipyard Rye   01797 222070

Surry Boatyard Shoreham-by-Sea
Marina (tidal berths)   01273 461491

Sussex Fishing Services Rye
Electronic repairs   01797 223895

Sussex Marine St Leonards on Sea
01424 425882

Sussex Marine Centre Shoreham
01273 454737

Sussex YC Shoreham-by-Sea
01273 464868

Templecraft Yacht Charters Lewes
01273 812333

UK Customs Nationwide 0845 0109000

Versatility Workboats Rye
Boatyard   01797 224422

Walton Marine Sales Brighton
Boat sales   01273 670707

**White Cliffs Motor Boat and Yacht
Club** Dover   01304 211666

XM Yachting Ltd Polegate
Chandler   01323 870092

Yachtowner Ltd Battle
Yacht charters; sailing holidays
0845 1300235

Yoldings Marine Eastbourne
Mechanical engineers, electricians
01323 470882

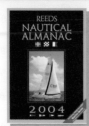

Waypoint Guide Area 3 – South East England - Selsey Bill to North Foreland

1	**Nab Tower** - 0·5M NW of	50°40'·41N	00°57'·64W
96	**Cherbourg** - 0·5M N of W entrance	49°40'·86N	01°39'·57W
132	**Owers SCM** - 1·8M SE of	50°36'·83N	00°40'·69W
133	**Boulder SHM** - 0·1M N of	50°41'·60N	00°49'·03W
134	**East Borough Hd ECM** - 0·1M N of	50°41'·63N	00°38'·83W
135	**Littlehampton entrance** - 1M 165°of on leading Lts	50°47'·03N	00°32'·11W
136	**Shoreham entrance** - 1M S of on leading Lts	50°48'·52N	00°14'·72W
137	**Brighton entrance** - 1M S of	50°47'·53N	00°06'·41W
138	**Newhaven entrance** - 1M S of	50°45'·56N	00°03'·56E
139	**Beachy Hd** - 1·5M S of	50°42'·52N	00°14'·51E
140	**Eastbourne** - 1·2M SE of Langney Pt	50°46'·29N	00°21'·00E
141	**Rye** - 0·1M S of Rye Fairway By	50°53'·93N	00°48'·03E
142	**Dungeness** - 1M SE of	50°54'·03N	00°59'·55E
143	**Folkestone** - 0·5M SE of breakwater	51°04'·20N	01°12'·25E
144	**Dover** - 1·2M SE of Western entrance	51°05'·83N	01°21'·00E
145	**South Foreland** - 2M E of	51°08·73N	01°26'·14E
146	**South Goodwin PHM** - 0·3M SE of	51°10'·43N	01°32'·59E
147	**East Goodwin Lt Float** - 0·8M W of	51°13'·26N	01°35'·14E
148	**East Goodwin ECM** - 0·2M E of	51°15'·77N	01°36'·02E
149	**Goodwin Knoll** - 1M SE of	51°18'·88N	01°33'·37E
150	**Ramsgate** - 1M E of; and for Pegwell Bay	51°19'·51N	01°27'·04E
151	**North Foreland** - 1M E of	51°22'·54N	01°28'·64E
152	**Foreness Pt** - 1M NNE of	51°24'·50N	01°26'·30E
153	**Margate** - 0·7M N of	51°24'·14N	01°22'·44E
197	**Cap Gris-Nez** - 2M NW of headland	50°53'·35N	01°32'·42E
198	**Boulogne** - 2M WNW of entrance	50°45'·16N	01°31'·08E
199	**Étaples** - 3M W of Le Touquet point	50°32'·24N	01°30'·70E
200	**St Valéry-sur-Somme** - 5M WNW Le Hourdel Pt	50°15'·34N	01°27'·00E
	Dieppe - 1M NW of entrance	49°57'·04N	01°03'·90E
	Fécamp - 1M NW of entrance	49°46'·74N	00°20'·70E
	Le Havre - 0·5M NE of Le Havre LHA	49°32'·00N	00°09'·04W

Distance Table - South East England

Approximate distances in nautical miles are by the most direct route while avoiding dangers and allowing for Traffic Separation Schemes

		1	2	3	4	5	6	7	8	9	10	11	12	13	14	15	16	17	18
1.	**Portland Bill Lt**	1																	
2.	**Nab Tower**	60	2																
3.	**Boulder Lt Buoy**	65	5	3															
4.	**Owers Lt Buoy**	69	11	8	4														
5.	**Littlehampton**	78	19	13	12	5													
6.	**Shoreham**	90	32	24	21	13	6												
7.	**Brighton**	93	35	28	24	17	5	7											
8.	**Newhaven**	97	40	34	29	24	12	7	8										
9.	**Beachy Head Lt**	104	46	41	36	30	20	14	8	9									
10.	**Eastbourne**	111	51	45	40	34	24	19	12	7	10								
11.	**Rye**	129	72	67	62	56	46	41	34	25	23	11							
12.	**Dungeness Lt**	134	76	71	66	60	50	44	38	30	26	9	12						
13.	**Folkestone**	152	92	84	81	76	65	60	53	43	40	23	13	13					
14.	**Dover**	157	97	89	86	81	70	65	58	48	45	28	18	5	14				
15.	**Ramsgate**	172	112	104	101	96	85	80	73	63	60	43	33	20	15	15			
16.	**N Foreland Lt**	175	115	107	104	99	88	83	76	66	63	46	36	23	18	3	16		
17.	**Sheerness**	206	146	139	135	132	119	114	107	97	96	79	67	54	49	34	31	17	
18.	**London Bridge**	248	188	184	177	177	161	156	149	139	141	124	109	96	91	76	73	45	18

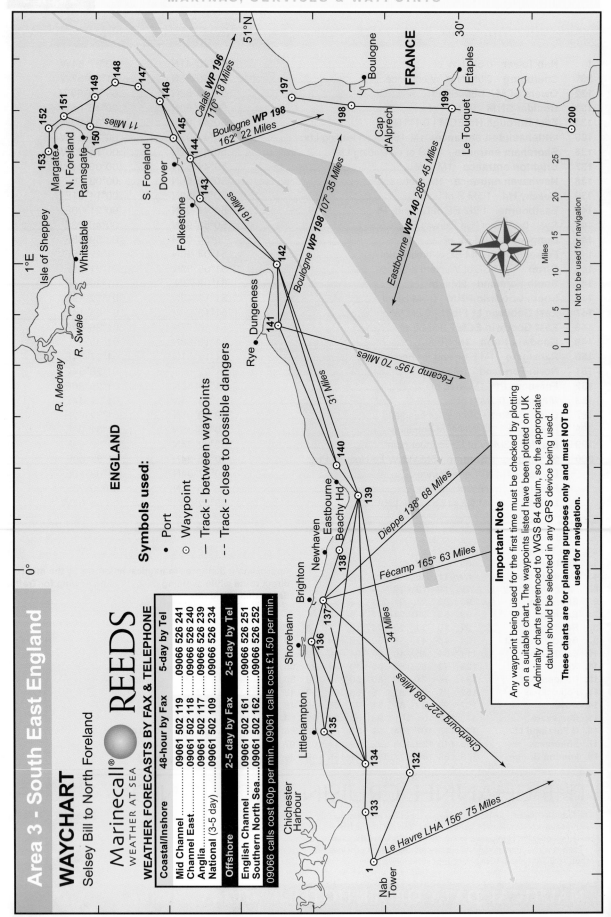

WAYCHART
Area 3 - South East England
Selsey Bill to North Foreland

Marinecall ● REEDS
WEATHER AT SEA

WEATHER FORECASTS BY FAX & TELEPHONE

Coastal/Inshore	48-hour by Fax	5-day by Tel
Mid Channel	09061 502 119	09066 526 241
Channel East	09061 502 118	09066 526 240
Anglia	09061 502 117	09066 526 239
National (3-5 day)	09061 502 109	09066 526 234

Offshore	2-5 day by Fax	2-5 day by Tel
English Channel	09061 502 161	09066 526 251
Southern North Sea	09061 502 162	09066 526 252

09066 calls cost 60p per min. 09061 calls cost £1.50 per min.

ENGLAND

FRANCE

Symbols used:
- ● Port
- ⊙ Waypoint
- — Track - between waypoints
- -- Track - close to possible dangers

Important Note

Any waypoint being used for the first time must be checked by plotting on a suitable chart. The waypoints listed have been plotted on UK Admiralty charts referenced to WGS 84 datum, so the appropriate datum should be selected in any GPS device being used.

These charts are for planning purposes only and must NOT be used for navigation.

Not to be used for navigation

Key to Marina Plans symbols

Calor Gas		P	Parking
Chandler			Pub/Restaurant
Disabled facilities			Pump out
Electrical supply			Rigging service
Electrical repairs			Sail repairs
Engine repairs			Shipwright
First Aid			Shop/Supermarket
Fresh Water			Showers
Fuel - Diesel			Slipway
Fuel - Petrol		WC	Toilets
Hardstanding/boatyard			Telephone
Laundry facilities			Trolleys
Lift-out facilities		V	Visitors berths

4

Area 4 - East England

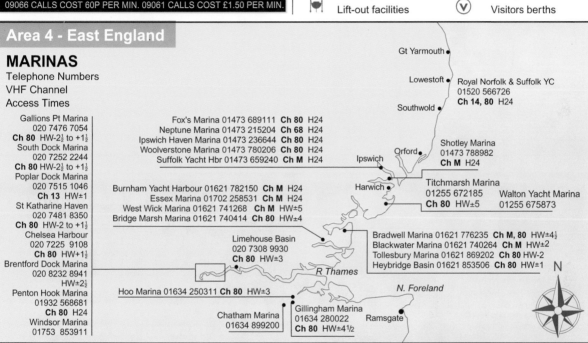

MARINAS
Telephone Numbers
VHF Channel
Access Times

Gallions Pt Marina
020 7476 7054
Ch 80 HW-2½ to +1½
South Dock Marina
020 7252 2244
Ch 80 HW-2½ to +1½
Poplar Dock Marina
020 7515 1046
Ch 13 HW±1
St Katharine Haven
020 7481 8350
Ch 80 HW-2 to +1½
Chelsea Harbour
020 7225 9108
Ch 80 HW+1½
Brentford Dock Marina
020 8232 8941
HW±2½
Penton Hook Marina
01932 568681
Ch 80 H24
Windsor Marina
01753 853911

Fox's Marina 01473 689111 **Ch 80** H24
Neptune Marina 01473 215204 **Ch 68** H24
Ipswich Haven Marina 01473 236644 **Ch 80** H24
Woolverstone Marina 01473 780206 **Ch 80** H24
Suffolk Yacht Hbr 01473 659240 **Ch M** H24

Burnham Yacht Harbour 01621 782150 **Ch M** H24
Essex Marina 01702 258531 **Ch M** H24
West Wick Marina 01621 741268 **Ch M** HW±5
Bridge Marsh Marina 01621 740414 **Ch 80** HW±4

Limehouse Basin
020 7308 9930
Ch 80 HW±3

Hoo Marina 01634 250311 **Ch 80** HW±3

Chatham Marina
01634 899200

Gt Yarmouth

Lowestoft
Royal Norfolk & Suffolk YC
01520 566726
Ch 14, 80 H24

Southwold

Orford
Shotley Marina
01473 788982
Ch M H24

Ipswich

Harwich
Titchmarsh Marina
01255 672185 Walton Yacht Marina
Ch 80 HW±5 01255 675873

Bradwell Marina 01621 776235 **Ch M, 80** HW±4½
Blackwater Marina 01621 740264 **Ch M** HW±2
Tollesbury Marina 01621 869202 **Ch 80** HW-2
Heybridge Basin 01621 853506 **Ch 80** HW±1

R Thames

N. Foreland

Gillingham Marina
01634 280022 Ramsgate
Ch 80 HW±4½

N

EAST COAST RIVERS
CRUISING COMPANION

Well established as 'the East Coast yachtsman's bible', this new edition of Jack Coote's highly regarded cruising companion covers the rivers, curlew-haunted creeks, and intricate shoals and swathways of the Thames Estuary. Edited by Jack's daughter, Janet Harber, the book now includes Lowestoft and contains completely redesigned charts and new colour photographs. Updated and extended shoreside information and essential pilotage details based on years of local knowledge make this an indispensable companion.

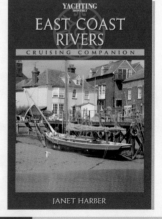

YACHTING MONTHLY
EAST COAST RIVERS
CRUISING COMPANION

JANET HARBER

NAUTICAL DATA ORDER HOTLINE: 01243 389898 Price £19.95

GILLINGHAM MARINA

Gillingham Marina
173 Pier Road, Gillingham, Kent, ME7 1UB
Tel: 01634 280022 Fax: 01634 280164
email: berthing@gillingham-marina.co.uk
www.gillingham-marina.co.uk

| VHF | Ch 80 |
| ACCESS | HW±4.5 |

Gillingham Marina comprises a locked basin, accessible four and a half hours either side of high water, and a tidal basin upstream which can be entered approximately two hours either side of high water. Deep water moorings in the river cater for yachts arriving at other times.

Visiting yachts are usually accommodated in the locked basin (beware that there are strong tides across its entrance), although it is best to contact the marina ahead of time. Lying on the south bank of the River Medway, the marina is approximately eight miles from Sheerness, at the mouth of the river, and five miles downstream of Rochester Bridge. Achieving the Five Gold Anchors award, its on site facilities include a well-stocked chandlery, brokerage and workshop.

FACILITIES AT A GLANCE

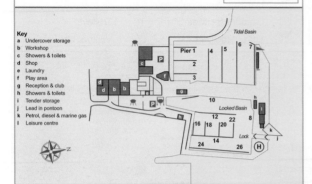

Key
a Undercover storage
b Workshop
c Showers & toilets
d Shop
e Laundry
f Play area
g Reception & club
h Showers & toilets
i Tender storage
j Lead in pontoon
k Petrol, diesel & marine gas
l Leisure centre

HOO MARINA

Hoo Marina
Vicarage Lane, Hoo, Rochester, Kent, ME3 9LE
Tel: 01634 250311 Fax: 01634 251761

| VHF | Ch 80 |
| ACCESS | HW±3 |

Hoo is a small village on the Isle of Grain, situated on a drying creek on the north bank of the River Medway approximately eight miles inland from Sheerness. Its marina was the first to be constructed on the East Coast and comprises finger berths supplied by all the usual services. It can be approached either straight across the mudflats near HW or, for a 1.5m draught, three hours either side of HW via a creek known locally as Orinoco. The entrance to this creek, which is marked by posts that must be left to port, is located a mile NW of Hoo Ness. Note that the final mark comprises a small, yellow buoy which you should pass close to starboard just before crossing the marina's sill.

Grocery stores can be found either in the adjacent chalet park or else in Hoo Village, while the Hoo Ness Yacht Club welcomes visitors to its bar and restaurant. There are also frequent bus services to the nearby town of Rochester.

FACILITIES AT A GLANCE

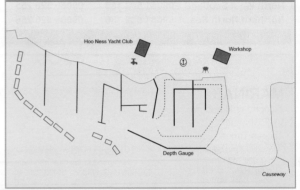

CHATHAM MARITIME MARINA

MDL, The Lock Building, Chatham Maritime Marina
Leviathan Way, Chatham Maritime, Chatham, Medway, ME4 4LP
Tel: 01634 899200 Fax: 01634 899201
email: chatham@mdlmarinas.co.uk   www.marinas.co.uk

VHF	Ch 80
ACCESS	H24*

Chatham Maritime Marina is situated on the banks of the River Medway in Kent, providing an ideal location from which to explore the surrounding area. There are plenty of secluded anchorages in the lower reaches of the Medway Estuary, while the river is navigable for some 13 miles from its mouth at Sheerness right up to Rochester, and even beyond for those yachts drawing less than 2m. Only 45 minutes from London by road, the marina is part of a multi-million pound leisure and retail development, currently accommodating 300 yachts.

FACILITIES AT A GLANCE

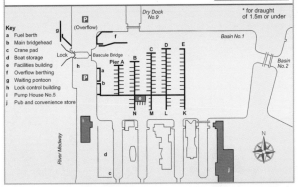

Key
a Fuel berth
b Main bridgehead
c Crane pad
d Boat storage
e Facilities building
f Overflow berthing
g Waiting pontoon
h Lock control building
i Pump House No.5
j Pub and convenience store

* for draught of 1.5m or under

When responding to adverts please mention Marina & Waypoint Guide 2004

4

GALLIONS POINT MARINA

Gallions Point Marina, Gate 14, Royal Albert Basin
Woolwich Manor Way, North Woolwich
London, E16 2NJ. Tel: 020 7476 7054 Fax: 020 7474 7056
Email: info@gallionspointmarina.co.uk
www.gallionspointmarina.co.uk

| VHF | Ch M, 80 |
| ACCESS | HW±5 |

Gallions Point Marina lies about 500 metres downstream of the Woolwich Ferry on the north side of Gallions Reach. Accessed via a lock at the entrance to the Royal Albert Basin, the marina offers deep water pontoon berths as well as hard standing. Future plans to improve facilities include the development of a bar/restaurant, a chandlery and an RYA tuition school. Diesel and gas are available from the fuel barge *Leonard*, moored off Gallions Pier just outside the lock entrance.

FACILITIES AT A GLANCE

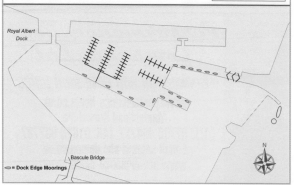

Royal Albert Dock

⊂= Dock Edge Moorings

Bascule Bridge

SOUTH DOCK MARINA

South Dock Marina
Rope Street, Off Plough Way
London, SE16 7SZ
Tel: 020 7252 2244 Fax: 020 7237 3806
garyb@sdockmarina.co.uk

| VHF | Ch M |
| ACCESS | HW-2.5 to +1.5 |

South Dock Marina is housed in part of the old Surrey Dock complex on the south bank of the River Thames. Its locked entrance is immediately downstream of Greenland Pier, just a few miles down river of Tower Bridge. For yachts with a 2m draught, the lock can be entered about two hours either side of high water, although if you arrive early there is a holding pontoon on the pier. The marina can be easily identified by the conspicuous arched rooftops of Baltic Quay, a luxury waterside apartment block. Once inside this secure, 350-berthed marina, you can take full advantage of all its facilities as well as enjoy a bar meal at the 'Wibbley Wobbley' floating pub.

FACILITIES AT A GLANCE

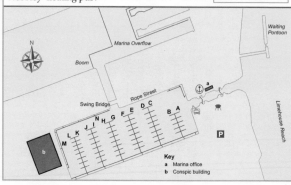

Marina Overflow

Boom

Waiting Pontoon

Swing Bridge   Rope Street

Limehouse Reach

Key
a Marina office
b Conspic building

POPLAR DOCK MARINA

Poplar Dock Marina
West India Dock Pierhead
420 Manchester Road
London, E14 9ST
Tel: 020 7517 5550 Fax: 020 7538 5537
email: sue@westindia.freeserve.co.uk

| VHF | Ch 13 |
| ACCESS | HW±1 0600-2000 |

Poplar Dock was originally designed and constructed to maintain the water level in the West India Docks. Nowadays, with Canary Wharf lying to the west and the Millennium Dome to the east, it has been converted into London's newest marina and was officially opened by the Queen in June 1999. Canary Wharf, boasting as many as 90 shops, bars and restaurants, is just a five minute walk away, while slightly further north of this is West India Quay, where Grade I listed warehouses have been converted into waterside eating places, a 12-screen cinema and fitness centre.

FACILITIES AT A GLANCE

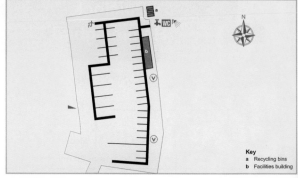

Key
a Recycling bins
b Facilities building

LIMEHOUSE BASIN

Limehouse Basin Marina
Cruising Association, CA House
1 Northey Street, London, E14 8BT
Tel: 020 7537 2828 Fax: 020 7537 2266
email: office@cruising.org.uk
www.cruising.org.uk

VHF	Ch 80
ACCESS	HW±3

Limehouse Basin Marina, situated where the canal system meets the Thames, is now considered the 'Jewel in the Crown' of the British inland waterways network. With complete access to 2,000 miles of inland waterway systems and with access to the Thames at most stages of the tide except at low water, the marina provides a superb location for river, canal and sea-going pleasure craft alike. Boasting a wide range of facilities and up to 90 berths, Limehouse Basin Marina is housed in the old Regent's Canal Dock.

FACILITIES AT A GLANCE

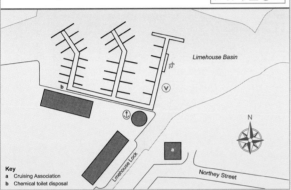

Limehouse Basin

Key
a Cruising Association
b Chemical toilet disposal

CHELSEA HARBOUR MARINA

Chelsea Harbour Marina
Estate Managements Office
C2-3 The Chambers, London, SW10 0XF
Tel: 020 7225 9108 Fax: 020 7352 7868
e-mail: paul.ray@chelsea-harbour.co.uk

VHF	Ch 80
ACCESS	HW±1.5

Chelsea Harbour is now widely thought of as one of London's most significant maritime sites. It is located in the heart of South West London, therefore enjoying easy access to the amenities of Chelsea and the West End. On site is the Chelsea Harbour Design Centre, where 80 showrooms exhibit the best in British and International interior design, while offering superb waterside views along with excellent cuisine is the Conrad Hotel.

The harbour lies approximately 48 miles up river from Sea Reach No 1 buoy in the Thames Estuary and is accessed via the Thames Flood Barrier in Woolwich Reach. With its basin gate operating one and a half hours either side of HW (+ 20 minutes at London Bridge), the marina welcomes visiting yachtsmen.

FACILITIES AT A GLANCE

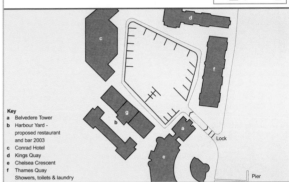

Key
a Belvedere Tower
b Harbour Yard -
   proposed restaurant
   and bar 2003
c Conrad Hotel
d Kings Quay
e Chelsea Crescent
f Thames Quay
   Showers, toilets & laundry

Lock

Pier

ST KATHARINE HAVEN

St Katharine Haven Ltd
50 St Katharine's Way, London, E1W 1LA
Tel: 020 7481 8350 Fax: 020 7702 2252
email: haven.reception@uk.taylorwoodrow.com
www.stkaths.co.uk

VHF	Ch 80
ACCESS	HW -2 to +1.5

St Katharine Docks has played a significant role in worldwide trade and commerce for over 1,000 years. Formerly a working dock, today it is an attractive waterside development housing a mixture of shops, restaurants, luxury flats and offices as well as a state-of-the-art marina. St Katharine Haven is ideally situated for exploring central London and taking full advantage of the West End's theatres and cinemas. Within easy walking distance are Tower Bridge, the Tower of London and the historic warship HMS *Belfast*. No stay at the docks is complete without a visit to the famous Dickens Inn, an impressive three storey timber building incorporating a pizza bar and stylish restaurant.

FACILITIES AT A GLANCE

Key
a Ivory House
b Dickens Inn
c Haven office
d Tower Hotel

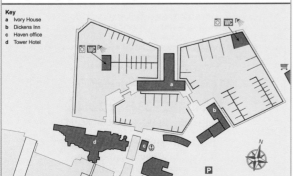

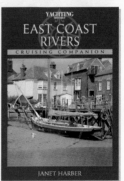

BRENTFORD DOCK MARINA

Brentford Dock Marina
2 Justine Close, Brentford, Middlesex, TW8 8QE
Tel: 020 8232 8941 Fax: 020 8560 5486
Mobile: 07920 143 987

VHF
ACCESS HW±2.5

Brentford Dock Marina is situated on the River Thames at the junction with the Grand Union Canal. Its hydraulic lock is accessible for up to two and a half hours either side of high water, although boats over 9.5m LOA enter on high water by prior arrangement. On site are the marina club, offering a full bar and restaurant service, as well as a Spar grocery store. The main attractions within the area are the Royal Botanic Gardens at Kew and the Kew Bridge Steam Museum at Brentford.

FACILITIES AT A GLANCE

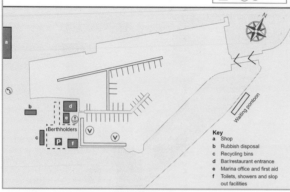

Key
a Shop
b Rubbish disposal
c Recycling bins
d Bar/restaurant entrance
e Marina office and first aid
f Toilets, showers and slop out facilities

PENTON HOOK MARINA

Penton Hook
Staines Road, Chertsey, Surrey, KT16 8PY
Tel: 01932 568681 Fax: 01932 567423
email: pentonhook@mdlmarinas.co.uk
www.marinas.co.uk

VHF Ch 80
ACCESS H24

Penton Hook Marina is situated on what is considered to be one of the most attractive reaches of the River Thames, close to Chertsey and about a mile downstream of Runnymede. Providing unrestricted access to the River Thames through a deep water channel below Penton Hook Lock, the marina can accommodate ocean-going craft of up to 21m LOA and is ideally placed for a visit to Thorpe Park, reputedly one of Europe's most popular family leisure attractions.

FACILITIES AT A GLANCE

Key
a Information point
b Dock manager's office

BISHAM ABBEY SAILING & NAVIGATION SCHOOL
National Sports Centre, Bisham, Nr Marlow, Bucks SL7 1RT
Tel: 01628 474960
Fax: 01628 474960
www.bishamabbeysailing.co.uk

RYA Training Centre. shore-based intensive and semi-inteneive: Dayskipper, Yachtmaster, Yachtmaster Ocean, VHF(SRC), 1st Aid, Radar, Diesel Engine Maintenance, Electronics, Boat Handling, IWHC, ICC coastal & inland, CEVNI, Powerboat 1&2. Dinghy Sailing. Boat Safety Scheme Inspections.

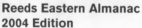

WINDSOR MARINA

Windsor Marina
Maidenhead Road, Windsor
Berkshire, SL4 5TZ
Tel: 01753 853911 Fax: 01753 868195
email: k.powell@mdlmarinas.co.uk www.marinas.co.uk

VHF Ch 33, M
ACCESS H24

Situated on the outskirts of Windsor town on the south bank of the River Thames, Windsor Marina enjoys a peaceful garden setting. On site are the Windsor Yacht Club as well as boat lifting and repair facilities, a chandlery and brokerage.

A trip to the town of Windsor, comprising beautiful Georgian and Victorian buildings, would not be complete without a visit to Windsor Castle. With its construction inaugurated over 900 years ago by William the Conqueror, it is the oldest inhabited castle in the world and accommodates a priceless art and furniture collection.

FACILITIES AT A GLANCE

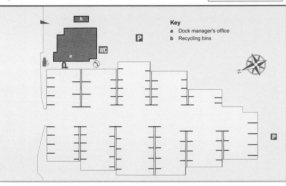

Key
a Dock manager's office
b Recycling bins

BURNHAM YACHT HARBOUR MARINA

Burnham Yacht Harbour Marina Ltd
Burnham-on-Crouch, Essex, CM0 8BL
Tel: 01621 782150 Fax: 01621785848
email: admin@burnhamyachtharbour.co.uk

VHF Ch 80
ACCESS HW±3

Boasting four major yacht clubs, each with comprehensive racing programmes, Burnham-on-Crouch has come to be regarded by some as 'the Cowes of the East Coast'. At the western end of the town lies Burnham Yacht Harbour, accessible three hours either side of high water. Offering a variety of on site facilities, its entrance can be easily identified by a yellow pillar buoy with an 'X' topmark.

The historic town, with its 'weatherboard' and early brick buildings, elegant quayside and scenic riverside walks, exudes plenty of charm. Among its attractions are a sports centre, a railway museum and a two-screen cinema.

FACILITIES AT A GLANCE

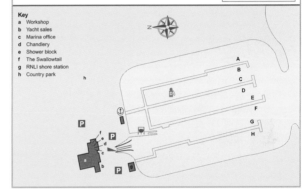

Key
a Workshop
b Yacht sales
c Marina office
d Chandlery
e Shower block
f The Swallowtail
g RNLI shore station
h Country park

ESSEX MARINA

Essex Marina
Wallasea Island, Essex, SS4 2HF
Tel: 01702 258531 Fax: 01702 258227
www.essexmarina.co.uk

VHF	Ch M
ACCESS	H24

Surrounded by beautiful countryside in an area of Special Scientific Interest, Essex Marina is situated in Wallasea Bay, about half a mile up river of Burnham on Crouch. Boasting 500 deep water berths, including 50 swinging moorings, the marina can be accessed at all states of the tide. On site are a 70 ton boat hoist, a chandlery and brokerage service as well as the Essex Marina Yacht Club.

Buses run frequently to Southend-on-Sea, just seven miles away, while a ferry service takes passengers across the river on weekends to Burnham, where you will find numerous shops and restaurants. Benefiting from its close proximity to London (just under an hour's drive away) and Rochford Airport (approximately four miles away), the marina provides a suitable location for crew changeovers.

FACILITIES AT A GLANCE

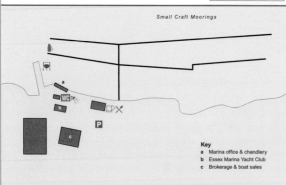

Small Craft Moorings

Key
a   Marina office & chandlery
b   Essex Marina Yacht Club
c   Brokerage & boat sales

WEST WICK MARINA

West Wick Marina Ltd
Church Road, North Fambridge, Essex, CM3 6LR
Tel: 01621 741268 Fax: 01621 742359

VHF	Ch M
ACCESS	HW±5

Just under a mile upstream of North Fambridge, Stow Creek branches off to the north of the River Crouch. The creek, marked with occasional starboard hand withies, leads to the entrance to West Wick Marina, which enjoys an unspoilt, tranquil setting between saltings and farmland. Home to West Wick Yacht Club, the marina has 180 berths and can accommodate vessels up to 15m LOA.

The nearby village of North Fambridge incorporates a small convenience store as well as the Ferryboat Inn, a favourite haunt with the boating fraternity. Only six miles down river lies Burnham-on-Crouch, while the Essex and Kent coasts are within easy sailing distance.

FACILITIES AT A GLANCE

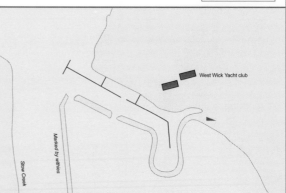

West Wick Yacht club

Stow Creek

Marked by withies

BRIDGEMARSH MARINA

Bridge Marsh Marine
Fairholme, Bridge Marsh Lane, Althorne, Essex
Tel: 01621 740414 Fax: 01621 740414

VHF | Ch 80
ACCESS | HW±4

On the north side of Bridgemarsh Island, just beyond Essex Marina on the River Crouch, lies Althorne Creek. Here Bridgemarsh Marine accommodates over 100 boats berthed alongside pontoons supplied with water and electricity. A red beacon marks the entrance to the creek, with red can buoys identifying the approach channel into the marina. Accessible four hours either side of high water, the marina has an on site yard with two docks, a slipway and crane. The village of Althorne is just a short walk away, from where there are direct train services (taking approximately one hour) to London.

FACILITIES AT A GLANCE

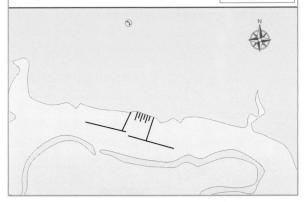

BRADWELL MARINA

Bradwell Marina, Port Flair Ltd, Waterside
Bradwell-on-Sea, Essex, CM0 7RB
Tel: 01621 776235 Fax: 01621 776393
email: info@bradwellmarina.com
www.bradwellmarina.com

VHF | Ch M, 80
ACCESS | HW±4.5

Opened in 1984, Bradwell is a privately-owned marina situated in the mouth of the River Blackwater, serving as a convenient base from which to explore the Essex coastline or as a departure point for cruising further afield to Holland and Belgium. The yacht basin can be accessed four and a half hours either side of HW and offers plenty of protection from all wind directions. With a total of 300 fully serviced berths, generous space has been allocated for manoeuvring between pontoons. Overlooking the marina is Bradwell Club House, incorporating a bar, restaurant, launderette and ablution facilities.

FACILITIES AT A GLANCE

Key
a   Clubhouse
b   Tower office

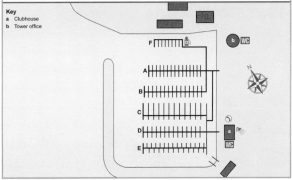

4

seaPro
Making Navigation Easy

Practical navigation features;

- Connects to a GPS & Autopilot
- Shows your position on a chart
- Enables tidal route planning
- Calculates best departure time
- Calculates course to steer
- Displays animated weather
- Supports multiple chart formats
- Versions to suit all budgets & needs

seaPro is the leading PC charting and navigation software that turns your laptop or PC into a complete navigation station. More powerful & flexible than a dedicated chart plotter, seaPro connects to your GPS to show your position on paper-quality charts and includes practical functions such as tidal and weather route planning. seaPro is used worldwide by thousands of sail and power boaters.

For more information or a demonstration visit **www.euronav.co.uk**

Euronav Ltd. 20 The Slipway, Port Solent, PO6 4TR
Tel : 023 92373855 Fax: 023 92325800

EURONAV
NAVIGATION
2004/NC29/d

SAILSPAR LTD
Tower Street, Brightlingsea, Essex CO7 0AW.
Tel: +44 (0) 1206 302679 Fax: +44 (0) 1206 302679
e-mail: info@sailspar.co.uk
www.sailspar.co.uk
Quality masts and spars. 'The Sailspar' Continuous Line Headsail Roller Reefing System. 'The Scott Boomlock' Gybe Preventer System. Standing and running rigging. RDM Sparcraft and Facnor agents.

BLACKWATER MARINA

Blackwater Marina
Marine Parade, Maylandsea, Essex
Tel: 01621 740264 Tel: 01621 742122
www.blackwater-marina.co.uk

VHF | Ch M
ACCESS | HW±2

Blackwater Marina is tucked away in Lawling Creek, the entrance to which lies about half a mile or so across the River Blackwater from Osea Island. Accessible two to three hours either side of high water for yachts drawing around 1.5m, the marina offers comprehensive facilities, including rigging, sail repair and shipwright services. The on site bar and restaurant provides a good menu, or else within easy walking distance is a cosmopolitan range of eating places as well as several convenience stores.

FACILITIES AT A GLANCE

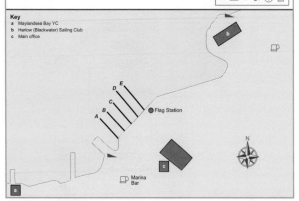

Key
a Maylandsea Bay YC
b Harlow (Blackwater) Sailing Club
c Main office

TOLLESBURY MARINA

Tollesbury Marina
The Yacht Harbour, Tollesbury, Essex, CM9 8SE
Tel: 01621 869202 Fax: 01621 868489
email: marina@woodrolfe.demon.co.uk

VHF | Ch M, 80
ACCESS | HW±2

Tollesbury Marina lies at the mouth of the River Blackwater in the heart of the Essex countryside. Within easy access from London and the Home Counties, it has been designed as a leisure centre for the whole family, with on-site activities comprising tennis courts and a covered heated swimming pool as well as a convivial bar and restaurant. Accommodating over 240 boats, the marina can be accessed two hours either side of HW and is ideally situated for those wishing to explore the River Crouch to the south and the Rivers Colne, Orwell and Deben to the north

FACILITIES AT A GLANCE

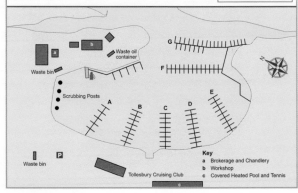

Key
a Brokerage and Chandlery
b Workshop
c Covered Heated Pool and Tennis

HEYBRIDGE BASIN

Heybridge Basin
Lock Hill, Heybridge Basin, Maldon, Essex, CM9 4RX
Tel: 01621 853506
email: colsnandmargaret@lockkeeping.fsnet.co.uk
www.cbn.co.uk

VHF Ch 80
ACCESS HW±1

Towards the head of the River Blackwater, not far from Maldon, lies Heybridge Basin. Situated at the lower end of the 14–mile long Chelmer and Blackwater Navigation Canal, it can be reached via a lock about one hour either side of HW for a yacht drawing around 2m. If you arrive too early, there is good holding ground in the river just outside the lock. Incorporating as many as 200 berths, the basin has a range of facilities, including shower and laundry amenities. Visiting yachts are advised to call ahead of time as it can get very crowded on weekends.

FACILITIES AT A GLANCE

TITCHMARSH MARINA

Titchmarsh Marina Ltd
Coles Lane, Walton on the Naze, Essex, CO14 8SL
Tel: 01255 672185 Fax: 01255 851901
email: office@titchmarshmarina.co.uk
www.titchmarshmarina.co.uk

VHF Ch 80
ACCESS HW±5

Titchmarsh Marina sits on the south side of The Twizzle in the heart of the Walton Backwaters. As the area is designated as a 'wetland of international importance', the marina has been designed and developed to function as a natural harbour. The 420 berths are well sheltered by the high-grassed clay banks, offering good protection in all conditions. Access to Titchmarsh is over a sill, which has a depth of about 1m at LWS, but once inside the basin, the depth increases to around 2m. Among the excellent facilities are an on site chandlery as well as the Harbour Lights Restaurant & Bar serving breakfasts, lunch and dinners.

FACILITIES AT A GLANCE

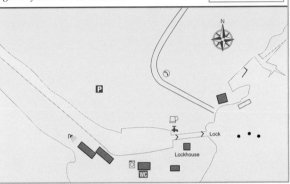

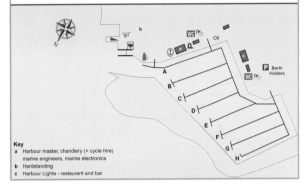

Key
a Harbour master, chandlery (+ cycle hire) marine engineers, marine electronics
b Hardstanding
c Harbour Lights - restaurant and bar

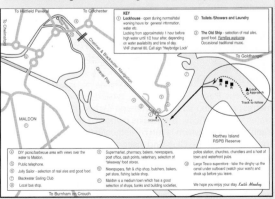

SHOTLEY MARINA

Shotley Marina Ltd
Shotley Gate, Ipswich, Suffolk, IP9 1QJ
Tel: 01473 788982 Fax: 01473 788868
Email: sales@shotley-marina.co.uk
www.shotley-marina.co.uk

| VHF | Ch 80 |
| ACCESS | H24 |

Based in the well protected Harwich Harbour where the River Stour joins the River Orwell, Shotley Marina is only eight miles from the county town of Ipswich. Entered via a lock at all states of the tide, its first class facilities include extensive boat repair and maintenance services as well as a well-stocked chandlery and on site bar and restaurant. The marina is strategically placed for sailing up the Stour to Manningtree, up the Orwell to Pin Mill or exploring the Rivers Deben, Crouch and Blackwater as well as the Walton Backwaters.

FACILITIES AT A GLANCE

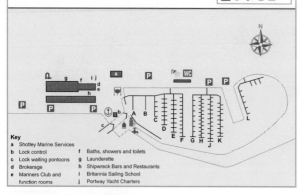

Key
a Shotley Marine Services
b Lock control
c Lock waiting pontoons
d Brokerage
e Mariners Club and function rooms
f Baths, showers and toilets
g Launderette
h Shipwreck Bars and Restaurants
i Britannia Sailing School
j Portway Yacht Charters

WALTON YACHT BASIN

Walton and Frinton Yacht Trust
Mill Lane, Walton on the Naze, CO14 8PF
Managed by Bedwell & Co Tel: 01255 675873
Fax: 01255 677405 After hours Tel: 01255 672655

| VHF | |
| ACCESS | HW-0.75,HW+0.25 |

Walton Yacht Basin lies at the head of Walton Creek, an area made famous in Arthur Ransome's *Swallows & Amazons* and *Secret Waters*. The creek can only be navigated two hours either side of HW, although yachts heading for the Yacht Basin should arrive on a rising tide as the entrance gate is kept shut once the tide turns in order to retain the water inside. Before entering the gate, moor up against the Club Quay to enquire about berthing availability.

A short walk away is the popular seaside town of Walton, full of shops, pubs and restaurants. Its focal point is the pier which, overlooking superb sandy beaches, offers various attractions including a ten-pin bowling alley. Slightly further out of town, the Naze affords pleasant coastal walks with striking panoramic views.

FACILITIES AT A GLANCE

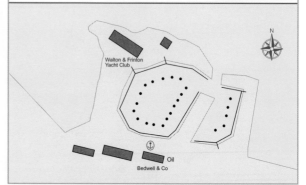

FOX'S MARINA

Fox's Marina Ltd
The Strand, Wherstead, Ipswich, Suffolk, IP2 8SA
Tel: 01473 689111 Fax: 01473 601737

VHF Ch 80
ACCESS H24

One of five marinas on the River Orwell, Fox's provides good shelter in all conditions and, dredged to 2m below chart datum, benefits from full tidal access from Ostrich Creek. Accommodating yachts up to 21m LOA, it has enough storage ashore for over 200 vessels and offers a comprehensive refit, repair and maintenance service. Since becoming part of the Oyster Group of Companies, Fox's facilities have further improved with ongoing investment. Besides several workshops, other services on hand include an osmosis centre, a spray centre, engineering, rigging and electronic specialists as well as one of the largest chandleries on the East Coast. In addition there are regular bus services to Ipswich, which is only about one to two miles away.

FACILITIES AT A GLANCE

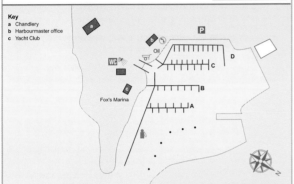

Key
a Chandlery
b Harbourmaster office
c Yacht Club

NEPTUNE MARINA

Neptune Marina Ltd
Neptune Quay, Ipswich, IP4 1AX
Tel: 01473 215204 Fax: 01473 215206
www.neptune-marina.com

VHF Ch M, 80
ACCESS H±2.5

The Wet Dock at Ipswich, which was opened in 1850, became the largest in Europe and was in use right up until the 1930s. Now the dock incorporates two modern marinas – Neptune Marina, situated at Neptune Quay on the Historic Waterfront, and Ipswich Haven Marina to the south. This 26-acre site is accessible through a 24-hr lock gate, with a waiting pontoon outside for those yachts wishing to enter. The town centre is a 10 minute walk away and offers a wealth of restaurants and shops, while Cardinal Park, a relatively new complex housing an 11-screen cinema and several eating places, is also nearby.

FACILITIES AT A GLANCE

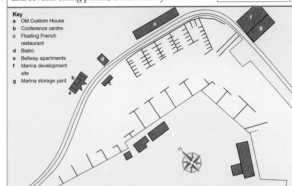

Key
a Old Custom House
b Conference centre
c Floating French restaurant
d Bistro
e Bellway apartments
f Marina development site
g Marina storage yard

4

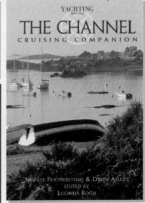

IPSWICH HAVEN MARINA

Ipswich Haven Marina
Associated British Ports
New Cut East, Ipswich, Suffolk, IP3 0EA
Tel: 01473 236644 Fax: 01473 236645
www.abports.co.uk email: ipswichhaven@abports.co.uk

VHF	Ch 80
ACCESS	H24

Lying at the heart of Ipswich, the Haven Marina enjoys close proximity to all the bustling shopping centres, restaurants, cinemas and museums that this County Town of Suffolk has to offer. The main railway station is only a 10-minute walk away, where there are regular connections to London, Cambridge and Norwich, all taking just over an hour to get to.

Within easy reach of Holland, Belgium and Germany, East Anglia is proving an increasingly popular cruising ground. The River Orwell, displaying breathtaking scenery, was voted one of the most beautiful rivers in Britain by the RYA.

FACILITIES AT A GLANCE

Key
a   Toilets, showers, laundry, office
b   Licensed bistro
c   R&J Marine Electronics
d   Boat sales
e   Fairline PDI Shed
f   Future restaurant retail
g   Peters Repair Shop

WOOLVERSTONE MARINA

Woolverstone Marina
Woolverstone, Ipswich, Suffolk, IP9 1AS
Tel: 01473 780206 Fax: 01473 780273
www.marinas.co.uk e mail: t.barnes@mdlmarinas.co.uk

| VHF | Ch 80 |
| ACCESS | H24 |

Set in 22 acres of parkland, within close proximity to the Royal Harwich Yacht Club, Woolverstone Marina boasts 210 pontoon berths as well as 120 swinging moorings, all of which are served by a water taxi. Besides boat repair services, an on site chandlery and excellent ablution facilities, the marina also incorporates a sailing school and yacht brokerage.

Woolverstone's location on the scenic River Orwell makes it ideally placed for exploring the various cruising grounds along the East Coast, including the adjacent River Stour, the Colne and Blackwater estuaries to the south and the River Deben to the north.

FACILITIES AT A GLANCE

Key

a Marina office, toilets, showers, launderette and boat sales
b Restaurant/bar
c Royal Harwich Yacht Club

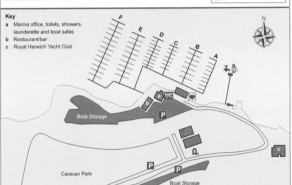

4

SUFFOLK YACHT HARBOUR

Suffolk Yacht Harbour Ltd
Levington, Ipswich, Suffolk, IP10 0LN
Tel: 01473 659240 Fax: 01473 659632
enquiries@suffolkyachtharbour.ltd.uk
www.suffolkyachtharbour.ltd.uk

VHF Ch M
ACCESS H24

A friendly, independently-run marina on the East Coast of England, Suffolk Yacht Harbour enjoys a beautiful rural setting on the River Orwell, yet is within easy access of Ipswich (a mile away), Woodbridge and Felixstowe. With approximately 500 berths, the marina offers extensive facilities while the Haven Ports Yacht Club provides a bar and restaurant.

FACILITIES AT A GLANCE

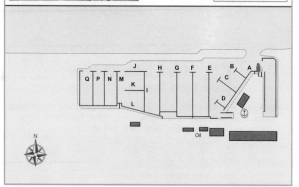

ROYAL NORFOLK & SUFFOLK YACHT CLUB

Royal Norfolk and Suffolk Yacht Club
Royal Plain, Lowestoft, Suffolk, NR33 0AQ
Tel: 01502 566726 Fax: 01502 517981
e-mail: rnsyc@ctc-net.co.uk

VHF Ch 14, 80
ACCESS H24

With its entrance at the inner end of the South Pier, opposite the Trawl Basin on the north bank, the Royal Norfolk and Suffolk Yacht Club marina occupies a sheltered position in Lowestoft Harbour. Lowestoft has always been an appealing destination to yachtsmen due to the fact that it can be accessed at any state of the tide, 24 hours a day. Note, however, that conditions just outside the entrance can get pretty lively when the wind is against tide. The clubhouse is enclosed in an impressive Grade 2 listed building overlooking the marina and its facilities include a bar and restaurant as well as a formal dining room with a full *à la carte* menu.

FACILITIES AT A GLANCE

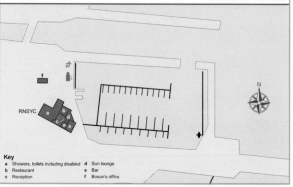

Key
a Showers, toilets including disabled
b Restaurant
c Reception
d Sun lounge
e Bar
f Bosun's office

4

A & B Textiles Gillingham
Sailmaker; boat covers   01634 579686

Absolute Gorleston on Sea
Customised sailing clothing
01493 442259

Adec Marine Croydon
Safety equipment   020 8686 9717

Adhesive Technologies Braintree
Adhesives; tapes   01376 346511

Akeron Ltd Southend on Sea
Stainless steel metalworker
01702 297101

Aldeburgh YC Aldeburgh 01728 452562

Alexandra YC   01702 340363

Allington Marina Maidstone
01622 752057

Anchor Marine Products Benfleet
Fenders and buoys   01268 566666

Anglia Yacht Brokerage
Bury St Edmunds
Brokerage   01359 271747

Aqua Bell Ltd Norwich
Marina moorings; boatbuilder; repairs
01603 713013

Aquafax Ltd Luton
Marine pumps & plumbing fittings
01582 568700

ARS Anglian Diesels Ltd Chedgrave
Hydraulic systems & equipment
01508 520555

Assured Boating Egham
Brokerage   01784 473300

Baker Marine (Medway) Ltd Rochester
Chandler   01634 843227

Barrus Ltd, EP Bicester
Inboard engine distributor 01869 363636

Bedwell and Co Walton-on-the-Naze
Chandler; boatyard – storage; repairs
01255 675873

Benfleet YC Canvey Island
01268 792278

Bigfish London
Marine finance, chartering in the Med,
syndicate ownership   020 8651 4096

Birch, ER
Boatbuilders   01268 696094

Bisham Abbey Sailing & Navigation School
RYA recognised establishment
01628 474960

Blackwater Marina Maylandsea
01621 740264

Bishop Skinner London
Boat Insurance   0800 783 8057

Blackwater SC Maldon   01621 853923

Blue Baker Yachts Ipswich
01473 780008

Boatacs Westcliffe on Sea
Chandler   01702 475057

Bradwell CC   01621 892970

Bradwell Chandlery Bradwell-on-Sea
01621 776147

Bradwell Marina Bradwell-on-Sea
01621 776235

Bradwell Quay YC Wickford
01268 776539

Brandy Hole YC Hullbridge
01702 230320

Bray Marina Bray   01628 623654

Brentford Dock Marina Brentford
020 8298 8941

Bridge Marsh Marina Althorpe
01621 740414

Brightlingsea Boatyard Brightlingsea
01206 302003/8

Brightlingsea SC Colchester
01206 303275

Bruntons Propellers Ltd
Clacton-on-Sea   01255 420005

Bure Marine Ltd Great Yarmouth
Storage; repairs; maintenance
01493 656996

Burnham Yacht Harbour Marina Ltd
Burnham-on-Crouch   01621 782150

Burnham-on-Crouch HM
01621 783602

Burnham-on-Crouch Police
01621 782121

Burnham-on-Crouch SC
Burnham-on-Crouch   01621 782812

Cabin Yacht Stores Rochester
Chandler   01634 718020

Cactus Navigation & Communication Ltd London
Supplier of marine electronics
020 7493 1115

Cannell, David M & Associates
Wivenhoe
Design of yachts and commercial craft to
80m   01206 823337

Captain O M Watts London
Chandler; brokerage   020 7493 4633

Casco Products Industrial Adhesives
St Neots   01480 476777

Charity & Taylor Ltd Lowestoft
Electronics   01502 581529

Chatham Maritime Marina Chatham
01634 899200

Chelsea Harbour Marina London
020 7225 9108

Chertsey Marine Ltd Penton Hook
Marina
Chandlery   01932 565195

Chiswick Quay Marina London
020 8994 8743

Cleghorn Waring Ltd Letchworth
Marine pumps; water systems;
compasses; searchlights 01462 480380

Colchester Police   01206 762212

Colne YC Brightlingsea   01206 302594

Cook's Diesel Service Ltd Faversham
Engine repairs; fuel injection equipment
01795 538553

Craftinsure.com Orpington
Marine insurance   01689 889507

Creeksea SC Burnham-on-Crouch
01245 320578

Crew Clothing London   020 8875 2300

Crouch YC Burnham-on-Sea
01278 782252

Cuxton Marina Ltd Rochester
01634 721941

Danson Marine Sidcup
Chandler   0208 304 5678

Dauntless Boatyard Ltd Canvey Island
Chandler; repairs; storage; rigging
01268 793782

Deben YC Woodbridge   01394 385400

Dinghy Store Whitstable 01227 274168

Dolphin Sails Harwich   01255 243366

Dove Marina London   020 8748 9474

East Anglian Sea School Levington
01473 659992

East Coast Sails Walton-on-the-Naze
01255 678353

Elmhaven Marina Halling
01634 240489

Energy Solutions Rochester
Onboard electrical power 01634 290772

Essex Marina Rochford   01702 258531

Essex YC Southend   01702 478404

Eurotech Marine Products Ltd London
Sailmaker; boat covers   020 7235 8273

Evans, Martin Kirby-Le-Soken
Surveyor   01255 677883

Exe Leisure Essex Marina
Broker   01702 258190

EYE Co Ltd Ipswich
New and used anchors & chains
01473 659666

Eyott SC Mayland   01245 320703

Fairways Chandlery
Burnham-on-Crouch   01621 782659

Fairways Marine Engineers Maldon
01621 852866

Felixarc Marine Ltd Felixstowe
01394 676497

Felixstowe Ferry Boatyard Felixstowe
01394 282173

Felixstowe Ferry SC Felixstowe
01394 283785

Fender-Fix Maidstone
Fenders & holders   01622 751518

Fox's Marina Ipswich Ltd Ipswich
01473 689111

Freeland Yacht Spars Ltd
Dorchester on Thames
Specialists in wooden spars; oars
01865 341277

French Marine Motors Ltd
Brightlingsea   01206 302133

Gallions Point Marina London
020 7476 7054

Gibbs Chandlery Shepperton
01932 242977

Gillingham Marina Gillingham
01634 280022

Goldfinch Sails Whitstable
01227 272295

Goodchild Marine Services
Great Yarmouth
Boatbuilders; repairs; marine engineers
01493 782301

Gorleston Marine Ltd Great Yarmouth
Outboards; spare parts; inflatables;
chandler   01493 661883

Gowen Ocean Sailmakers W Mersea
01206 384412

Gravesend SC Gravesend
01474 533974

Great Yarmouth HM   01493 335501

Great Yarmouth Police 01493 336200

Great Yarmouth Police 01493 336200

Greenwich YC London 020 8858 7339

GUARDIAN FIRE LTD Norwich
Fire extinguishers   01603 787679

Halcon Marine Ltd Canvey Island
01268 511611

Halfway YC   01702 582025

Halls & Son, Frank Walton on the Naze
Boatbuilders & repairs   01255 675596

Hampton Pier YC Herne Bay
01227 364749

Harbour Lights Restaurant
Walton-on-the-Naze   01255 851887

Harbour Marine Services Ltd (HMS)
Southwold   01502 724721

Harwich Town SC Harwich
01255 503200

Haven Ports YC Woodbridge
01394 659658

Hawkins Marine Shipstores, John
Rochester   01634 840812

Herne Bay SC Herne Bay
01227 375650

Heybridge Basin Maldon
01621 853506

Holman & Pye West Mersea
Yacht designer   01206 382478

Hoo Marina Rochester 01634 250311

Hoo Ness YC Sidcup   01634 250052

Hullbridge YC   01702 231797

Hurlingham YC London 020 8788 5547

Hyde Sails (Benfleet) Benfleet
01268 756254

IBS Boats South Woodham Ferrers
Distributor of inflatables and RIBS
01245 323211/425551

Ipswich Haven Marina Ipswich
01473 236644

Iron Wharf Boatyard Faversham
01795 536296

Island YC Canvey Island 01268 510360

Jeckells and Son Ltd Lowestoft
Sailmaker; covers; upholsterer
01502 565007

Keypart Watford
Inboard engine distributor; spare parts
01923 330570

Kew Marina London   020 8940 8364

Lawrence, J Sailmakers Brightlingsea
01206 302863

Leigh-on-Sea SC   01702 476788

Limehouse Basin Marina London
020 7537 2828

Lowestoft CC Lowestoft 01502 574376

Lowestoft HM   01502 572286

Lowestoft Police   01986 855321

MacGregor, WA Felixtowe
Surveyor   01394 676034

Maldon Little Ship Club
01621 854139

Marconi Marine Lowestoft
Marine electronics   01502 572365

Mardon Insurance Shrewsbury
0800 515629

Margate YC Margate   01227 292602

Marine Electrical Repair Service
London
Marine electrical repair specialist
020 7228 1336

Marine & Industrial Sealants Norwich
01692 538263

Marine Maintenance Tollesbury
Marine engineers; chandler; engine sales;
spares; custom made stainless steel
products   01621 860441

Marine Store Maldon
Chandler   01621 854280

Marine Store Walton on the Naze
Chandler   01255 679028

Mariners Farm Boatyard Gillingham
01634 233179

Martello Yacht Services Canvey Island
01268 681970

McKillop Sails (Sail Locker) Ipswich
01473 780007

McNamara Sails, Michael Great
Yarmouth   01692 584186

Medusa Marine Ipswich
Shipwrights and engineers 01473 780090

Medway Bridge Marina Rochester
01634 843576

Medway Diving Contractors Ltd
Gillingham   01634 851902

Medway Pier Marina Gillingham
01634 851113

Medway Police   01634 811281

Medway YC Rochester 01634 718399

Mercia Marine Malvern
Insurance   01684 564457

Microcustom Ltd Ipswich
Electrical equipment   01473 780724

Morgan & Sons Marine, LH
Brightlingsea
Boat storage; repairs; moorings; boat
sales; chandlery   01206 302003

Musto Ltd Laindon
Foul weather gear   01268 491555

Nautical World London
Chandler   020 7247 0521

Navtronics Lowestoft
Marine electronics   01502 587696

Neptune Marina Ltd Ipswich
01473 215204

Newens Marine, Chas Putney
Engine Sales/repairs
020 8788 4587

Norfolk Marine Great Yarmouth
01692 670272

Norfolk Marine Chandlery Shop
Norwich   01603 783150

North Fambridge Yacht Centre
01621 740370

North Sea Sails Tollesbury
01621 869367

Ocean Leisure Ltd London
Chandler; surfing & diving equipment
020 7930 5050

One Stop Chandlery Chelmsford
01245 380680

Orford SC Woodbridge 01394 450444

Orwell YC Ipswich   01473 602288

Oulton Broad Yacht Station
01502 574946

Oyster Brokerage Ltd Ipswich
Broker for used Oyster yachts
01473 602263

Oyster Marine Ltd Ipswich
High performance yachts 01473 688888

Parker & Kay Sailmakers East Ipswich
01473 659878

Penton Hook Chertsey 01932 568681

Pin Mill SC Woodbridge 01394 780271

Pirates Cave Ltd Rochester
Chandlery, stocking leading brands
01634 295233

Poplar Dock Marina London
020 7515 1046

Port Medway Marina Rochester
01634 720033

Port of London Authority Gravesend
01474 560311

Portway Yacht Charters Ipswich
01473 787018

Premium Liferaft Services
Burnham-on-Crouch
Hires/sells liferafts and safety equipment
01621 782150

Premium Liferaft Services Colchester
As above   01206 579245

Premium Liferaft Services Levington
As above   01473 659465

Premium Liferaft Services London
As above   020 8519 2227

Premium Liferaft Services
West Mersea
As above   01206 382545

Priors Boatyard Burnham-on-Crouch
Moorings; boatbuilders; repairs; storage
01621 782160

Pro-Boat Ltd Burnham-on-Crouch
Yacht equipment; antifouling
01621 785455

Purcell, D – Crouch Sailing School
Burnham-on-Crouch
Diver   01621 784140

Queenborough Harbour
Queenborough, Isle of Sheppey
01795 662051

Queenborough HM   01795 662051

Queenborough Police   01795 477055

Queenborough YC Queenborough
01795 663955

Racecourse Yacht Basin (Windsor) Ltd
Marina with full facilities   01753 851501

Radiocommunications Agency London
Radio licence   020 7211 0211

RF Upson and Co Aldeburgh
01728 453047

Rice and Cole Ltd Burnham-on-Crouch
01621 782063

River Blackwater HM   01621 856487

River Colne (Brightlingsea) HM
01206 302200

River Colne Police   01255 221312

River Deben HM   01394 270106

River Deben Police   01394 383377

River Medway HM   01795 596593

River Orwell HM   01473 231010

River Orwell Police   01473 233000

River Roach HM   01621 783602

River Stour HM   01255 243000

River Stour Police   01255 241312

Rivers Alde & Ore HM   01473 450481

Rivers Alde and Ore Police
01394 613500

Robertsons Boatyard Woodbridge
01394 382305

Rochester CC Rochester 01634 841350

Royal Burnham YC Burnham-on-Crouch
01621 782044

Royal Corinthian YC
Burnham-on-Crouch   01621 782105

Royal Harwich YC Ipswich
01473 780319

Royal Institute of Navigation London
Navigation for air, sea, land and space
020 7591 3130

Royal Norfolk & Suffolk YC Lowestoft
01502 566726

Royal Norfolk and Suffolk Yacht Club
Lowestoft   01502 566726

Rule – ITT Industries Hoddesdon
Compasses; bilge pumps; winches;
ventilation products   01992 450145

RW Munro Ltd Woodford Green
Meteorological & hydrographic instrument
manufacturers   020 8551 7000

Sailspar Ltd Brightlingsea
Quality masts and spars ready made or in
kit form   01206 302679

St Margarets Insurances Penge,
London   020 8778 6161

Seamark-Nunn & Co Felixstowe
Chandler; boat repairs; outboard
services/spares; insurance 01394 275327

Seasalter SC Whitstable 01227 264784

Seath Instruments (1992) Ltd
Lowestoft
Gas alarm & control systems
01502 573811

Shanly Investments Ltd, Michael
Beaconsfield
Saxon moorings Old Windsor
01494 671331

Shepperton Marina London
01932 247427

Ship Shape Marine Chandlers
King's Lynn   01553 764058

Shotley Marina Ipswich 01473 788982

Shotley Marine Services Ltd Ipswich
Boat repairs   01473 788913

Sika Ltd Welwyn Garden City
Adhesives   01707 394444

Sillette–Sonic Ltd Sutton
020 8715 0100

Slaughden SC Duxford   01223 835395

Small Craft Deliveries Ltd Woodbridge
01394 382655

Smith AM (Marine) Ltd London
British Admiralty chart supplier & nautical
instruments   020 8529 6988

Smith & Son Ltd, EC Luton
Yacht equipment – hardware to paints
01582 729721

South Dock Marina London
020 7252 2244

South Eastern Marine Services Ltd
Basildon
Liferafts; safety equipment 01268 534427

South Woodham Ferrers YC
Chelmsford   01245 325391

Southend-on-Sea HM   01702 611889

Southend-on-Sea Police
01702 341212

Southwold HM   01502 724712

Southwold Police   01986 855321

Southwold SC   01502 716776

Spencer Sailing Services, Jim
Brightlingsea
Boatbuilder   01206 302911

St Katharine Haven London
020 7481 8350

Stanford Charts West Mersea
Charts; publications   01206 381580

Stanford's International Map Centre
London   020 7836 1321

Stoke SC Ipswich   01473 780815

Stour SC   01206 393924

Strood YC Aylesford   01634 718261

Suffolk Sails Woodbridge
01394 386323

Suffolk Yacht Harbour Ltd Ipswich
01473 659240

Swale HM   01795 561234

Swale Marina Ltd Teynham
01795 521562

Swale Police   01795 536639

TCS Chandlery Grays   01375 374702

TCS Chandlery Southend-on-Sea
01702 444444

Thames Estuary HM   01474 562200

Thames Estuary Police 020 7275 4421

Thames Estuary YC   01702 345967

The Dinghy Store Whitstable
Chandlers   01227 274168

Thorpe Bay YC   01702 587563

Thurrock YC Grays   01375 373720

Tide Mill Yacht Harbour Woodbridge
01394 385745

Timage & Co Ltd Braintree
Brass, chrome, stainless steel fittings
01376 343087

Titchmarsh Marina Walton-on-the-Naze
01255 672185

Tollesbury CC Tollesbury 01621 869561

Tollesbury Marina Tollesbury
01621 869202

Sunchaser Yachting   020 8760 9900
Sailing holidays worldwide

UK Customs Nationwide
0845 0109000

Up River YC Hullbridge   01702 231654

Upnor SC Upnor   01634 718043

W Sails Leigh-on-Sea
Sailmaker   01702 714550

Wakering YC Rochford   01702 530926

Waldringfield SC Wickham Market
01728 736633

Walton & Frinton YC
Walton-on-the-Naze   01255 675526

Walton and Frinton Yacht Trust
Walton on the Naze   01255 675873

Walton Backwaters Police
01255 241312

Walton-on-the-Naze HM
01255 851899

West Mersea Police   01206 382930

West Mersea YC Colchester
01206 382947

West Wick Marina Ltd Nr Chelmsford
01245 741268

Whitstable HM   01227 274086

Whitstable Marine
Mercury outboards, inflatables etc
01227 262525

Whitstable Police   01227 770055

Whitstable YC Whitstable
01227 272343

Wilkinson Sails Teynham 01795 521503

Windsor Marina Windsor
01753 853911

Wivenhoe SC Colchester
01206 822132

Wolstenholme Yacht Design Coltishall
Yacht designer   01603 737024

Woodbridge CC Woodbridge
01394 386737

Woodrolfe Boatyard Maldon
01621 869202

Woolverstone Marina Ipswich
01473 780206

Wyatts Chandlery Ltd Colchester
01206 384745

Yachtbits.co.uk Lowestoft
On-line electrical and electronic products
01502 569079

4

Waypoint Guide Area 4 – East England - North Foreland to Great Yarmouth

149	**Goodwin Knoll** - 1M SE of	51°18'·88N	01°33'·37E
150	**Ramsgate** -1M E of Pegwell Bay	51°19'·47N	01°27'·04E
151	**North Foreland** - 1M E of	51°22'·54N	01°28'·64E
152	**Foreness Point** - 1M NNE of	51°24'·50N	01°26'·30E
153	**Margate** - 0·7M N of	51°24'·14N	01°22'·44E
154	**Fisherman's Gat** - SE turning waypoint	51°33'·33N	01°24'·90E
155	**Fisherman's Gat** - NW turning waypoint	51°36'·33N	01°20'·60E
156	**Black Deep/Sunk Sand** - turning wayoint	51°40'·97N	01°24'·90E
157	**Barrow No 2 PHM** - 0·3M NE of	51°42'·19N	01°23'·24E
158	**Barrow No 3 ECM** - 0·3M N of	51°42'·32N	01°20'·25E
159	**Whitaker Channel** - for River Crouch (6M)	51°40'·43N	01°05'·20E
160	**Swin Spitway SWM** - 0·1M SSW of	51°41'·84N	01°08'·26E
161	**Spitway North** - turning waypoint	51°43'·73N	01°07'·00E
162	**Colne, Blackwater** - 0·3M W of Eagle SHM	51°44'·13N	01°03'·33E
163	**NE Gunfleet ECM** - 0·5M NW of	51°50'·28N	01°27'·25E
164	**Medusa SHM** - 0·3M SW of	51°51'·03N	01°19'·90E
165	**Kentish Knock ECM** - 0·2M E of	51°38'·53N	01°40'·70E
166	**Trinity SCM** - 0·6M N of	51°49'·68N	01°36'·35E
167	**Sunk light F** - 0·2M SW of	51°50'·90N	01°34'·70E
168	**Cork Sand Beacon NCM** - Harwich Yacht Channel ent	51°55'·24N	01°25'·19E
171	**Orfordness** - 1·5M ESE of	52°04'·24N	01°36'·94E
172	**Southwold** - 2M ESE of entrance	52°18'·03N	01°43'·60E
173	**Lowestoft** - 2·8M E of entrance	52°28'·33N	01°50'·00E
174	**Gt Yarmouth** - 0·5M SSW of S Corton SCM	52°32'·10N	01°49'·26E
175	**Gt Yarmouth** - 4·7M E of entrance	52°34'·36N	01°52'·05E

Distance Table - East England

Approximate distances in nautical miles are by the most direct route while avoiding dangers and allowing for Traffic Separation Schemes

	1	2	3	4	5	6	7	8	9	10	11	12	13	14	15	16	17	18	19	20
1. Ramsgate	1																			
2. Whitstable	22	2																		
3. Sheerness	34	14	3																	
4. Gravesend	56	36	22	4																
5. London Bridge	76	55	45	23	5															
6. Southend-on-Sea	35	17	6	20	43	6														
7. Havengore	33	15	12	32	55	12	7													
8. Burnham-on-Crouch	44	36	34	53	76	33	30	8												
9. West Mersea	43	38	29	49	72	30	29	22	9											
10. Brightlingsea	41	36	28	47	71	28	26	22	8	10										
11. Walton-on-the-Naze	40	40	46	59	82	39	37	25	23	23	11									
12. Harwich	40	40	50	65	83	40	41	31	24	24	6	12								
13. Ipswich	49	49	59	74	92	49	50	40	33	33	15	9	13							
14. River Deben (ent)	45	45	55	71	89	46	46	35	38	38	10	6	15	14						
15. River Ore (ent)	47	47	60	75	93	50	51	38	43	43	14	10	19	4	15					
16. Southwold	62	67	80	95	113	70	71	58	63	63	33	30	39	23	20	16				
17. Lowestoft	72	77	90	105	123	80	81	68	73	73	43	40	49	33	30	10	17			
18. Great Yarmouth	79	84	97	112	130	87	88	76	81	80	51	52	61	41	38	18	7	18		
19. Blakeney	123	128	141	156	174	131	132	120	125	124	95	96	105	85	82	62	51	44	19	
20. Bridlington	207	198	224	226	244	201	215	204	205	204	181	175	184	169	165	145	135	114	79	20

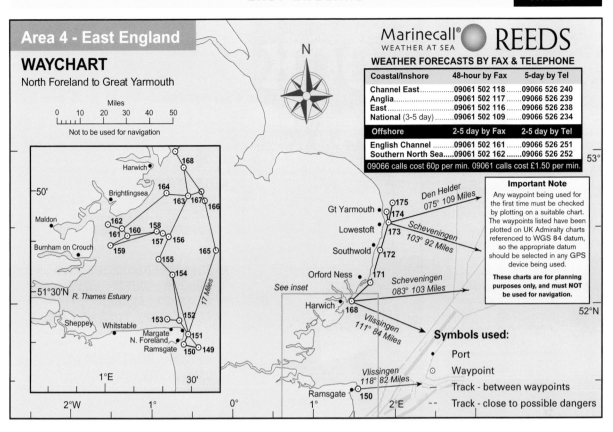

Area 4 - East England

WAYCHART

North Foreland to Great Yarmouth

Miles
0 10 20 30 40 50

Not to be used for navigation

Marinecall® REEDS
WEATHER AT SEA

WEATHER FORECASTS BY FAX & TELEPHONE

Coastal/Inshore	48-hour by Fax	5-day by Tel
Channel East	09061 502 118	09066 526 240
Anglia	09061 502 117	09066 526 239
East	09061 502 116	09066 526 238
National (3-5 day)	09061 502 109	09066 526 234

Offshore	2-5 day by Fax	2-5 day by Tel
English Channel	09061 502 161	09066 526 251
Southern North Sea	09061 502 162	09066 526 252

09066 calls cost 60p per min. 09061 calls cost £1.50 per min.

Important Note
Any waypoint being used for the first time must be checked by plotting on a suitable chart. The waypoints listed have been plotted on UK Admiralty charts referenced to WGS 84 datum, so the appropriate datum should be selected in any GPS device being used.

These charts are for planning purposes only, and must NOT be used for navigation

Symbols used:

• Port
◎ Waypoint
— Track - between waypoints
-- Track - close to possible dangers

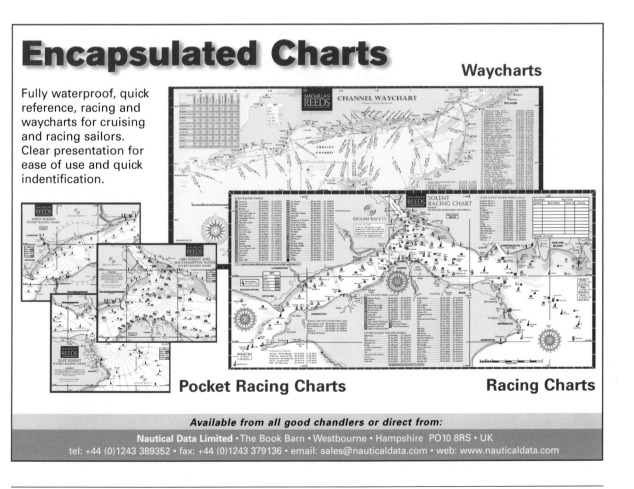

Encapsulated Charts

Waycharts

Fully waterproof, quick reference, racing and waycharts for cruising and racing sailors. Clear presentation for ease of use and quick indentification.

Pocket Racing Charts

Racing Charts

NORTH EAST ENGLAND - Great Yarmouth to Berwick-upon-Tweed

Marinecall® REEDS
WEATHER AT SEA
WEATHER FORECASTS BY FAX & TELEPHONE

Coastal/Inshore	2-day by Fax	5-day by Phone
Anglia	09061 502 117	09066 526 339
East..............................	09061 502 116	09066 526 238
North East	09061 502 115	09066 526 237
Scotland East	09061 502 114	09066 526 236
National (3-5 day)........	09061 502 109	09066 526 234

Offshore	2-5 day by Fax	2-5 day by Phone
English Channel..........	09061 502 161	09066 526 251
Southern North Sea......	09061 502 162	09066 526 252
Northern North Sea......	09061 502 166	09066 526 256
North West Scotland.....	09061 502 165	09066 526 255

09066 CALLS COST 60P PER MIN. 09061 CALLS COST £1.50 PER MIN.

Key to Marina Plans symbols

Calor Gas		P	Parking
Chandler			Pub/Restaurant
Disabled facilities			Pump out
Electrical supply			Rigging service
Electrical repairs			Sail repairs
Engine repairs			Shipwright
First Aid			Shop/Supermarket
Fresh Water			Showers
Fuel - Diesel			Slipway
Fuel - Petrol		WC	Toilets
Hardstanding/boatyard			Telephone
Laundry facilities			Trolleys
Lift-out facilities		V	Visitors berths

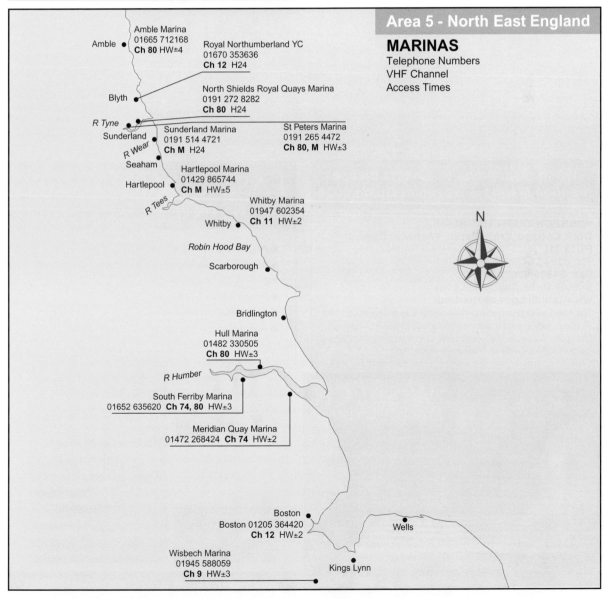

Area 5 - North East England

MARINAS
Telephone Numbers
VHF Channel
Access Times

Amble
Amble Marina
01665 712168
Ch 80 HW±4

Royal Northumberland YC
01670 353636
Ch 12 H24

Blyth

North Shields Royal Quays Marina
0191 272 8282
Ch 80 H24

R Tyne
Sunderland

Sunderland Marina
0191 514 4721
Ch M H24

St Peters Marina
0191 265 4472
Ch 80, M HW±3

R Wear
Seaham

Hartlepool
Hartlepool Marina
01429 865744
Ch M HW±5

R Tees

Whitby Marina
01947 602354
Ch 11 HW±2

Whitby

Robin Hood Bay

Scarborough

Bridlington

Hull Marina
01482 330505
Ch 80 HW±3

R Humber

South Ferriby Marina
01652 635620 **Ch 74, 80** HW±3

Meridian Quay Marina
01472 268424 **Ch 74** HW±2

Boston
Boston 01205 364420
Ch 12 HW±2

Wells

Wisbech Marina
01945 588059
Ch 9 HW±3

Kings Lynn

N

5

WISBECH YACHT HARBOUR

Wisbech Yacht Harbour
Harbour Master, Harbour Office, Dock Cottage
Wisbech, Cambridgeshire PE13 3JJ
Tel: 01945 588059 Fax: 01945 580589
email: wyh@pdh.co.uk www.fenland.gov.uk

| VHF | Ch 9 |
| ACCESS | HW±3 |

Regarded as the capital of the
English Fens, Wisbech is situated
about 25 miles north east of
Peterborough and is a market
town of considerable character
and historical significance. Rows
of elegant houses line the banks
of the River Nene, with the North
and South Brink still deemed two
of the finest Georgian streets in England.

Wisbech Yacht Harbour, linking Cambridgeshire with the sea,
is proving increasingly popular as a haven for small
craft, despite the busy commercial shipping. In
recent years the facilities have been developed and
improved upon and the HM is always on hand to
help with passage planning both up or downstream.

FACILITIES AT A GLANCE

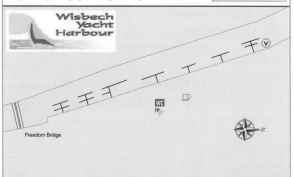

BOSTON MARINA

Boston Marina
5/7 Witham Bank East, Boston, Lincs, PE21 9JU
Tel: 01205 364420 Fax: 01205 364420
www.bostonmarina.co.uk email: bostonmarina@5witham.fsnet

| VHF | Ch 12 |
| ACCESS | H±2 |

Boston Marina, located near Boston
Grand Sluice in Lincolnshire, is an
ideal location for both seagoing
vessels and for river boats wanting
to explore the heart of the Fens.
However, berths are only available
from 1 April to 31 October when all
vessels must leave the marina to find
winter storage. The on site facilities

include a fully-stocked chandlery and brokerage service, while nearby
is the well-established Witham Tavern, decorated in a rustic theme to
reflect the pub's close proximity to The Wash.

The old maritime port of Boston has numerous
modern-day and historical attractions, one of the
most notable being St Botolph's Church, better
known as the 'Boston Stump'.

FACILITIES AT A GLANCE

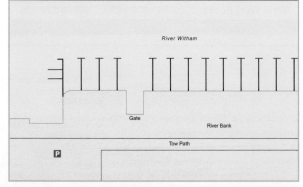

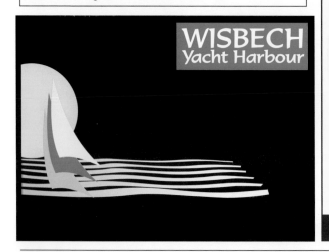

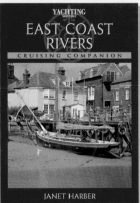

MERIDIAN QUAY MARINA

Humber Cruising Assn
Meridian Quay Marina, Meridian Quay
Auckland Road, Fish Dock, Grimsby
Tel: 01472 268424 Fax: 01472 269832
www.hca-grimsby.freeserve.co.uk

| VHF | Ch 74 |
| ACCESS | HW±2 |

Situated in the locked fish dock of Grimsby, at the mouth of the River Humber, Meridian Quay Marina is run by the Humber

Cruising Association and comprises approximately 160 alongside berths plus 30 more for visitors. Accessed two hours either side of high water via lock gates, the marina should be contacted on VHF Ch 74 (call sign 'Fish Dock Island') as you make your final approach. The pontoon berths are equipped with water and electricity, while the fully licensed clubhouse serves light meals and incorporates a pool table, television and laundry facilities.

FACILITIES AT A GLANCE

SOUTH FERRIBY MARINA

South Ferriby Marina
Barton on Humber, Lincolnshire, DN18 6JH
Tel: 01652 635620 (Lock 635219) Fax: 01652 660517
www.clapsons.co.uk email: marina@clapsons.co.uk

| VHF | Ch 74, 80 |
| ACCESS | HW±3 |

South Ferriby Marina is run by Clapson & Sons, an established company founded in 1912. The marina site was developed in 1967 and today offers a comprehensive range of services, including heated workshops for osmosis repairs, general boat repairs and ample storage space. Its well stocked on site chandlery is open until 1700 seven days a week.

Situated at Barton upon Humber, the marina lies on the south bank of the River Humber at the southern crossing of the Humber Bridge, approximately eight miles south west of Kingston upon Hull. Good public transport links to nearby towns and villages include train services to Cleethorpes and Grimsby, and bus connections to Scunthorpe and Hull.

FACILITIES AT A GLANCE

Key
a Chandlery
b Shipwrights workshop

HULL MARINA

Hull Marina
Railway Street Hull, HU1 2DQ
Tel: 01482 330505 Fax: 01482 224148
www.britishwaterways.co.uk

VHF	Ch 80
ACCESS	HW±3

Situated on the River Humber, Hull Marina is literally a stone's throw from the bustling city centre with its array of arts and entertainments. Besides the numerous historic bars and cafés surrounding the marina itself, there are plenty of traditional taverns to be sampled in the Old Town, while also found here is the Street Life Museum, vividly depicting the history of the city.

Yachtsmen enter the marina via a tidal lock, operating HW±3, and should try to give 15 minutes' notice of arrival via VHF Ch 80. Hull is perfectly positioned for exploring the Trent, Ouse and the Yorkshire coast as well as for hopping across the North Sea to Holland or Belgium.

FACILITIES AT A GLANCE

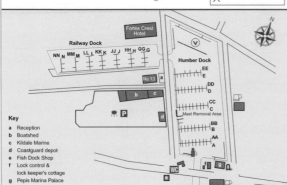

Key
a Reception
b Boatshed
c Kildale Marine
d Coastguard depot
e Fish Dock Shop
f Lock control &
   lock keeper's cottage
g Pepis Marina Palace

WHITBY MARINA

Whitby Marina
Whitby Harbour Office, Endeavour Wharf
Whitby, North Yorkshire YO21 1DN
Tel: 01947 602354 Fax: 01947 600380
email: portofwhitby@btinternet.com

VHF	Ch 11,16
ACCESS	HW±2

The only natural harbour between the
Tees and the Humber, Whitby lies some
20 miles north of Scarborough on the
River Esk. The historic town is said to
date back as far as the Roman times,
although it is better known for its abbey,
which was founded over 1,300 years
ago by King Oswy of Northumberland.
Another place of interest is the Captain
Cook Memorial Museum, a tribute to
Whitby's greatest seaman.

FACILITIES AT A GLANCE

A swing bridge divides the harbour into upper
and lower sections, with the marina being in the
Upper Harbour. The bridge opens on request
(VHF Ch 11) each half hour for two hours either
side of high water.

Town centre
Pubs etc

N

Key
a Marina office
b Waste oil bin

River Esk

WC

P

Coates
Chandlery
100 yards

Parkol
Dry Dock

Weir

HARTLEPOOL MARINA

Hartlepool Marina
Lock Office, Slake Terrace, Hartlepool, TS24 0UR
Tel: 01429 865744 Fax: 01429 865947
email: lockoffice@hartlepool-marina.com

VHF	Ch 80, M
ACCESS	HW±5

As part of a £60 million development project, Hartlepool Marina is one of the major boating facilities in the North of England, boasting 500 fully serviced berths and one of the biggest boat hoists in Europe. Surrounded by a cosmopolitan selection of shops, restaurants and hotels, its focal point is the award-winning Historic Quay, an impressive replica of an 18th century seaport demonstrating what life was like during the time of Nelson. The marina can be accessed five hours either side of high water via a lock: note that yachtsmen wishing to enter should contact the marina on VHF Ch 80 about 15 minutes before arrival.

FACILITIES AT A GLANCE

Key
a Brittania House - amenity/cafe
b Neptune House - restaurant & bar
c Lock office and marina reception
d 220m complex with retail, restaurants and cafes
e Hartlepool Diving Club and HMS Abdiel sea cadet unit
f Fisherman's stores & landing area
g Office units
h Old West Quay Pub, restaurant and travel inn
i Trincomalee visitors centre

SUNDERLAND MARINA

The Marine Activities Centre
Sunderland Marina, Sunderland, SR6 0PW
Tel: 0191 514 4721 Fax: 0191 514 1847

VHF	Ch 80, M
ACCESS	H24

Sunderland Marina sits on the north bank of the River Wear and is easily accessible through two outer breakwaters except in very strong north east to south easterly winds. Among the extensive range of facilities on site are a newsagent, café, hairdresser and top quality Italian restaurant. Both the Wear Boating Association and the Sunderland Yacht Club are also located in the vicinity and welcome yachtsmen to their respective bars and lounges.

FACILITIES AT A GLANCE

Key
a. Marina Reception
b. Marine News - Newsagent & Shop
c. Snow Goose - Café
d. Hairdresser
e. Trattoria Due - Italian Restaurant
f. Wear Boating Association
g. Hard stand compound
h. Refuse Compound

NORTH SHIELDS ROYAL QUAYS MARINA

North Shields Royal Quays Marina
Coble Dene Road, North Shields, NE29 6DU
Tel: 0191 272 8282 Fax: 0191 272 8288
www.crestnicholsonmarinas.co.uk
email: royalquaysmarina@crestnicholson.com

VHF	Ch 80
ACCESS	H24

North Shields Royal Quays Marina enjoys close proximity to the entrance to the River Tyne, allowing easy access to and from the open sea as well as being ideally placed for cruising further up the Tyne. Just over an hour's motoring upstream brings you to the heart of the city of Newcastle, where you can tie up on a security controlled visitors' pontoon right outside the Pitcher and Piano Bar.

With a reputation for a high standard of service, the marina accommodates 255 pontoon berths, all of which are fully serviced. It is accessed via double sector lock gates which operate at all states of the tide and 24 hours a day.

FACILITIES AT A GLANCE

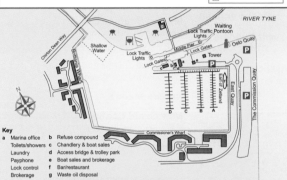

RIVER TYNE

Key
a Marina office
   Toilets/showers
   Laundry
   Payphone
   Lock control
   Brokerage
b Refuse compound
c Chandlery & boat sales
d Access bridge & trolley park
e Boat sales and brokerage
f Bar/restaurant
g Waste oil disposal

ST PETERS MARINA

St Peters Marina, St Peters Basin
Newcastle upon Tyne, NE6 1HX
Tel: 0191 2654472 Fax: 0191 2762618
Email: info@stpetersmarina.co.uk
www.stpetersmarina.co.uk

VHF	Ch 80, M
ACCESS	HW±3

Nestling on the north bank of the River Tyne, some eight miles upstream of the river entrance, St Peters Marina is a fully serviced, 150-berth marina with the capacity to accommodate large vessels of up to 37m LOA. Situated on site is the Bascule Bar and Bistro, while a few minutes away is the centre of Newcastle. This city, along with its surrounding area, offers an array of interesting sites, among which are Hadrian's Wall, the award winning Gateshead Millennium Bridge and the Baltic Art Centre.

FACILITIES AT A GLANCE

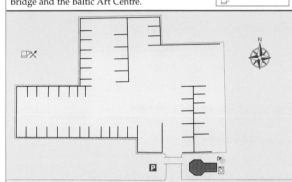

ROYAL NORTHUMBERLAND YACHT CLUB

Royal Northumberland Yacht Club
South Harbour, Blyth, Northumberland, NE24 3PB
Tel: 01670 353636

VHF	Ch 12
ACCESS	H24

The Royal Northumberland Yacht Club is based at Blyth, a well-sheltered port that is accessible at all states of the tide and in all weathers except for when there is a combination of low water and strong south-easterly winds. The yacht club is a private club with approximately 75 pontoon berths and a further 20 fore and aft moorings.

Visitors usually berth on the north side of the most northerly pontoon and are welcome to use the clubship, HY *Tyne* – a wooden lightship built in 1880 which incorporates a bar, showers and toilet facilities. The club also controls its own boatyard, providing under cover and outside storage space.

FACILITIES AT A GLANCE

South Harbour

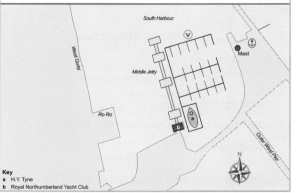

Key
a H.Y. Tyne
b Royal Northumberland Yacht Club

AMBLE MARINA

Amble Marina Ltd
Amble, Northumberland, NE65 0YP
Tel: 01665 712168 Fax:01665 713363
www.amble.co.uk email: marina@amble.co.uk

VHF	Ch 80
ACCESS	HW±4

Amble Port, marketing itself as 'The Friendliest Port', was formerly the largest exporter of coal on the North Northumberland coast, but is now a vibrant fishing and leisure port. Tucked away on the banks of the River Coquet amidst unspoilt Northumbrian countryside, Amble Marina has 250 fully serviced berths for residential and visiting yachts. Cafés, bars and restaurants are all within easy walking distance of the marina, while all your shopping needs can be met in Queen Street in the town centre. Situated just one mile from Amble is Coquet Island, a bird sanctuary that is home to thousands of puffins, terns and eider ducks.

FACILITIES AT A GLANCE

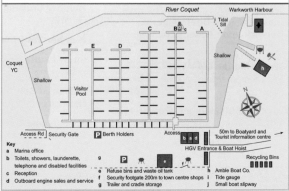

Key
a Marina office
b Toilets, showers, launderette, telephone and disabled facilities
c Reception
d Outboard engine sales and service
e Refuse bins and waste oil tank
f Security footgate 200m to town centre shops
g Trailer and cradle storage
h Amble Boat Co.
i Tide gauge
j Small boat slipway

Amble Boat Co Ltd Amble
Boat repairs and slipping facilities,
engines, chandlery, marine surveyors,
yacht spraying and painting
01665 710267

Amble HM 01665 710306

Amble Marina Amble 01665 712168

Autosound Marine Bradford
Electronics 01274 688990

Berwick-upon-Tweed HM
01289 307404

Berwick-upon-Tweed Police
01289 307111

Bettabond Adhesives Leeds
0113 278 5088

Blyth HM 01670 352678

Blyth Marina Blyth 01679 353636

Blyth Police 01661 872555

Boston HM 01205 362328

Boston Marina Boston 01205 364420

Boston Police 01205 366222

**Brancaster Sailing and Sailboard
Centre** Kings Lynn 01485 210236

Brancaster Staithe SC 01485 210249

Bridlington HM 01262 670148/9

Bridlington Police 01262 672222

Burgh Castle Marina Norfolk
01493 780331

Burnham Overy Staithe SC
01328 730961

C & J Marine Services
Newcastle Upon Tyne
Repairs; storage; shipwright
0191 295 0072

C & M Marine Bridlington
Chandler; marine supplies 01262 672212

Castlegate Marine Club
Stockton on Tees 01642 583299

Clapson & Son (Shipbuilders) Ltd
Barton-on-Humber
Moorings, chandlery, repairs
01652 635620

Clark Insurance, Graham Tyneside
0191 455 8089

**Coastal Marine Boatbuilders
(Berwick upon Tweed)** Eyemouth
01890 750328

Coates Marine Ltd Whitby
Boat storage, repairs, rigging, chandlery
01947 604486

Cook Boatbuilders and Repairers, S
Whitby 01947 820521

Cooke & Son Ltd, B Hull
British Admiralty chart agents;
manufacturers of nautical instruments
01482 223454

Coquet YC 01665 711179

CTC Marine & Leisure Middlesbrough
Chandler, boat repairs, electronic and
engine supplier 01642 230123

Denney & Son, EL Redcar
Chandler, engine services/repairs;
outboard sales 01642 483507

Divesafe Sunderland 0191 567 8423

Divetech UK King's Lynn 01485 572323

Donnelly, R South Shields
Diver 07973 119455

Eccles Marine Co Middlesbrough
Chandler; outboard engine & fibre-glass
repairs 01642 230123

Essex Marina Wallsea Island
01702 258531

Euro Rope Ltd Scunthorpe
Ropes 01724 280480

Farrow & Chambers Yacht Builders
Humberston 01472 632424

**Fishermans Mutual Association
(Eyemouth) Ltd** Eyemouth
01890 750373

Gibbons Ship Chandlers Ltd
Sunderland 0191 567 2101

Grimsby Dockmaster 01472 359181

Grimsby Police 01472 359171

Grimsby and Cleethorpes YC Grimsby
01472 356678

Hartlepool Marina Hartlepool
01429 865744

Hartlepool Marine Engineering
Hartlepool 01429 867883

Hartlepool Marine Supplies Hartlepool
01429 862932

Hartlepool Police 01429 221151

Hartlepool YC Hartlepool
01429 233423

Hewitt, George Binham
Boatbuilder; repairs 01328 830078

Holy Island HM 01289 389217

Hull Marina Hull 01482 330505

Hull Police 01482 210031

Humber Cruising Association Marina
Grimsby 01472 268424

Humber Yawl Club 01724 733458

Imray Laurie Norie and Wilson Ltd
Huntingdon 01480 462114

Industrial Self Adhesives Ltd
Nottingham 0115 9681895

Jeckells and Son Ltd Wroxham
Sailmaker; covers; upholsterer
01603 782223

Joules Market Harborough
Clothing 01858 461156

Kildale Marine Hull
Chandler 01482 227464

Lilley & Gillie Ltd, John North Shields
Navigation equipment & chart agents
0191 257 2217

Lincoln Marina Lincoln
Repairs, chandlery, boat sales
01522 526896

Lynch Ltd, PA Morpeth
Electronics, engines, boat sales
01670 512291

Marconi Marine Newcastle Upon Tyne
Marine electronics 0191 2650374

Meridian Quay Marina Grimsby
01472 268424

Moncur Sailing, Bob
Newcastle upon Tyne
RYA Sailing School 0191 265 4472

Morton Boats Lincoln
Repairs, chandlery, boat sales
01522 868689

Mr Splice Thurmaston, Leicester
Discount marine ropes 0800 1697178

Naburn Marina 01904 621021

New Guard Coatings Ltd Wetherby
Paint; varnish; lacquer 01937 568311

North Sunderland Marine Club
Sunderland 01665 721231

Northern Divers (Engineering) Ltd Hull
01482 227276

Northshore King's Lynn
Chandlery & Sailcraft Sea School
01485 210236

Oliver, A & Sons Nr Boston
Service & repairs for outboard engines
01205 820207

Ouse Amateur SC Kings Lynn
01553 772239

Parker Lift Keel Yachts Ltd Nr Boston
Boatbuilder 01205 722697

Pennine Marine Ltd Skipton
Chandler; watersports equipment
01756 792335

Port of Boston Ltd Boston
Harbour authorities 01205 365571

Pratt and Sons, VJ King's Lynn
01553 764058

Premium Liferaft Services Morpeth
Hire/sale of liferafts and safety equipment
01670 512291

Premium Liferaft Services
Scarborough
As above 01723 859480

Premium Liferaft Services Whitby
As above 01947 606299

Redcar Fish Company
Stockton-on-Tees
Marine electronics 01642 633638

Reynolds, Cliff Hartlepool
Chandler; marine engine service & repairs
01429 272049

Richardson Electronics (Europe) Ltd
Lincoln   01522 542631

River Humber HM   01482 327171

River Tees Engineering & Welding Ltd
Middlesbrough
Boat repairs; marine engineering
01642 226226

River Tyne Police   0191 232 3451

River Tyne/North Shields HM
0191 257 2080

Royal Northumberland YC Blyth
01670 353636

Royal Quays Marina North Shields
0191 272 8282

Royal Yorkshire YC Bridlington
01262 672041

Scarborough HM   01723 373530

Scarborough Marine Engineering Ltd
Scarborough
Boat repairs, slipping facilities, chandler,
engine repairs, sales   01723 375199

Scarborough Police   01723 500300

Scarborough YC Scarborough
01723 373821

Seaham HM   0191 581 3246

Seaham Police   0191 581 2255

Shipshape Marine King's Lynn
01553 764058

South Bank Marine (Charts) Ltd
Grimsby   01472 361137

South Bank Marine (Charts) Ltd
Immingham   01469 576757

**South Dock (Seaham Harbour Dock
Co)** Seaham   0191 581 3877

South Ferriby Marina
Barton on Humber   01652 635620

**South Gare Marine Club – Sail
Section** Middlesbrough   01642 453031

South Shields SC South Shields
0191 456 5821

Speedings Ltd Sunderland
Flags; banners; bunting   0191 565 7525

St Peter's Marina Newcastle upon Tyne
0191 265 4472

Standard House Boatyard
Wells-next-the-Sea   01328 710593

Standard House Chandlery
Wells-next-the-Sea   01328 710593

Stanley Sail & Cover Makers, G Hull
01482 225590

Storrar Marine Store
Newcastle upon Tyne
Chandler   0191 266 1037

Sub Aqua Services North Ormesby
01642 230209

Sunderland HM   0191 567 2626

Sunderland Marina Sunderland
0191 5144721

Sunderland Police   0191 4547555

Sunderland YC Sunderland
0191 567 5133

Tees & Hartlepool Port Authority
01429 277205

Tees & Hartlepool YC   01429 233423

Tees SC Aycliffe Village   01429 265400

Trident UK Gateshead
Sails; boat covers; clothing; trailers
0191 490 1736

Tynemouth SC Newcastle upon Tyne
0191 257 2167

UK Customs Nationwide
0845 0109000

Walton Marine Sales Ltd Wroxham
Boat sales   01603 781178

Ward & McKenzie (North East)
Pocklington
Professional yacht & powerboat surveyors
01759 304322

Wear Boating Association
0191 567 5313

Wells SC Wells-next-the-sea
01328 711190

Wells-next-the-Sea HM 01328 711646

Wells-next-the-Sea Police
01493 336200

Whitby HM   01947 602354

Whitby Marina Whitby   01947 602354

Whitby Police   01947 603443

Whitby YC Whitby   01947 603623

William Woolford Bridlington
Commercial diver   01262 671710

Wisbech Yacht Harbour Wisbech
01945 588059

Witham SC Boston   01205 363598

Waypoint Guide Area 5 – North East England - Great Yarmouth to Berwick-upon-Tweed

174	**Gt Yarmouth** - 0·5M SSW of S Corton SCM		52°32'·10N	01°49'·26E
175	**Gt Yarmouth** - 4·7M E of entrance		52°34'·36N	01°52'·05E
177	**Winterton** - 5·2M NE of		52°46'·90N	01°48'·40E
178	**Cromer light** - 3M NNE of		52°58'·17N	01°21'·10E
179	**North Well SWM** - 0·5M NE		53°03'·37N	00°28'·50E
180	**Inner Dowsing light float** - 0·5M NE of		53°20'·12N	00°34'·40E
181	**Spurn Head** - 2·6M NE of Spurn Lightship		53°34'·82N	00°17'·70E
182	**Flamborough Head** - 2M E of		54°07'·12N	00°01'·20W
183	**Scarborough** - 1M E of entrance		54°16'·88N	00°21'·66W
184	**Robin Hood's Bay** - 2·6M NE of		54°26'·41N	00°27'·40W
185	**Whitby** - 1·6M N of entrance		54°31'·11N	00°36'·70W
186	**River Tees** - Fairway Buoy		54°40'·94N	01°06'·48W
187	**Seaham** - 0·9M E of entrance		54°50'·24N	01°17'·75W
188	**Sunderland** - 1·7M E of entrance		54°55'·21N	01°18'·15W
189	**R Tyne** - 1·7M E by N of entrance		55°01'·16N	01°21'·20W
190	**Blyth** - 1·5M E of entrance		55°07'·00N	01°26'·60W
191	**Amble** - 2·5M NE of entrance		55°21'·86N	01°30'·80W
192	**Farne Island** - 2M NE of Longstone light		55°40'·01N	01°34'·05W
193	**Holy Island** - 1M NE of Emmanuel Hd		55°41'·95N	01°45'·60W
194	**Berwick-upon-Tweed** - 1·5M E of Breakwater		55°45'·90N	01°56'·40W

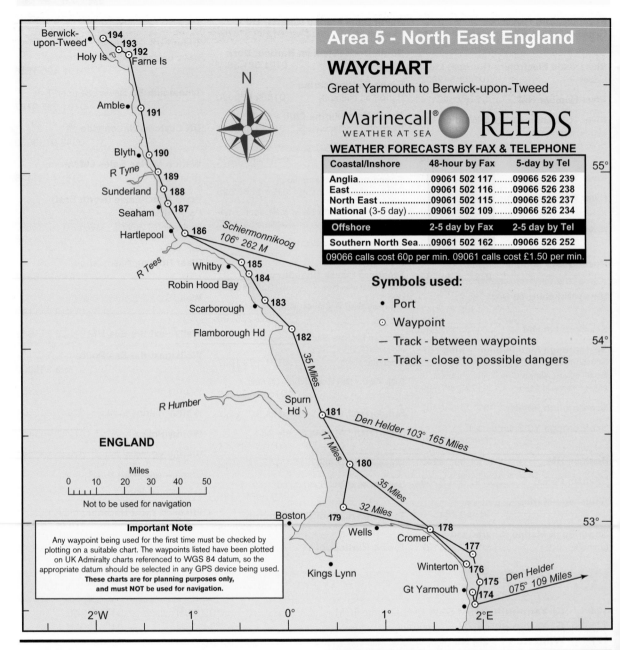

Area 5 - North East England

WAYCHART
Great Yarmouth to Berwick-upon-Tweed

Marinecall® REEDS
WEATHER AT SEA

WEATHER FORECASTS BY FAX & TELEPHONE

Coastal/Inshore	48-hour by Fax	5-day by Tel
Anglia	09061 502 117	09066 526 239
East	09061 502 116	09066 526 238
North East	09061 502 115	09066 526 237
National (3-5 day)	09061 502 109	09066 526 234
Offshore	**2-5 day by Fax**	**2-5 day by Tel**
Southern North Sea	09061 502 162	09066 526 252

09066 calls cost 60p per min. 09061 calls cost £1.50 per min.

Symbols used:

- • Port
- ⊙ Waypoint
- — Track - between waypoints
- -- Track - close to possible dangers

Important Note

Any waypoint being used for the first time must be checked by plotting on a suitable chart. The waypoints listed have been plotted on UK Admiralty charts referenced to WGS 84 datum, so the appropriate datum should be selected in any GPS device being used.

These charts are for planning purposes only, and must NOT be used for navigation.

Miles
0 10 20 30 40 50
Not to be used for navigation.

Distance Table - North East England

Approximate distances in nautical miles are by the most direct route while avoiding dangers and allowing for Traffic Separation Schemes

SOUTH EAST SCOTLAND - Eyemouth to Rattray Head

Marinecall® REEDS
WEATHER AT SEA
WEATHER FORECASTS BY FAX & TELEPHONE

Coastal/Inshore	2-day by Fax	5-day by Phone
East	09061 502 116	09066 526 238
North East	09061 502 115	09066 526 237
Scotland East	09061 502 114	09066 526 236
Scotland North	09061 502 110	09066 526 235
National (3-5 day)	09061 502 109	09066 526 234

Offshore	2-5 day by Fax	2-5 day by Phone
English Channel	09061 502 161	09066 526 251
Southern North Sea	09061 502 162	09066 526 252
Northern North Sea	09061 502 166	09066 526 256
North West Scotland	09061 502 165	09066 526 255

09066 CALLS COST 60P PER MIN. 09061 CALLS COST £1.50 PER MIN.

Key to Marina Plans symbols

Calor Gas		P	Parking
Chandler			Pub/Restaurant
Disabled facilities			Pump out
Electrical supply			Rigging service
Electrical repairs			Sail repairs
Engine repairs			Shipwright
First Aid			Shop/Supermarket
Fresh Water			Showers
Fuel - Diesel			Slipway
Fuel - Petrol		WC	Toilets
Hardstanding/boatyard			Telephone
Laundry facilities			Trolleys
Lift-out facilities		V	Visitors berths

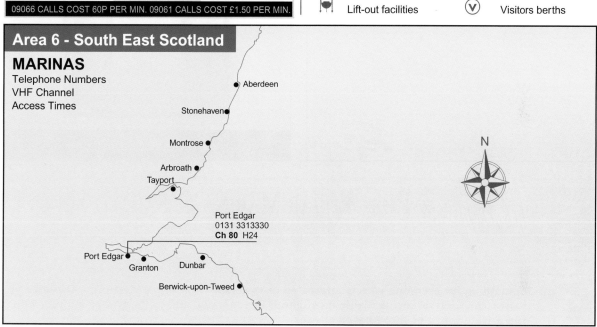

Area 6 - South East Scotland

MARINAS
Telephone Numbers
VHF Channel
Access Times

Aberdeen

Stonehaven

Montrose

Arbroath

Tayport

Port Edgar
0131 3313330
Ch 80 H24

N

Port Edgar

Granton Dunbar

Berwick-upon-Tweed

6

PORT EDGAR MARINA

Port Edgar Marina
Shore Road, South Queensferry
West Lothian, EH3 9SX
Tel: 0131 331 3330 Fax: 0131 331 4878
www.portedgar.co.uk

VHF	Ch 80
ACCESS	H24

Port Edgar is a large watersports centre and marina found on the south bank of the sheltered Firth of Forth. Situated in the village of South Queensferry, just west of the Forth Road Bridge, it is managed by Edinburgh Leisure on behalf of the City of Edinburgh Council and is reached via a deep water channel just west of the suspension bridge.

The nearby village offers a sufficient range of shops and restaurants, while Port Edgar is only a 20-minute walk from Dalmeny Station from where trains run regularly to Edinburgh.

FACILITIES AT A GLANCE

Key
a Changing rooms and toilets
b Landing and trolleys
c Port Edgar Yacht Club
d Sail loft
e Cafe
f Marina office
g Ferry Marine
h Blue V
i Bosuns Locker

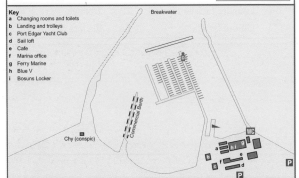

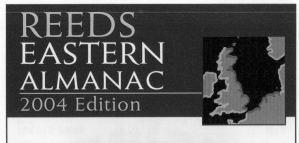

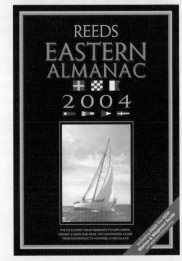
Welcome to PORT EDGAR MARINA & SAILING SCHOOL

Our programme has something to offer all types of sailor whatever their experience. To find out more please telephone **0131 331 3330**

PORT EDGAR MARINA

What's on offer?

Something for everyone who is interested in Watersports at every level from beginner to instructor. Courses are available throughout the summer, and in the winter months we run a wide range of shore based classes.

Activities include: -

◆ **Dinghy Sailing At All Levels.**

◆ **Children's Holiday Sailing Courses**

◆ **SPLASH! Multi Activity Courses for Youngsters**

◆ **Catamaran Courses**

◆ **Dinghy Crusing**

◆ **Dinghy Racing**

◆ **Powerboating**

◆ **Safety Boat Handling**

◆ **Advanced Powerboating**

◆ **Canoeing - BCU 1 & 2 Star Courses**

◆ **SRC/DSC Radio Operators Course**

◆ **GPS Operator**

◆ **Yachtmaster, Coastal Skipper, Day Skipper**

The Marina

The marina is fully serviced with power and water to 300 berths. We have storage facilities for craft in boat sheds or boat parks. Cranage is available throughout the year via our fixed crane for craft up to 4.3/4 tons. Other services on site are Chandlery, Sailmakers, Marine engineers, Electronics, Port Edgar Yacht Club.

2004/M&WC72/d

Aberdeen and Stonehaven SC
Nr Inverurie   01569 764006

Aberdeen HM   01224 597000

Aberdeen Police   01224 386000

Aberdour BC   01383 860632

Allison-Gray Dundee
Sailmaker; boat covers   01382 505888

Anchorwatch Edinburgh
Measures anchor cable tension up to
1,000kg   0131447 5057

Anstruther HM   01333 310836

Anstruther Police   01333 592100

Arbroath Fishermens Association
Arbroath   01241 873132

Arbroath HM   01241 872166

Arbroath Police   01241 872222

Argonaut Marine Aberdeen
                            01224 706526

Bissett and Ross Aberdeen
Sailmaker   01224 580659

Bosuns Locker South Queensferry
                       0131 331 3875/4496

Bruce Anchor (Scotland) Ltd Livingston
Anchor manufacturer   01506 415454

Buchan & Son Ltd, J Peterhead
                            01779 475395

CDL Aberdeen
Electronics   01224 706655

Chattan Security Ltd Edinburgh
Admiralty agents; charts; hydrographic
books   0131 555 3155

**Coastal Marine Boatbuilders Ltd
(Dunbar)** Eyemouth   01890 750328

Coastcraft Ltd Cockenzie
Boatbuilding; repairs   01875 812150

Cosalt International Ltd Aberdeen
Liferaft servicing   01224 588327

Crail HM   01333 450820

Cramond BC   0131 336 1356

Dunbar HM   01368 863206

Dunbar Police   01368 862718

Dunbar SC Cockburnspath
                            01368 86287

Dundee HM   01382 224121

East Lothian YC   01620 892698

Elie HM   01333 330051

**Enterprise Marine Electronic &
Technical Services Ltd** Aberdeen
Electronic supplies; services
                            01224 593281

Eyemouth HM   01890 750223

Eyemouth Police   01890 750217

Ferry Marine South Queensferry
                            0131 331 1233

Fettes & Rankine Engineering
Aberdeen
Engine sales, spares & services
                            01224 573343

Fisherrow HM   0131 665 5900

Forth Corinthian YC Haddington
                            0131 552 5939

Forth YCs Association Edinburgh
                            0131 552 3006

Gourdon HM   01569 762741

JNW Services Peterhead
Ship chandler   01779 477346

Johnshaven HM   01561 362262

Kongsberg Simrad Ltd Aberdeen
Marine electronics; underwater electronic
equipment   01224 226500

Land & Sea Electronics Aberdeen
Marine electronics & communications
                            01224 593281

Mackay Boatbuilders (Arbroath) Ltd
Aberdeen
Boat repairs; maintenance; slipping
facilities, chandlers; electronic
supplies/services   01241 872879

Marconi Marine Aberdeen
Marine electronics   01224 585334

Methil HM   01333 462725

Methil Police   01592 418888

Montrose HM   01674 672302

Montrose Police   01674 672222

Montrose SC Montrose   01674 672554

Noskab Group plc Aberdeen
Wire, cable & electrical component
manufactuer   01224 786004

Peterhead Bay Marina Peterhead
                            01779 474020

Peterhead HM   01779 483630

Peterhead Police   01779 472571

Peterhead SC Ellon   01779 75527

Peterhead Watersports Centre
Peterhead   01779 480888

Pittenweem HM   01333 312591

Port Edgar Marina & Sailing School
South Queensferry   0131 331 3330

Port Edgar YC Penicuik 01968 674210

Royal Forth YC Edinburgh
                            0131 552 3006

Royal Tay YC Dundee   01382 477516

S Queensferry Police   0131 331 1798

Safe Marine Ltd Aberdeen
Marine electronics   01224 338338

Sea & Shore Ship Chandler Dundee
Boat repairs; sail repairs, chandlery, boat
sales   01382 202666

Sea Information Systems Ltd
Aberdeen
Electronics; computer software
                            01224 621326

Sea Span Edinburgh
Chandler   0131 552 2224

Seatronics Aberdeen   01224 853100
Marine Electronics

Silva Ltd Livingston
Electronics   01506 419555

St Monans HM   01333 350055

Stenmar Ltd Aberdeen
Electronics; underwater equipment
                            01224 827288

Stonehaven HM   01569 762741

Stonehaven Police   01569 762963

Tay Corinthian BC Dundee
                            01382 553534

Tay YCs Association   01738 621860

Tayport Harbour   01382 553679

Thomas Gunn Navigation Services
Aberdeen   01224 595045

UK Customs Nationwide
                            0845 0109000

WA Simpson Marine Ltd Dundee
Chandlery; boat sales; boat repairs;
boatbuilder   01382 566670

Woodsons of Aberdeen Ltd Aberdeen
Electronics; underwater electronic
equipment   01224 722884

Wormit BC   01382 553878

6

Waypoint Guide Area 6 – South East Scotland - Eyemouth to Rattray Head

194	**Berwick-upon-Tweed** - 1·5M E of		55°45'·90N	01°56'·40W
423	**Rattray Head light** - 1·8M ENE of		57°37'·40N	01°46'·00W
424	**Peterhead** - 2·1M ESE		57°29'·30N	01°42'·71W
425	**Aberdeen** - 2M E by N of Girdle Ness		57°08'·80N	01°59'·06W
426	**Stonehaven** - 2M E of		56°57'·60N	02°08'·04W
427	**Todhead Point light** - 2·5M E of		56°53'·03N	02°08'·35W
428	**Montrose** - 2·1M E of Scurdie Ness light		56°42'·10N	02°22'·40W
429	**Red Head** - 1·8M E of		56°37'·02N	02°25'·98W
430	**Tayport** - 0·5M E of Fairway Buoy		56°29'·25N	02°37'·32W
431	**Fife Ness** - 2·8M ESE of		56°15'·95N	02°30'·39W
432	**Granton** - 0·5M N of Firth of Forth Fairway Buoy		56°04'·00N	03°00'·09W
433	**Bass Rock light** - 1·5M N of		56°06'·10N	02°38'·44W
434	**Dunbar** - 1·5M NNE of		56°01'·76N	02°30'·30W
435	**St Abb's Head light** - 1·5M NE of		55°56'·11N	02°06'·50W
	Hoek van Holland - 1·2M WNW of		51°59'·90N	04°00'·80E

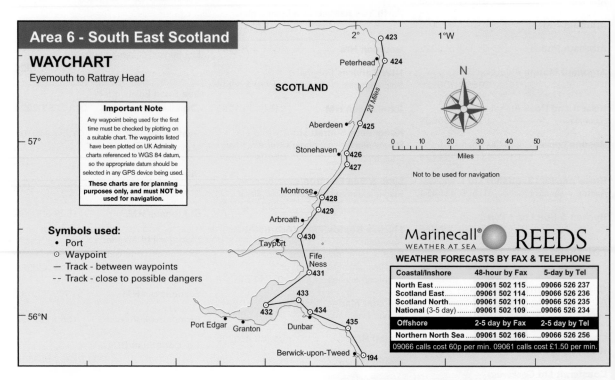

Area 6 - South East Scotland

WAYCHART
Eyemouth to Rattray Head

Important Note

Any waypoint being used for the first time must be checked by plotting on a suitable chart. The waypoints listed have been plotted on UK Admiralty charts referenced to WGS 84 datum, so the appropriate datum should be selected in any GPS device being used.

These charts are for planning purposes only, and must NOT be used for navigation.

Symbols used:
- • Port
- ⊙ Waypoint
- — Track - between waypoints
- -- Track - close to possible dangers

Marinecall® WEATHER AT SEA **REEDS**

WEATHER FORECASTS BY FAX & TELEPHONE

Coastal/Inshore	48-hour by Fax	5-day by Tel
North East	09061 502 115	09066 526 237
Scotland East	09061 502 114	09066 526 236
Scotland North	09061 502 110	09066 526 235
National (3-5 day)	09061 502 109	09066 526 234

Offshore	2-5 day by Fax	2-5 day by Tel
Northern North Sea	09061 502 166	09066 526 256

09066 calls cost 60p per min. 09061 calls cost £1.50 per min.

Distance Table - South East Scotland

Approximate distances in nautical miles are by the most direct route while avoiding dangers and allowing for Traffic Separation Schemes

		1	2	3	4	5	6	7	8	9	10	11	12	13	14	15	16	17	18	19	20
1.	**Great Yarmouth**	**1**																			
2.	**Berwick-on-Tweed**	232	**2**																		
3.	**Eyemouth**	240	10	**3**																	
4.	**Dunbar**	257	26	17	**4**																
5.	**North Berwick**	266	35	25	9	**5**															
6.	**Granton**	285	54	44	27	19	**6**														
7.	**Port Edgar**	290	58	50	34	26	7	**7**													
8.	**Burntisland**	283	53	43	26	18	5	8	**8**												
9.	**Methil**	276	45	36	20	13	14	20	12	**9**											
10.	**Anstruther**	269	38	29	14	10	23	29	22	11	**10**										
11.	**Fife Ness**	269	38	29	17	14	28	34	27	16	5	**11**									
12.	**Bell Rock**	276	43	36	27	25	40	47	39	28	17	12	**12**								
13.	**Dundee**	289	58	49	37	34	48	54	47	36	25	20	20	**13**							
14.	**Arbroath**	284	51	44	34	31	45	51	44	33	22	17	10	15	**14**						
15.	**Montrose**	291	59	51	43	41	55	61	54	43	32	27	17	27	12	**15**					
16.	**Stonehaven**	300	72	66	60	58	72	78	71	60	49	44	32	45	30	20	**16**				
17.	**Aberdeen**	308	82	78	73	70	84	90	83	72	61	56	44	57	42	32	13	**17**			
18.	**Peterhead**	318	105	98	93	95	106	108	105	94	83	78	68	80	64	54	35	25	**18**		
19.	**Fraserburgh**	334	121	114	109	108	122	128	121	110	99	94	83	96	79	68	51	39	16	**19**	
20.	**Wick**	391	178	171	166	165	179	185	178	167	156	151	140	153	136	125	108	96	72	57	**20**

Marinecall® REEDS
WEATHER AT SEA
WEATHER FORECASTS BY FAX & TELEPHONE

Coastal/Inshore	2-day by Fax	5-day by Phone
North East	09061 502 115	09066 526 237
Scotland East	09061 502 114	09066 526 236
Scotland North	09061 502 110	09066 526 235
Minch	09061 502 126	09066 526 248
National (3-5 day).........	09061 502 109	09066 526 234

Offshore	2-5 day by Fax	2-5 day by Phone
Southern North Sea	09061 502 162	09066 526 252
Northern North Sea	09061 502 166	09066 526 256
North West Scotland ...	09061 502 165	09066 526 255
Irish Sea	09061 502 163	09066 526 253

09066 CALLS COST 60P PER MIN. 09061 CALLS COST £1.50 PER MIN.

Key to Marina Plans symbols

Calor Gas		P	Parking
Chandler			Pub/Restaurant
Disabled facilities			Pump out
Electrical supply			Rigging service
Electrical repairs			Sail repairs
Engine repairs			Shipwright
First Aid			Shop/Supermarket
Fresh Water			Showers
Fuel - Diesel			Slipway
Fuel - Petrol		WC	Toilets
Hardstanding/boatyard			Telephone
Laundry facilities			Trolleys
Lift-out facilities		V	Visitors berths

Area 7 - North East Scotland

MARINAS
Telephone Numbers
VHF Channel
Access Times

7

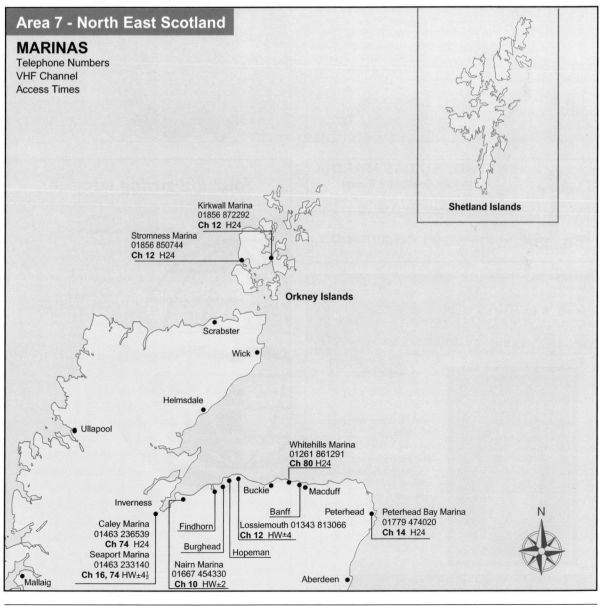

Shetland Islands

Kirkwall Marina
01856 872292
Ch 12 H24

Stromness Marina
01856 850744
Ch 12 H24

Orkney Islands

Scrabster

Wick

Helmsdale

Ullapool

Whitehills Marina
01261 861291
Ch 80 H24

Buckie

Macduff

Inverness

Banff

Peterhead

Peterhead Bay Marina
01779 474020
Ch 14 H24

Caley Marina
01463 236539
Ch 74 H24
Seaport Marina
01463 233140
Ch 16, 74 HW±4½

Findhorn

Lossiemouth 01343 813066
Ch 12 HW±4

Burghead

Hopeman

Nairn Marina
01667 454330
Ch 10 HW±2

Mallaig

Aberdeen

N

PETERHEAD BAY MARINA

Peterhead Bay Marina
Bath House, Bath Street, Peterhead, AB42 1DX
Tel: 01779 474020 Fax: 01779 475712
email: marina@peterhead-bay.co.uk
www.peterhead-bay.co.uk

VHF Ch 14
ACCESS H24

Based in the south west corner of Peterhead Bay Harbour, the marina provides one of the finest marine leisure facilities in the east of Scotland. In addition to the services on site, there are plenty of nautical businesses in the vicinity, ranging from ship chandlers and electrical servicing to boat repairs and surveying.

Due to its easterly location, Peterhead affords an ideal stopover for those yachts heading to or from Scandinavia as well as for vessels making for the Caledonian Canal.

FACILITIES AT A GLANCE

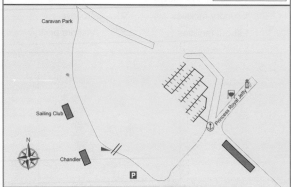

WHITEHILLS MARINA

Whitehills Harbour Commissioners
Whitehills, Banffshire AB45 2NQ
Tel: 01261 861291 Fax: 01261 861291
www.whitehillsharbour.co.uk
e mail: whitehillsharbour@lineone.co.uk

VHF Ch 80
ACCESS H24

Built in 1900, Whitehills is a Trust Harbour which is fully maintained and run by nine commissioners elected from the village. It was a thriving fishing port up until 1999, but due to changes in the fishing industry, was converted into a marina during the following year.

Just three miles west of Banff Harbour, it has become increasingly popular over the last few years, especially as it benefits from full tidal access. The marina comprises 38 serviced berths, with electricity provided for each berth, as well as eight non-serviced berths.

Close to the harbour is a gift centre and coffee shop, while the nearby village of Whitehills boasts a newsagent, convenience store, post office and a couple of pubs. A coastal path leads from the marina to the top of the headland, affording striking views across the Moray Firth to the Caithness Hills.

FACILITIES AT A GLANCE

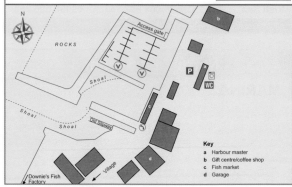

Key
a Harbour master
b Gift centre/coffee shop
c Fish market
d Garage

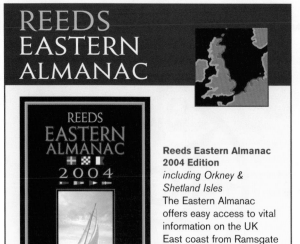
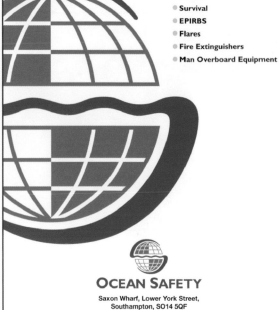

LOSSIEMOUTH MARINA

The Harbour Office
Lossiemouth, Moray, IV31 6NT
Tel: 01343 813066 Fax: 01343 813066

VHF	Ch 12
ACCESS	HW±4

Situated on the beautiful Moray Firth coastline, Lossiemouth Marina provides 50 well serviced berths in its East Basin and several new berths for larger vessels in its West Basin. Although the berths are primarily taken up by residential yachts, during the summer months a certain number are allocated to visitors who can benefit from the friendly, efficient service. The marina lies within easy walking distance of the town, which has a good range of shops and restaurants and boasts an array of leisure facilities, a championship standard golf course and acres of sandy beaches.

FACILITIES AT A GLANCE

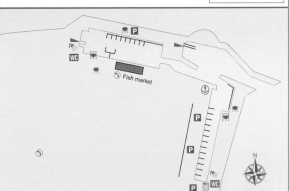

NAIRN MARINA

Nairn Marina
Nairn Harbour, Nairnshire, Scotland
Tel: 01667 454330 Fax: 01667 454330
Email: alex.taylor@highland.gov.uk

VHF	Ch 10
ACCESS	HW±2

Nairn is a small town on the coast of the Moray Firth. Formerly renowned both as a fishing port and as a holiday resort dating back to Victorian times, it boasts miles of award-winning, sandy beaches, famous castles such as Cawdor, Brodie and Castle Stuart, and two championship golf courses. Other recreational activities include horse riding or walking through spectacular countryside that is rich in plant and wildlife.

The marina lies at the mouth of the River Nairn, entry to which should be avoided in strong north to north-easterly winds. The approach is made from the north west at or around high water as the entrance is badly silted and dries out.

FACILITIES AT A GLANCE

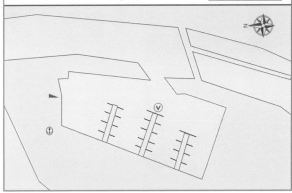

CALEY MARINA

Caley Marina
Canal Road, Inverness, IV3 8NF
Tel: 01463 236539 Fax: 01463 238323
email: info@caleymarina.com
www.caleycruisers.com

| VHF | Ch 74 |
| ACCESS | H24 |

Caley Marina is a family run business based near Inverness. With the four flight Muirtown locks and the Kessock Bridge providing a dramatic backdrop, the marina runs alongside the Caledonian Canal which, opened in 1822, is regarded as one of the most spectacular waterways in Europe. Built as a short cut between the North Sea and the Atlantic Ocean, thus avoiding the potentially dangerous Pentland Firth on the north coast of Scotland, the canal is around 60 miles long and takes about three days to cruise from east to west. With the prevailing winds behind you, it takes slightly less time to cruise in the other direction.

FACILITIES AT A GLANCE

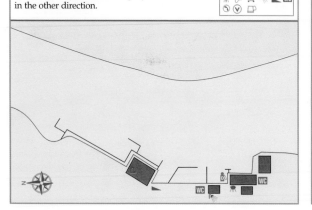

SEAPORT MARINA

Seaport Marina
Muirtown Wharf, Inverness, IV3 5LE
Tel: 01463 233140 Fax: 01463 710942
www.scottishcanals.co.uk

| VHF | Ch 16, 74 |
| ACCESS | HW±4.5 |

Seaport Marina is situated at Inverness at the head of the Caledonian Canal. Although it only incorporates 29 berths, it proves a popular location for long term berthing and is accessible four and half hours either side of HW. The centre of Inverness is just a 15-minute walk away, where you will find a full range of shops, pubs and restaurants, while entertainment venues include a theatre, bowling alley and multiplex cinema.

As the capital of the Highlands, Inverness attracts thousands of visitors each year, providing the ideal base from which to explore the surrounding area by road, coach or train. In addition, Inverness airport is only 20 minutes by taxi from the marina.

FACILITIES AT A GLANCE

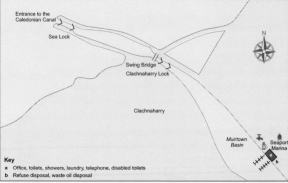

Entrance to the Caledonian Canal
Sea Lock
Swing Bridge
Clachnaharry Lock
Clachnaharry
N
Muirtown Basin
Seaport Marina

Key
a Office, toilets, showers, laundry, telephone, disabled toilets
b Refuse disposal, waste oil disposal

KIRKWALL MARINA

Kirkwall Marina
Harbour Street, Kirkwall, Orkney, KW15
Tel: 01856 872292
www.orkneymarinas.co.uk

VHF Ch 12
ACCESS H24

The Orkney Isles, comprising 70 islands in total, provides some of the finest cruising grounds in Northern Europe. The Main Island, incorporating the ancient port of Kirkwall, is the largest, although 16 others have lively communities and are rich in archaeological sites as well as spectacular scenery and wildlife.

Kirkwall Marina is due to open around October 2003 and will offer excellent facilities along with 24hr access and good shelter. The site is very close to the historic Kirkwall, whose original town is one of the best preserved examples of an ancient Norse dwelling.

FACILITIES AT A GLANCE

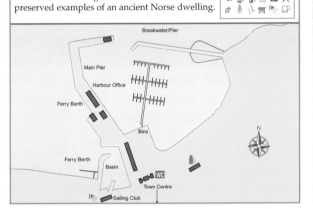

STROMNESS MARINA

Stromness Marina
Stromness
Orkney, KW16
Tel: 01856 850744 Fax: 01856 851457
www.orkneymarinas.co.uk

VHF Ch 12
ACCESS H24

Just 16 miles to the west of Kirkwall, Stromness lies on the south-western tip of the Orkney Isles' Mainland. Sitting beneath the rocky ridge known as Brinkie's Brae, it is considered one of Orkney's major seaports, with sailors first attracted to the fine anchorage provided by the bay of Hamnavoe.

Stromness, like Kirkwall, is a brand new marina (due to be completed in Autumn 2003), offering comprehensive facilities including a chandlery and repair services. Also on hand are an internet café, a fitness suite and swimming pool as well as car and bike hire.

FACILITIES AT A GLANCE

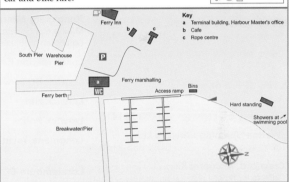

Key
a   Terminal building, Harbour Master's office
b   Cafe
c   Rope centre

Sail Orkney

Airylea Motors Aberdeen
Diesel fuel injection specialists
01224 872891

Banff HM 01261 815544

Banff SC Cults 01261 815296

British Waterways Scotland
01463 233140

Brown Son & Ferguson Ltd Glasgow
Nautical publishers 0141 429 1234

Buckie HM 01542 831700

Buckie Police 01542 832222

Buckie Shipyard Ltd Buckie
01542 831245

Burghead Boat Centre Findhorn
Boat repairs; cranage; chandler
01309 690099

Burghead HM 01343 835337

Caley Cruisers Inverness
Yacht charter 01463 236328

Caley Marina & Chandlery Inverness
01463 236328

Canal Office (Inverness) HM
01463 233140

Chanonry SC Fortrose 01463 221415

Chattan Shipping Services Ltd
Edinburgh 0131 555 3155

Crawford, Margaret Kirkwall
Canvas work; sail repairs; upholstery
01856 875692

Cromarty Firth HM 01381 600479

Cullen HM 01261 842477

Denholm Fishselling Scrabster
Fish selling & vessel management
01847 896968

DH Marine (Shetland) Ltd Shetland
Marine engineers 01595 690618

Duncan Ltd, JS Wick
Ship chandler 01955 602689

Fathoms Ltd Wick
Diving company; hydrographic surveys
01955 605956

Findhorn Boatyard Findhorn
01309 690099

Findhorn Police 01309 672224

Findhorn YC Findhorn 01309 690247

Findochty HM 01542 831466

Fleetwood & Sons Ltd, Henry
Lossiemouth
Engine sales, spares and services
01343 813015

Flotta HM 01856 701411

Fraserburgh HM 01346 515858

Fraserburgh Police 01346 513121

Grampian Diving Services New Deer
01771 644206

Helmsdale HM 01431 821692

Helmsdale Police 01431 821222

HNP Engineers (Lerwick Ltd) Lerwick
Marine engineers & electronic repairs
01595 692493

Hopeman HM 01343 835337

Hopeman Police 01343 830222

Invergordon BC 01349 877612

Inverness HM 01463 715715

Inverness Police 01463 715555

Jacobite Cruises Inverness
Cruise boats 01463 233999

Kettletoft Bay HM 01857 600227

Kirkwall HM 01856 872292

Kirkwall Marina Kirkwall 01856 872292

Kirkwall Police 01856 872241

Kongsberg Simrad Ltd Wick
Marine electronics; underwater electronic
equipment 01955 603606

Leask Marine Kirkwall 01856 874725

Lerwick BC Lerwick 01595 696954

Lerwick HM 01595 692991

Lerwick Police 01595 692110

Longmans Yacht Haven Inverness
01463 715715

Lossiemouth CC Fochabers
01348 812121

Lossiemouth HM 01343 813066

Lossiemouth Marina Lossiemouth
01343 813066

Lossiemouth Police 01343 812022

Lyness HM 01856 791387

Macduff and Banff Police
01261 812555

Macduff HM 01261 832236

Macduff Shipyard Ltd Macduff
01261 832234

Malakoff and Moore Lerwick
Boat repairs, maintenance; chandlers;
engines; sailmakers and repairs
01595 695544

Marconi Marine Fraserburgh
Marine electronics 01346 518187

Marconi Marine Peterhead
Marine electronics 01779 480921

McCaughty (Boatbuilders), J Wick
01955 602858

Montrose Rope and Sails Montrose
01674 672657

Nairn Marina 01667 454330

Nairn Police 01667 452222

Nairn SC Nairn 01667 453897

**North of England Yachting
Association** Kirkwall 01856 872331

Orkney SC Kirkwall 01856 872331

Paterson, A Macduff 01261 832784
Chandler

Pentland Firth YC Thurso
01847 891803

**Peter Georgeson Marina – Vaila
Sound (Walls)** Lerwick 01595 809273

Peterhead Bay Authority Peterhead
Moorings 01779 474020

Peterhead Bay Marina Peterhead
01779 474020

Pierowall HM 01857 677216

Pirie & Co, John S Fraserburgh
Marine engineers 01346 513314

Portknockie HM 01542 840833

Richardson Boatbuilders, Ian
Stromness
Boat repairs; maintenance 01856 850321

Scalloway BC Lerwick 01595 880409

Scalloway HM 01595 880574

Scrabster HM 01847 892779

Scrabster Police 01847 893222

Seaport Marina Inverness
01463 233140

Seaway Marine Macduff 01261 832877

Sperry Marine Ltd Peterhead
Marine electronics 01779 473475

St Margaret's Hope HM 01856 831454

STN Atlas Marine UK Ltd Peterhead
Marine electronics 01779 478233

Stromness HM 01856 850744

Stromness Marina Stromness
01856 850744

Stromness Police 01856 850222

Stronsay HM 01857 616317

Stronsay Police 01857 872241

Sullom Voe HM 01806 242551

Thulecraft Ltd Lerwick
Chandler; boat sales 01595 693192

UK Customs Nationwide
0845 0109000

Veripos Precise Navigation
Fraserburgh
Marine electronics 01346 511411

Walls Regatta Club Lerwick
01595 809273

Westray Marina Westray 01857 677216

Whitehills HM 01261 861291

Wick HM 01955 602030

Wick Police 01955 603551

Wyko Industrial Services Inverness
Generators; marine engineering; engine
repairs 01463 224747

Waypoint Guide Area 7 – North East Scotland - Rattray Head to Cape Wrath

399	**Cape Wrath** - 2M NW of	58°38'·87N	05°02'·89W
400	**Whiten Head** - 4·4M N of	58°39'·18N	04°34'·90W
401	**Scrabster** - 1·4M NE of Holborn Head	58°38'·58N	03°30'·80W
402	**Dunnet Head light** -1·7M NW of	58°41'·58N	03°24'·39W
403	**Pentland Firth** - 1·5M NE by N of Stroma	58°42'·98N	03°05'·31W
404	**Duncansby Head** - 2M NE of	58°39'·78N	02°58'·49W
405	**Stromness** - 2·8M NW of Graemsay light	58°57'·07N	03°23'·80W
406	**Stronsay** - 0·8M NW Ness light	59°09'·97N	02°35'·90W
407	**Kirkwall** - 1·5M NW of Mull Head	58°59'·37N	02°40'·50W
408	**Copinsay light** - 2·5M E of	58°54'·07N	02°35'·20W
409	**Lerwick** - 1·1M SW of Bressay light	60°06'·57N	01°08'·50W
410	**Wick** - 1·6M E of South Head	58°25'·78N	03°01'·10W
411	**Sarclet Head** - 2M E by S of	58°21'·88N	03°02'·60W
412	**Helmsdale** - 1·8M SE of ent	58°05'·48N	03°36'·90W
413	**Tarbat Ness light** - 2M E of	57°51'·88N	03°42'·78W
414	**Inverness** - 0·5 NE of Fairway Buoy	57°40'·28N	03°53'·40W
415	**Findhorn** - 2·2M NW of bay	57°41'·43N	03°40'·11W
416	**Lossiemouth** - 1·7M N of	57°45'·20N	03°16'·90W
417	**Buckie** - 2M WNW of	57°41'·68N	03°00'·99W
418	**Scar Nose** - 1·6M N of	57°43'·98N	02°51'·01W
419	**Banff** - 1·3M N of Meavie Point	57°41'·64N	02°31'·30W
420	**Troup Head** - 1·8M N of	57°43'·50N	02°17'·75W
421	**Kinnairds Head** - 1·6M N of	57°43'·50N	02°00'·16W
422	**Cairnbulg Point light** - 1·9M NE of	57°42'·20N	01°53'·81W
423	**Rattray Head light** - 1·8M ENE of	57°37'·40N	01°46'·00W
424	**Peterhead** - 2·1M ESE	57°29'·30N	01°42'·71W
425	**Aberdeen** - 2M E by N of Girdle Ness	57°08'·80N	01°59'·06W
426	**Stonehaven** - 2M E of	56°57'·60N	02°08'·04W
427	**Todhead Point light** - 2·5M E of	56°53'·03N	02°08'·35W
428	**Montrose** - 2·1M E of Scurdie Ness light	56°42'·10N	02°22'·40W
429	**Red Head** - 1·8M E of	56°37'·02N	02°25'·98W
430	**Tayport** - 0·5M E of Fairway Buoy	56°29'·25N	02°37'·32W
431	**Fife Ness** - 2·8M ESE of	56°15'·95N	02°30'·39W
432	**Granton** - 0·5M N of Firth of Forth Fairway Buoy	56°04'·00N	03°00'·09W
433	**Bass Rock light** - 1·5M N of	56°06'·10N	02°38'·44W
434	**Dunbar** - 1·5M NNE of	56°01'·76N	02°30'·30W
435	**St Abb's Head light** - 1·5M NE of	55°56'·11N	02°06'·50W
	Hoek van Holland - 1·2M WNW of	51°59'·90N	04°00'·80E

Distance Table - North East Scotland

Approximate distances in nautical miles are by the most direct route while avoiding dangers and allowing for Traffic Separation Schemes

		1	2	3	4	5	6	7	8	9	10	11	12	13	14	15	16	17	18	19	20
1.	**Peterhead**	1																			
2.	**Fraserburgh**	16	2																		
3.	**Banff/Macduff**	33	18	3																	
4.	**Buckie**	46	31	15	4																
5.	**Lossiemouth**	56	41	25	11	5															
6.	**Findhorn**	69	54	38	24	13	6														
7.	**Nairn**	79	64	48	34	23	10	7													
8.	**Inverness**	90	75	59	45	34	23	13	8												
9.	**Tarbat Ness**	72	57	41	27	18	14	17	27	9											
10.	**Helmsdale**	74	59	44	33	26	28	32	43	16	10										
11.	**Wick**	72	57	50	46	44	51	58	69	42	29	11									
12.	**Duncansby Head**	82	67	62	58	57	64	71	81	54	41	13	12								
13.	**Scrabster**	100	85	80	76	75	82	89	99	72	59	31	18	13							
14.	**Kirkwall**	115	100	95	91	90	97	104	114	87	74	46	34	50	14						
15.	**Stromness**	104	89	84	80	79	85	92	103	76	63	35	22	25	32	15					
16.	**Fair Isle**	122	111	116	118	120	130	137	148	121	108	79	68	85	55	77	16				
17.	**Lerwick**	160	150	156	160	162	172	170	190	162	148	120	109	124	95	110	42	17			
18.	**Loch Eriboll (ent)**	137	122	117	113	112	119	126	136	109	96	68	55	37	80	50	110	150	18		
19.	**Cape Wrath**	145	130	125	121	120	127	126	144	117	104	76	63	47	79	58	120	155	13	19	
20.	**Ullapool**	198	183	178	174	173	180	179	197	170	157	129	116	100	132	111	173	208	66	53	20

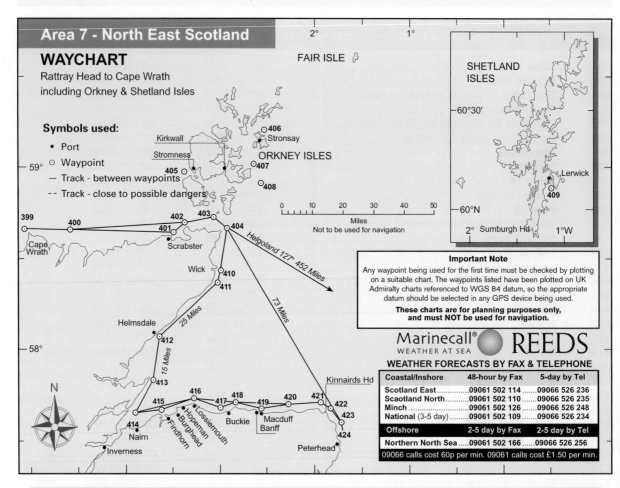

Area 7 - North East Scotland

WAYCHART
Rattray Head to Cape Wrath
including Orkney & Shetland Isles

FAIR ISLE

Symbols used:

- ● Port
- ○ Waypoint
- — Track - between waypoints
- -- Track - close to possible dangers

SHETLAND ISLES

Kirkwall
Stromness
ORKNEY ISLES

● 406 Stronsay
○ 407
○ 405
○ 408

Lerwick
○ 409

Scrabster
Cape Wrath
399 ○—○ 400 ——○ 401 ○ 402 ○ 403 ○ 404

Sumburgh Hd

Miles
Not to be used for navigation
0 10 20 30 40 50

Wick
○ 410
○ 411

Helgoland 127° 452 Miles

73 Miles

Helmsdale
25 Miles
○ 412
15 Miles
○ 413

Kinnairds Hd

N

○ 414 Nairn
○ 415
○ 416
○ 417 ○ 418 ○ 419 ○ 420 ○ 421 ○ 422
○ 423
○ 424
Lossiemouth
Hopeman
Burghead
Findhorn
Buckie
Macduff
Banff
Peterhead
Inverness

Important Note
Any waypoint being used for the first time must be checked by plotting on a suitable chart. The waypoints listed have been plotted on UK Admiralty charts referenced to WGS 84 datum, so the appropriate datum should be selected in any GPS device being used.

These charts are for planning purposes only, and must NOT be used for navigation.

Marinecall®
WEATHER AT SEA

REEDS

WEATHER FORECASTS BY FAX & TELEPHONE

Coastal/Inshore	48-hour by Fax	5-day by Tel
Scotland East	09061 502 114	09066 526 236
Scaotland North	09061 502 110	09066 526 235
Minch	09061 502 126	09066 526 248
National (3-5 day)	09061 502 109	09066 526 234

Offshore	2-5 day by Fax	2-5 day by Tel
Northern North Sea	09061 502 166	09066 526 256

09066 calls cost 60p per min. 09061 calls cost £1.50 per min.

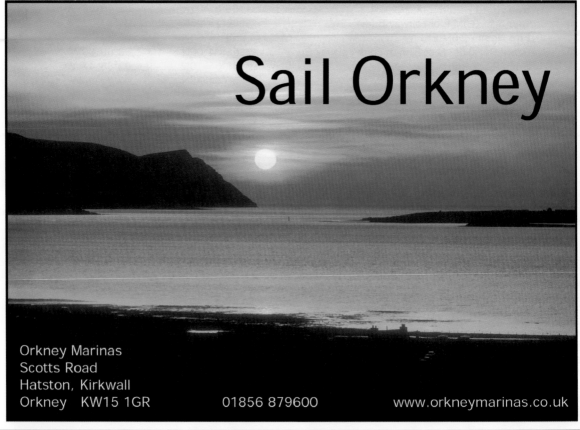

Sail Orkney

Orkney Marinas
Scotts Road
Hatston, Kirkwall
Orkney KW15 1GR

01856 879600

www.orkneymarinas.co.uk

Marinecall® WEATHER AT SEA **REEDS**

WEATHER FORECASTS BY FAX & TELEPHONE

Coastal/Inshore	2-day by Fax	5-day by Phone
Scotland North	09061 502 110	09066 526 235
Minch	09061 502 126	09066 526 248
Caledonia	09061 502 125	09066 526 247
Clyde	09061 502 124	09066 526 246
National (3-5 day)	09061 502 109	09066 526 234

Offshore	2-5 day by Fax	2-5 day by Phone
Southern North Sea	09061 502 162	09066 526 252
Northern North Sea	09061 502 166	09066 526 256
North West Scotland ...	09061 502 165	09066 526 255
Irish Sea	09061 502 163	09066 526 253

09066 CALLS COST 60P PER MIN. 09061 CALLS COST £1.50 PER MIN.

Key to Marina Plans symbols

Calor Gas		P	Parking
Chandler			Pub/Restaurant
Disabled facilities			Pump out
Electrical supply			Rigging service
Electrical repairs			Sail repairs
Engine repairs			Shipwright
First Aid			Shop/Supermarket
Fresh Water			Showers
Fuel - Diesel			Slipway
Fuel - Petrol		WC	Toilets
Hardstanding/boatyard			Telephone
Laundry facilities			Trolleys
Lift-out facilities		V	Visitors berths

Area 8 - North West Scotland

MARINAS
Telephone Numbers
VHF Channel
Access Times

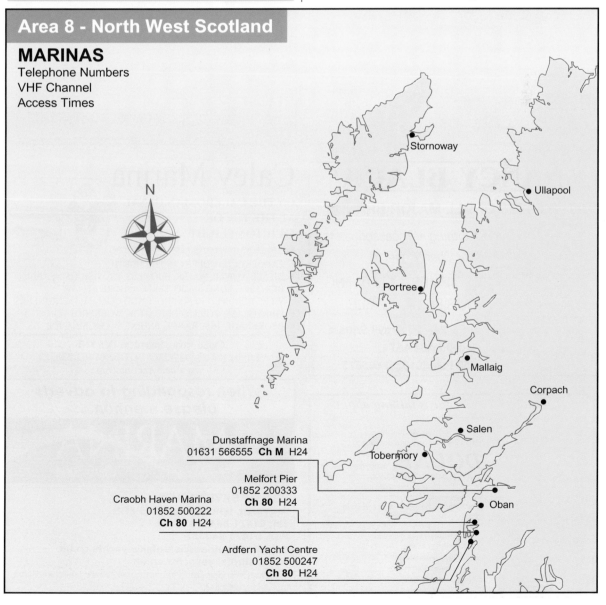

Stornoway

Ullapool

Portree

Mallaig

Corpach

Salen

Tobermory

Oban

Dunstaffnage Marina
01631 566555 **Ch M** H24

Melfort Pier
01852 200333
Ch 80 H24

Craobh Haven Marina
01852 500222
Ch 80 H24

Ardfern Yacht Centre
01852 500247
Ch 80 H24

DUNSTAFFNAGE MARINA

Dunstaffnage Marina Ltd
Dunbeg, by Oban, Argyll, PA37 1PX
Tel: 01631 566555 Fax: 01631 567422
e-mail: lizzy@dunstaffnage.sol.co.uk

VHF Ch M
ACCESS H24

Located just two to three miles north of Oban, Dunstaffnage Marina has recently been renovated to include an additional 36 fully serviced berths, a new breakwater providing shelter from NE'ly to E'ly winds and an increased amount of hard standing. Also on site is the Wide Mouthed Frog, offering a convivial bar and restaurant with spectacular views of the 13th century Dunstaffnage Castle.

The marina is perfectly placed to explore Scotland's stunning west coast and Hebridean Islands. Only 10 miles NE up Loch Linnhe is Port Appin, while sailing 15 miles S, down the Firth of Lorne, brings you to Puldohran where you can walk to an ancient hostelry situated next to the C18 Bridge Over the Atlantic.

FACILITIES AT A GLANCE

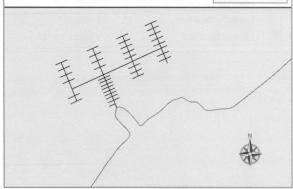

MELFORT PIER AND HARBOUR

Melfort Pier and Harbour
Kilmelford, by Oban, Argyll
Tel: 01852 200333 Fax: 01852 200329
email: melharbour@aol.com

VHF Ch 80
ACCESS H24

Melfort Pier and Harbour is situated on the shores of Loch Melfort, one of the most peaceful lochs on the south west coast of Scotland. Overlooked by the Pass of Melfort and the Braes of Lorn, it lies approximately 18 miles north of Lochgilphead and 16 miles south of Oban. Its on site facilities include showers, electricity and water supplies, while boat and engine repairs can be carried out at the neighbouring Kimelford Yacht Haven. Within easy walking distance of the pier are village shops in Kimelford and a nearby pub, the Shower of Herring. For those who want a few nights on dry land, Melfort Pier and Harbour offer five star self-catering houses, each one equipped with a sauna, spa bath and balcony offering views over the loch.

FACILITIES AT A GLANCE

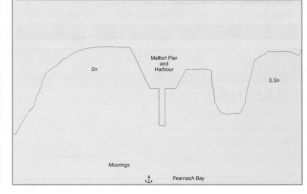

CRAOBH HAVEN MARINA

Craobh Haven Marina
By Lochgilphead, Argyll, Scotland, PA31 8UA
Tel: 01852 50022 Fax: 01852 500252
email: craobh@talk21.com
www.kipmarina.co.uk/pages/craobhcontent.html

| VHF | Ch M, 80 |
| ACCESS | H24 |

Pronounced 'Croove', Craobh Marina has been developed from a natural harbour and lies at the heart of Scotland's spectacular west coast cruising grounds. It is strategically placed for entering the Crinan Canal, making a short trip to the Mull of Kintyre and Oban, or visiting Jura and Islay. With 250 berths and the capacity to accommodate yachts up to 33m LOA, Craobh Marina enjoys deep water at all states of the tide. It sits adjacent to the village of Craobh Haven, where you can find a convenience store, a pub-cum-restaurant and a convivial bistro. Alternative activities to sailing include a well-equipped dive centre as well as a large number of walks through exquisite countryside.

FACILITIES AT A GLANCE

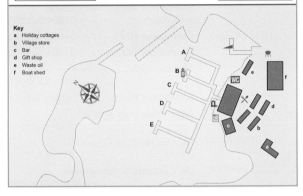

Key
a Holiday cottages
b Village store
c Bar
d Gift shop
e Waste oil
f Boat shed

ARDFERN YACHT CENTRE

Ardfern Yacht Centre
Ardfern, by Lochgilphead, Argyll, PA31 8QN
Tel: 01852 500247 Fax: 01852 500624
www.ardfernyacht.co.uk email: office@ardfernyacht.co.uk

| VHF | Ch 80 |
| ACCESS | H24 |

Developed around an old pier once frequented by steamers, Ardfern Yacht Centre lies at the head of Loch Craignish, one of Scotland's most sheltered and picturesque sea lochs. With several islands and protected anchorages nearby, Ardfern is an ideal place from which to cruise the west coast of Scotland and the Outer Hebrides.

The Yacht Centre comprises pontoon berths and swinging moorings as well as a workshop, boat storage and well-stocked chandlery, while a grocery store and several eating places can be found in the village. Among the onshore activities available locally are horse riding, cycling, walking and golf.

FACILITIES AT A GLANCE

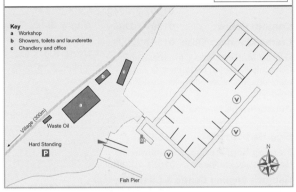

Key
a Workshop
b Showers, toilets and launderette
c Chandlery and office

CRINAN BOATYARD LTD
Crinan, Lochgilphead, Argyll PA31 8SW
Tel: (01546) 830232
Fax: (01546) 830281
Fully stocked chandlery, slipway, engineering and shipwright work and repairs, swinging moorings, water and diesel, shower and laundry facilities, undercover and outside storage.

PREMIUM LIFERAFT SERVICES
KYLE OF LOCHALSH
Tel: (01599) 534541
Freephone: 0800 243673
e-mail: info@liferafts.com
www.liferafts.com
Hire and sales of DoT and RORC approved liferafts and safety equipment.

PREMIUM LIFERAFT SERVICES
OBAN
Tel: (01631) 562849
Freephone: 0800 243673
e-mail: info@liferafts.com
www.liferafts.com
Hire and sales of DoT and RORC approved liferafts and safety equipment.

SLEAT MARINE SERVICES
Ardvasar, Isle of Skye IV45 8RS
Tel: (01471) 844216
Fax: (01471) 844387
e-mail: services@sleatmarineservices.com
www.sleatmarineservices.co.uk
Yacht Charter - we offer a choice of yachts in the 10-12 metre size range. Services to visiting yachts include: 15 ton hoist, general repairs, diesel, water, mooring and showers. We look forward to seeing you.

8

Ardoran Marine Oban
Boat repairs; boat sales; chandler
01631 566123

Ardmair Boat Centre Ullapool
Moorings; boat/engine repairs; boat sales;
yacht charter   01854 612054

Ardoran Marine Oban, Argyll
01631 566123

Arinagour Piermaster   01879 230347

Arisaig Marine Inverness-shire
Moorings, wintering, services, repairs
01687 450224

C I Diving Services Ltd Invergordon
01349 852500

Chattan Shipping Services Ltd
Edinburgh   0131 555 3155

Corpach Boatbuilding Company
Fort William   01397 772861

Corpach Canal Sea Lock HM
01397 772249

Corpach Police   01397 702361

Creran Moorings Oban 01631 720265

Doune Marine Mallaig, Inverness-shire
Gaff cutter charter, restaurant, 2 x free
moorings, shorebased walking/wildlife
holidays   01687 462667

Dunstaffnage Marina Ltd Oban
01631 566555

Eigg Harbour HM   01687 482428

Fleming Engineering, J Stornoway
Boat repairs; engines   01851 703488

Gairloch Angling Centre & Chandlery
Gairloch   01445 712458

Johnston Brothers Mallaig
Ship chandler   01687 462215

KG McColl Oban
Boat repairs; moorings; winter storage
01852 200248

Kinlochbervie HM   01971 521235

Kinlochbervie Police   01971 521222

Loch Gairloch HM   01445 712140

Loch Inver HM   01571 844265

Loch Melfort Police   01852 562213

Lochaber YC Fort William 01397 772361

MacDougalls Marine Services
01681 700294

**Mallaig Boat Building and
Engineering** Mallaig   01687 462304

Mallaig Police   01687 462177

Marine Resource Centre Ltd Oban
Boat storage; repairs; rigging; engineering
01631 720291

Melfort Pier & Harbour Kilmelford
Moorings; harbour bus   01852 200333

Morrison Engineering, Sandy Uig
01470 542300

Murray, Alex Stornoway
Diver; welder   01851 704978

Nancy Black Oban
Chandler   01631 562550

North Pier Oban
Mobile cranage; fresh water; fuel by road
tanker   01631 562892

Oban HM   01631 562892

Oban Marine Centre Oban
Storage   01631 562472

Oban Police   01631 562213

Oban SC Ledaig Nr Oban
01631 563999

Oban Yachts and Marine Services
Nr Oban
Boat repairs; chandlery   01631 565333

Owen Sails Nr Oban
Sailmaker; chandlery   01631 720485

Plockton HM   01599 534589

Portree HM   01478 612926

Portree Police   01478 612888

Premium Liferaft Services
Kyle of Lochalsh
Hire/sale of liferafts and safety equipment
01599 534541

Premium Liferaft Services Oban
As above   01631 562849

Robertson, MK Oban
Marine electronics   01631 563836

Royal Highland YC Connel
01546 510261

Seafare Tobermory
Chandler   01688 302277

Sleat Marine Services Isle of Skye
Yacht charter; boat repairs; cranage
01471 844216

Sperry Marine Ullapool
Electronics   01854 612024

Stealaway Diving Oban 01631 566349

Stornoway Fishermen's Co-op
Stornoway   01851 702563

Stornoway HM   01851 702688

Stornoway Police   01851 702222

Stornoway SC Stornoway
01851 705412

Tobermory Police   01688 302016

Tobermory Port Manager
01688 302017

Thorpe, Norman Portree
Diver   01478 612274

UK Customs Nationwide
0845 0109000

Ullapool HM   01854 612091

Ullapool Police   01854 612017

WB Leitch and Son Tarbert
01880 820287

Western Battery Service Mallaig
Marine electronics   01687 462044

Western Isles YC   01688 302371

Waypoint Guide Area 8 – North West Scotland - Cape Wrath to Crinan Canal

348	**Skerryvore light** - 6·8M W by N of		56°20'·78N	07°18'·86W
370	**Sound of Insh** - 1M SSW of Insh Island		56°17'·60N	05°41'·06W
371	**Kerrera Sound** - 0·7M SSW of Rubha Seanach		56°21'·70N	05°33'·96W
372	**Oban** - 0·5M WNW of Maiden Isle		56°26'·00N	05°30'·36W
373	**Between Lady's Rock and Eilean Musdile**		56°27'·19N	05°36'·75W
374	**Sound of Mull** - 1·6M SE of Ardtornish Pt		56°30'·15N	05°42'·81W
375	**Loch Aline** - 0·7M S by W of entrance		56°31'·30N	05°46'·86W
376	**Sound of Mull** - 1·8M N of Salen		56°33'·00N	05°56'·36W
377	**Tobermory** - 0·9M NE of harbour entrance		56°38'·39N	06°02'·46W
378	**Ardmore Point (Mull)** - 0·7M N of		56°40'·00N	06°07'·66W
379	**Point of Ardnamurchan** - 2·8M S of		56°40'·90N	06°13'·36W
380	**Point of Ardnamurchan** - 1·3M W of		56°43'·60N	06°15'·96W
381	**Mallaig** - 1·5M WNW of harbour entrance		57°00'·98N	05°52'·17W
382	**Neist Point light** - 4M W of		57°25'·42N	06°54'·57W
383	**Sound of Shiant** - 2·2M E of Eilean Glas light		57°51'·20N	06°34'·40W
384	**Sound of Shiant** - 0·3M NW of Shiants SHM		57°54'·78N	06°26'·07W
385	**Kebock Head** - 2·3M E of		58°02'·38N	06°17'·10W
386	**Stornoway** - 1·2M SE of harbour entrance		58°10'·28N	06°20'·67W
387	**Chicken Head** - 1·2M S of		58°09'·60N	06°15'·28W
388	**Sandaig Islands light** - 0·6M W by N of		57°10'·22N	05°43'·27W

389	**Kyle Rhea (S approach)** - 0·6M W of Glenelg	57°12'·62N	05°38'·86W
390	**Loch Alsh (W approach)** - 1M NW of entrance	57°17'·18N	05°46'·17W
391	**Crowlin Islands** - 1·5M W of	57°20'·68N	05°53'·87W
392	**Inner Sound** - 1·7M E Rubha Ard Ghlaisen	57°29'·55N	05°55'·57W
393	**Portree** - 1·8M E of town	57°24'·98N	06°08'·07W
394	**Sd of Raasay** - 3·1M SE of Rubha nam Brathairean	57°33'·28N	06°03'·86W
395	**Rubha Reidh** - 3M W of	57°51'·58N	05°54'·40W
396	**Greenstone Point** - 1·6M NW of	57°56'·58N	05°39'·27W
397	**Ullapool** - 1·7M NE of Cailleach Head light	57°56'·88N	05°21'·87W
398	**Stoerhead light** - 2M NW of	58°15'·77N	05°26'·87W
399	**Cape Wrath** - 2M NW of	58°38'·87N	05°02'·89W
400	**Whiten Head** - 4·4M N of	58°39'·18N	04°34'·90W

Distance Table - North West Scotland

Approximate distances in nautical miles are by the most direct route while avoiding dangers and allowing for Traffic Separation Schemes

		1	2	3	4	5	6	7	8	9	10	11	12	13	14	15	16	17	18	19	20
1.	Cape Wrath	**1**																			
2.	Ullapool	54	**2**																		
3.	Stornoway	53	45	**3**																	
4.	East Loch Tarbert	75	56	33	**4**																
5.	Portree	83	57	53	42	**5**															
6.	Loch Harport	110	82	65	45	66	**6**														
7.	Kyle of Lochalsh	91	63	62	63	21	53	**7**													
8.	Mallaig	112	82	83	84	42	33	21	**8**												
9.	Eigg	123	98	97	75	54	34	35	14	**9**											
10.	Castlebay (Barra)	133	105	92	69	97	43	76	59	46	**10**										
11.	Tobermory	144	114	115	87	74	52	53	32	20	53	**11**									
12.	Loch Aline	157	127	128	100	87	65	66	45	33	66	13	**12**								
13.	Fort William	198	161	162	134	121	99	98	75	63	96	43	34	**13**							
14.	Oban	169	138	139	111	100	76	77	56	44	77	24	13	29	**14**						
15.	Loch Lathaich	160	130	124	98	91	62	67	49	35	56	31	53	77	48	**15**					
16.	Loch Melfort	184	154	155	117	114	92	93	69	61	92	40	27	45	18	45	**16**				
17.	Craobh Haven	184	155	155	117	114	93	92	70	60	93	40	27	50	21	43	5	**17**			
18.	Loch Craignish	188	158	159	131	118	95	96	76	64	98	44	31	55	26	46	17	14	**18**		
19.	Crinan	187	157	158	129	112	95	95	74	63	97	42	30	54	25	45	14	9	6	**19**	
20.	Mull of Kintyre	232	203	189	175	159	133	143	121	105	120	89	87	98	72	78	62	57	54	51	**20**

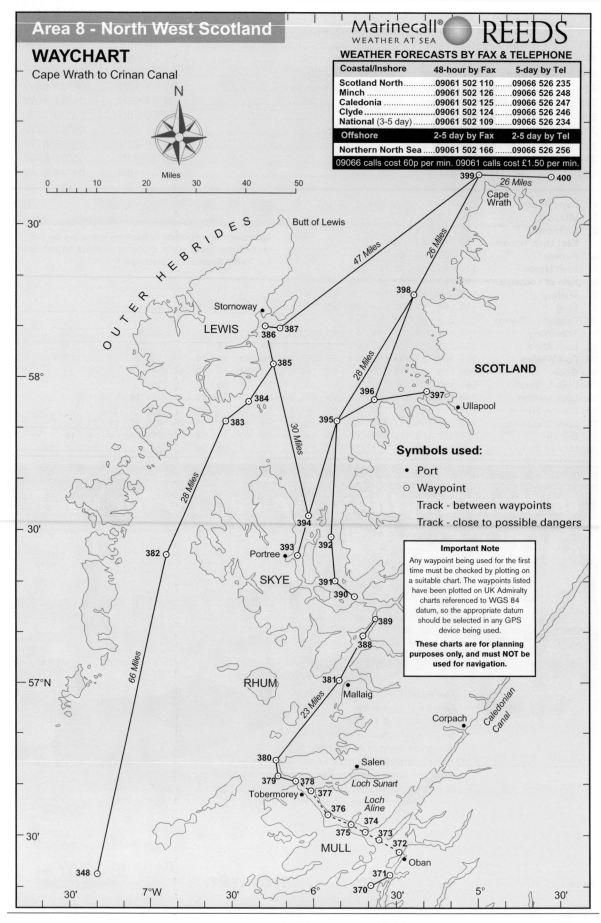

Area 8 - North West Scotland

WAYCHART
Cape Wrath to Crinan Canal

Marinecall®
WEATHER AT SEA

REEDS

WEATHER FORECASTS BY FAX & TELEPHONE

Coastal/Inshore	48-hour by Fax	5-day by Tel
Scotland North.............	09061 502 110	......09066 526 235
Minch	09061 502 126	......09066 526 248
Caledonia	09061 502 125	......09066 526 247
Clyde	09061 502 124	......09066 526 246
National (3-5 day)	09061 502 109	......09066 526 234

Offshore	2-5 day by Fax	2-5 day by Tel
Northern North Sea	09061 502 166	......09066 526 256

09066 calls cost 60p per min. 09061 calls cost £1.50 per min.

Symbols used:

- • Port
- ⊙ Waypoint
- Track - between waypoints
- Track - close to possible dangers

Important Note

Any waypoint being used for the first time must be checked by plotting on a suitable chart. The waypoints listed have been plotted on UK Admiralty charts referenced to WGS 84 datum, so the appropriate datum should be selected in any GPS device being used.

These charts are for planning purposes only, and must NOT be used for navigation.

Key to Marina Plans symbols

Calor Gas		P	Parking
Chandler		✕	Pub/Restaurant
Disabled facilities			Pump out
Electrical supply			Rigging service
Electrical repairs			Sail repairs
Engine repairs			Shipwright
First Aid			Shop/Supermarket
Fresh Water			Showers
Fuel - Diesel			Slipway
Fuel - Petrol		WC	Toilets
Hardstanding/boatyard			Telephone
Laundry facilities			Trolleys
Lift-out facilities		V	Visitors berths

Area 9 - South West Scotland

MARINAS
Telephone Numbers
VHF Channel
Access Times

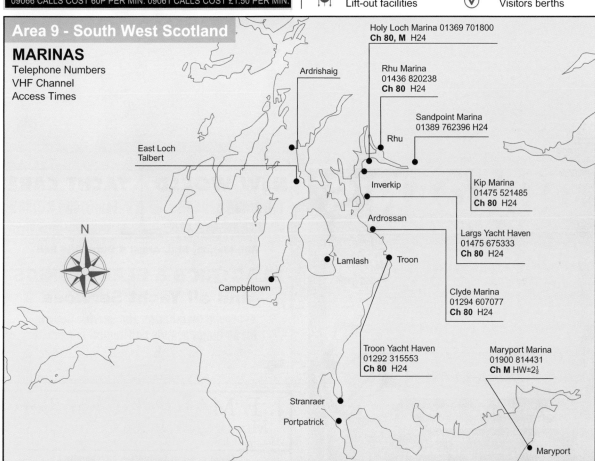

Holy Loch Marina 01369 701800
Ch 80, M H24

Rhu Marina
01436 820238
Ch 80 H24

Sandpoint Marina
01389 762396 H24

Kip Marina
01475 521485
Ch 80 H24

Largs Yacht Haven
01475 675333
Ch 80 H24

Clyde Marina
01294 607077
Ch 80 H24

Troon Yacht Haven
01292 315553
Ch 80 H24

Maryport Marina
01900 814431
Ch M HW±2½

Ardrishaig
East Loch Talbert
Rhu
Inverkip
Ardrossan
Lamlash
Troon
Campbeltown
Stranraer
Portpatrick
Maryport

9

HOLY LOCH MARINA

Holy Loch Marina
Rankin's Brae, Sandbank, Dunoon, PA23 8QB
Tel: 01369 701800 Fax: 01369 704749
Email: info@holylochmarina.co.uk

VHF | Ch 80, M
ACCESS | H24

Holy Loch Marina, reputed for being the Clyde's newest marina, lies on the south shore of the loch, roughly half a mile west of Lazaretto Point. Holy Loch is among the Clyde's most beautiful natural harbours and, besides being a peaceful location, offers an abundance of wildlife, places of local historical interest as well as excellent walking and cycling through the Argyll Forest Park.

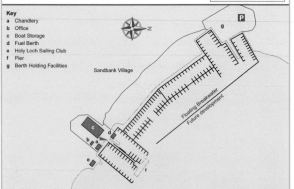

The marina can be entered in all weather conditions and is within easy sailing distance of Loch Long and Upper Firth.

FACILITIES AT A GLANCE

Key
a Chandlery
b Office
c Boat Storage
d Fuel Berth
e Holy Loch Sailing Club
f Pier
g Berth Holding Facilities

Sandbank Village

RHU MARINA

Rhu Marina Ltd
Rhu, Dunbartonshire, G84 8LH
Tel: 01436 820238 Fax: 01436 821039
email: any@rhumarina.force9.co.uk

VHF | Ch 80, M
ACCESS | H24

Located on the north shore of the Clyde Estuary, Rhu Marina is accessible at all states of the tide and can accommodate yachts up to 18m in length. It also operates 60 swinging moorings in the bay adjacent to the marina, with a ferry service provided.

Within easy walking distance of the marina is Rhu village, a conservation village incorporating a few shops, a pub and the beautiful Glenarn Gardens as well as the Royal Northern & Clyde Yacht Club. A mile or two to the east lies the holiday town of Helensburgh, renowned for its attractive architecture and elegant parks and gardens, while Glasgow city is just 40 miles away and can be easily reached by train

FACILITIES AT A GLANCE

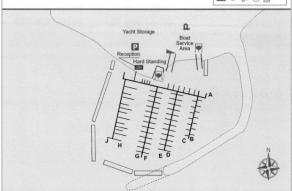

Yacht Storage

Boat Service Area

Reception
Hard Standing

J H
G F E D
C B
A

SANDPOINT MARINA

Sandpoint Marina Ltd
Sandpoint, Woodyard Road, Dumbarton, G82 4BG
Tel: 01389 762396 Fax: 01389 732605
email: sales@sandpoint-marina.co.uk
www.sandpoint-marina.co.uk

VHF	CH M
ACCESS	HW±3

Lying on the north bank of the Clyde estuary on the opposite side of the River Leven from Dumbarton Castle, Sandpoint Marina provides easy access to some of the most stunning cruising grounds in the United Kingdom. It is an independently run marina, offering a professional yet personal service to every boat owner. Among the facilities to hand are an on site chandlery, storage areas, a 40 ton travel hoist and 20 individual workshop units.

Within a 20-minute drive of Glasgow city centre, the marina is situated close to the shores of Loch Lomond, the largest fresh water loch in Britain.

FACILITIES AT A GLANCE

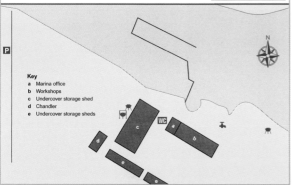

Key
a Marina office
b Workshops
c Undercover storage shed
d Chandler
e Undercover storage sheds

KIP MARINA

Kip Marina, The Yacht Harbour
Inverkip, Renfrewshire, Scotland, PA16 0AS
Tel: 01475 521485 Fax: 01475 521298
www.kipmarina.co.uk

VHF	Ch 80
ACCESS	H24

Inverkip is a small village which lies on the south shores of the River Kip as it enters the Firth of Clyde. Once established for fishing, smuggling and, in the 17th century, witch-hunts, it became a seaside resort in the 1860s as a result of the installation of the railway. Today it is a yachting centre, boasting a state-of-the-art marina with over 600 berths and full boatyard facilities. With the capacity to accommodate yachts of up to 23m LOA, Kip Marina offers direct road and rail access to Glasgow and its international airport, therefore making it an ideal location for either a winter lay up or crew changeover.

FACILITIES AT A GLANCE

Key
a Boat sales, chandlery and reception
b Workshop and contractors
c Chartroom and superloos

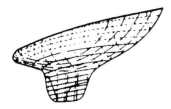

LARGS YACHT HAVEN

Largs Yacht Haven Ltd
Irvine Road, Largs, Ayrshire, KA30 8EZ
Tel: 01475 675333 Fax: 01475 672245
www.yachthavens.com e mail: largs@yachthavens.com

VHF Ch 80, M
ACCESS H24

Largs Yacht Haven offers a superb location among lochs and islands, with numerous fishing villages and harbours nearby. Sheltered cruising can be enjoyed in the inner Clyde, while the west coast and Ireland are only a day's sail away. With a stunning backdrop of the Scottish mountains, Largs incorporates 630 fully serviced berths and provides a range of on site facilities from chandlers and sailmakers to divers and engineers.

A 20-minute coastal walk brings you to the town of Largs, which has all the usual amenities as well as good road and rail connections to Glasgow.

FACILITIES AT A GLANCE

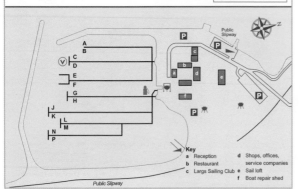

Key
a Reception
b Restaurant
c Largs Sailing Club
d Shops, offices, service companies
e Sail loft
f Boat repair shed

CLYDE MARINA

Clyde Marina Ltd
The Harbour, Ardrossan, Ayrshire
Scotland, KA22 8DB
Tel: 01294 607077 Fax: 01294 607076
www.clydemarina.com email: info@clydemarina.com

VHF Ch 80
ACCESS H24

CLYDE MARINA

Situated between Glasgow and Ayr, Clyde Marina enjoys a sheltered location in Ardrossan harbour. Set amidst the fine cruising waters of the Clyde, the marina is within easy reach of the Scottish Western Isles. Accommodating yachts up to 30m LOA with draughts of up to 5m, it can be accessed at all states of the tide and offers a complete range of facilities. Further developments this year include a new winter storage shed, a secure hard standing area equipped with a power and water supply for every boat, and a repositioned hoist bay.

FACILITIES AT A GLANCE

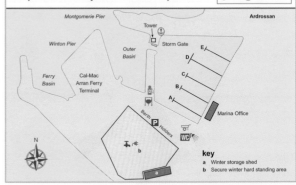

key
a Winter storage shed
b Secure winter hard standing area

TROON YACHT HAVEN

Troon Yacht Haven Ltd
The Harbour, Troon, Ayrshire, KA10 6DJ
Tel: 01292 315553 Fax: 01292 312836
email: troon@yachthavens.com
www.yachthavens.com

VHF	Ch 80, M
ACCESS	H24

Troon Yacht Haven, situated on the Southern Clyde Estuary, benefits from deep water at all states of the tide. Tucked away in the harbour of Troon, it is well sheltered and within easy access of the town centre. There are plenty of cruising opportunities to be had from here, whether it be hopping across to the Isle of Arran, with its peaceful anchorages and mountain walks, sailing round the Mull or through the Crinan Canal to the Western Isles, or heading for the sheltered waters of the Clyde.

FACILITIES AT A GLANCE

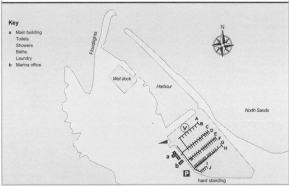

Key
a Main building
   Toilets
   Showers
   Baths
   Laundry
b Marina office

MARYPORT MARINA

Maryport Harbour and Marina
Bridge Street, Maryport, Cumbria, CA15 8AE
Tel: 01900 814431/818447 Fax: 01900 810212
www.maryportmarina.com
email: enquires@maryportmarina.com

VHF	Ch M
ACCESS	HW±2.5

Maryport Marina lies in the historic Senhouse Dock, which was originally built for sailing clippers. The old stone harbour walls provide good shelter to this 161-berth, Blug Flag marina in all wind directions. Set within a quiet spot, although still within easy walking distance of Maryport town centre, it affords a perfect location from which to explore the west coast of Scotland as well as the Isle of Man and the Galloway Coast. For those who wish to venture inland, then the Lake District is only seven miles away.

FACILITIES AT A GLANCE

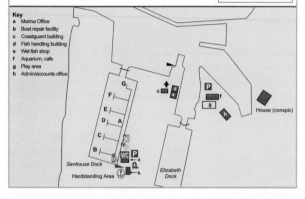

Key
a Marina Office
b Boat repair facility
c Coastguard building
d Fish handling building
e Wet fish shop
f Aquarium, cafe
g Play area
h Admin/accounts office

House (conspic)

Senhouse Dock
Hardstanding Area
Elizabeth Dock

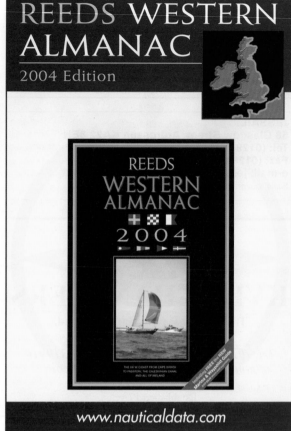

REEDS WESTERN ALMANAC

2004 Edition

www.nauticaldata.com

Amsbrisbeg Ltd Port Bannatyne
Boatyard; storage   01700 502719

Ardfern Yacht Centre Ltd Lochgilphead
Boatyard and marina facilities; chandlers;
engines   01852 500247

Ardlui Hotel, Marina & Holiday Home Park Arrochar
Marina; boat repairs   01301 704243

Ardmaleish Boat Building Co
Rothesay
Boat repairs; maintenance 01700 502007

Ardminish Port Port Ellen
01583 505254

Ardrishaig Boatyard Lochgilphead
01546 603280

Ardrishaig Police   01546 603233

Ardrossan Control Tower HM
01294 463972

Ardrossan Police   01294 468236

Ayr Yacht and CC Ayr   01292 476034

Bellanoch Marina Ardrishaig
01546 603210

Boat Electrics & Electronics Ltd Troon
01292 315355

Bowling Basin (Dumbarton)
Dumbarton   01389 877969

British Polar Engines Ltd Glasgow
Diesel engine manufacturer
0141 445 2455

British Waterways Aedrishaig, Argyll
Scottish canals with marina berthing
01546 603210

Brown Son & Ferguson Ltd Glasgow
Nautical publishers   0141 429 1234

Bruce Anchor Ltd Isle of Man
Anchor manufacturer   01624 629203

C & C Marine Services Largs
Diving equipment & supplies
01475 687180

Caledonian Marine Rhu Marina
Marine engineers   01436 821184

Campbeltown HM   01586 552552

Campbeltown Police   01586 552253

Campbeltown SC Campbeltown
01586 552488

Chattan Shipping Services Ltd
Edinburgh   0131 555 3155

CJ Marine Mechanical Troon
Engine sales; services; parts; boat sales
01292 313400

Clyde CC (Glasgow) Glasgow
0141 221 2774

Clyde Marina Ltd Ardrossan
01294 607077

Clyde Yacht Clubs Association
Helensburgh   01436 821234

Craobh Haven HM   01852 502222

Craobh Marina by Lochgilphead, Argyll
01852 500222

Crinan Boatyard Ltd Crinan
Engineering, shipwright work, repairs,
swinging moorings, storage, diesel,
shower, laundry   01546 830232

Crinan Canal Office HM
01546 603210

Crinan Canal Police   01546 602222

Duncan Yacht Chandlers Glasgow
0141 429 6044

Duthie Marine Safety, Arthur Glasgow
0141 429 4553

East Loch Tarbert HM   01859 502444

East Loch Tarbert Police
01880 820200

Elton Boatbuilding Co Kirkcudbright
Boat repairs; boatbuilder   01557 330177

Estuary Control – Dumbarton HM
01389 726211

Fairlie Quay Fairlie
Boat repairs; storage   01475 568267

Fairlie YC   01294 213940

Fergulsea Engineering Ayr
Boat repairs; haul out facilities
01292 262978

Ferguson Munro and Parker Ltd
Glasgow
Electrical equipment   0141 779 2172

Floetree Ltd (Loch Lomond Marina)
Balloch
Boat repairs; chandlery; engines;
electronics; boat sales   01389 752069

Gael Sail Offshore Sailing School
Troon   01292 315727

Helensburgh SC Rhu   01436 672778

Henderson, J Shiskine
Boatyard services & supplies
01770 860259

Holy Loch Marina Dunoon
01369 701800

Hook Marine Ltd Troon
Marine engineers 01292 679500

Inverkip Diving Services Inverkip
01475 521281

Inverkip Police 01475 521222

Irvine HM 01294 487286

Isle of Bute SC Rothesay
01700 502819

Jessail Ardrossan
Sails, covers, upholstery 01294 467311

JF Marine Chandlery Rhu Marina
01436 820584

Johnstons Marine Stores Lamlash
Chandler 01770 600333

JSB Tarbert Ltd Tarbert
Ship chandler 01880 820180

Kip Chandlery Inverkip 01475 521485

Kip Marina Inverkip 01475 521485

Kippford Slipway Ltd Dalbeattie
Boat repairs; chandlery; electronics;
engines; boat sales 01556 620249

Kirkcudbright HM 01557 331135

Kyle Chandlers Troon 01293 311880

Lamlash Police 01770 302573

Largs Chandlers Largs 01475 686026

Largs Police 01475 674651

Largs SC Largs 01475 670000

Largs Yacht Haven Largs
01475 675333

Loch Lomond Marina (Floetree Ltd)
Balloch
Marine & chandlery 01389 752069

Loch Ryan SC Stranraer 01776 706322

Lomond Boat Covers Alexandria
Boat covers 01389 602734

MacDonald & Co Ltd, JN Glasgow
Inboard engine sales, services & parts
0141 334 6171

MacFarlane & Son Glasgow
Moorings; boat hire 01360 870214

Malcolm Sails Fairlie 01475 568500

Maramarine Helensburgh
Moorings 01436 810971

Maritek Ltd Glasgow
Marine software & electronics
0141 571 9164

Maritime Craft Services (Clyde) Ltd
Largs
Yacht haven; owners of tugboats/work
boats 01475 675338

McCallum, A & Co Boat Builders
Tarbert 01880 820209

McGruer and Co Ltd Helensburgh
Boat repairs 01436 831313

McIntosh Marine Electronics
Helensburgh 01436 831285

McKellar's Slipway Ltd Helensburgh
Boatbuilders; repairs 01436 842334

Mitchell Outboard Services Ltd
Glasgow
Outboard engines 0141 221 1449

New World Yacht Care Helensburgh
Chandler; engines; electronics
01436 820586

Nicholson, Ian Helensburgh
Surveyors 01436 842224

Nicholson Hughes Sails Rosneath
01436 831356

NLB Marine Clyde Marina, Ardrossan
Osmosis treatment 01563 521509

Noble and Sons, Alexander Girvan
Boat repairs; cranage facilities; chandler
01465 712223

North Sails (UK) Ltd Largs
Sailmaker 01475 568500

North Western Automarine Engineers
Largs
Marine engineers 01475 687139

Owen Sails Gourock 01475 636196

Portpatrick HM 01776 810355

Portpatrick Police 01776 702112

Prestwick SC Prestwick 01292 671117

Prosser Marine Sales Ltd Glasgow
Boat sales 0141 552 2005

Queens Gareloch/Rhu HM
01436 674321

Rhu Chandlery Rhu 01436 820584

Rhu Marina Ltd Rhu 01436 820238

Rhu Police 01436 672141

Rothesay HM 01700 503842

Rothesay Police 01700 502121

Royal Gourock YC Gourock
01475 632983

Royal Northern and Clyde YC Rhu
01436 820322

Royal Scottish Motor YC
0141 881 1024

Sails.UK Helensburgh
Sailmaker 07000 724562

Sandpoint Marina Dumbarton
01389 762396

Saturn Sails Largs 01475 689933

Seaward Engineering Glasgow
Marine engineers 0141 632 4910

Shearwater Engineering Services Ltd
Dunoon
Chandler; marine workshop
01369 706666

Silvers Marine Ltd Helensburgh
Boatbuilders; repairs
01436 831222/831881

SP Engineering Helensburgh
Marine electronics 01436 820260

Sterling Yacht Services Port Bannatyne
Boat repairs 01700 502716

Tarbert Lochfyne YC Tarbert
01880 820376

Tayvallich Inn, The by Lochgilphead,
Argyll
Bar and restaurant on shores of Loch
Sween 01546 870282

Teltale Sails Prestwick
Sailmakers & cover work 01292 475125

Troon HM 01292 281687

Troon Marine Services Ltd Troon
Engineers, repairs, painting, osmosis
treatment 01292 316180

Troon Police 01292 313100

Troon Yacht Haven Troon
01292 315553

Troon YC 01292 315315

UK Customs Nationwide
0845 0109000

Wilson & Co Ltd, DB Glasgow
0141 647 0161

9

Marinecall®

WEATHER AT SEA

NEW SERVICES

Revised Content and New Services for even better Boating

Coastal/Inshore Area	BY TELEPHONE Localised 6-Hour Forecasts plus 5-Day Outlook 09066 526 + Area No.	BY FAX Localised 6-Hour Forecasts plus 48-Hour Outlook 09061 502 + Area No.
Cape Wrath - Rattray Head	235	110
Rattray Head - Berwick	236	114
Berwick - Whitby	237	115
Whitby - The Wash	238	116
The Wash - North Foreland	239	117
North Foreland - Selsey Bill	240	118
Selsey Bill - Lyme Regis	241	119
Lyme Regis - Hartland Point	242	120
Hartland Point - St. Davids Head	243	121
St. Davids Head - Colwyn Bay	244	122
Colwyn Bay - Mull of Galloway	245	123
Mull of Galloway - Mull of Kintyre	246	124
Mull of Kintyre - Ardnamurchan	247	125
Ardnamurchan - Cape Wrath	248	126
Lough Foyle - Carlingford Lough	249	127
Channel Islands	250	-
National Inshore Waters	234	-

Offshore Area	2-5 Day Planning Forecasts 09066 526 + Area No.	2-5 Day Planning Forecasts plus Wave Height Contour Graph 09061 502 + Area No.
English Channel	251	161
Southern North Sea	252	162
Irish Sea	253	163
Biscay	254	164
North West Scotland	255	165
Northern North Sea	256	166

09066 calls cost 60p/min.   09061 calls cost £1.50p/min. * Localised 6-Hour Forecasts are not available for these Inshore/Coastal areas.
Marinecall is a brand of iTouch UK Ltd and produced in partnership with Met Office. Customer Helpdesk 0870 600 4219 (Mon-Fri)
E-mail: Marinecall@itouch.co.uk Website: www.marinecall.co.uk
Met Office and the Met Office logo are registered trademarks

Marinecall Met Book - 2003 Edition -
Packed full of forecasting techniques, tide tables and other useful information.

To reserve your copy call: 09065 22 33 12.   Calls cost £1.50p/min. Max call length is one minute.

Met Office

Waypoint Guide Area 9 – South West Scotland - Crinan Canal to Mull of Galloway

269	**Kirkcudbright** - 1.5M S of Little Ross Light	54°44'.50N	04°05'.07W
341	**South Rock light Vessel** - 1.1M E of	54°24'.30N	05°20'.07W
342	**Burrow Head** - 2M S of	54°38'.60N	04°23'.65W
343	**Mull of Galloway light** - 1.7M S of	54°36'.40N	04°51'.50W
344	**Crammag Head light** - 1.8M SW of	54°38'.60N	05°00'.07W
345	**Mull of Kintyre light** - 2.5M SW of	55°16'.90N	05°51'.37W
346	**Mull of Kintyre light** - 10.3M NW of	55°25'.50N	06°01'.57W
347	**Rhinns of Islay light** - 2.2M SW of	55°38'.85N	06°33'.56W
348	**Skerryvore light** - 6.8M W by N of	56°20'.80N	07°18'.87W
349	**Killantringan light** - 4.2M NW of	54°54'.20N	05°14'.76W
350	**Corsewall Pt light** - 1.8M WNW of	55°01'.20N	05°12'.26W
351	**Stranraer** - 1M NNW of entrance to Loch Ryan	55°02'.40N	05°05'.17W
352	**Bennane Head** - 1.5M NW of	55°09'.25N	05°01'.87W
353	**Troon** - 2.1M W of harbour entrance	55°33'.10N	04°44'.77W
354	**Little Cumbrae Island light** - 0.8M SW of	55°42'.75N	04°59'.07W
355	**Rothesay** - Entrance to Rothesay Sound	55°50'.90N	04°59'.67W
356	**Firth of Clyde, Cloch Point light** - 1.3M WSW of	55°55'.95N	04°54'.82W
357	**R Clyde, Kempock Point** - 0.9M WNW of	55°58'.10N	04°50'.57W
358	**Lamlash** - 1M SE of S entrance	55°29'.80N	05°03'.60W
359	**Lamlash** - 1M E of N entrance	55°32'.90N	05°03'.07W
360	**Isle of Arran** - 2M NNE of Sannox Bay	55°41'.60N	05°08'.07W
361	**West Kyle** - 1.3M SSE of Ardlamont Point	55°48'.35N	05°11'.80W
362	**East Loch Tarbert** - 1M E of Loch	55°52'.20N	05°22'.07W
363	**Ardrishaig** - 1.3M SSE of hbr entrance	55°59'.50N	05°25'.67W
364	**Campbeltown** - 1M NE of Loch entrance	55°26'.40N	05°31'.07W
365	**Gigha Island** - 1.5M W of Cath Sgeir WCM	55°39'.69N	05°50'.07W
366	**Sound of Jura** - 2.5M NW of Island of Danna	55°58'.80N	05°45'.56W
367	**Loch Crinan** - 0.6M NW of Ardnoe Point	56°06'.00N	05°35'.46W
368	**Sound of Jura** - 2M SSW Reisa an t-Sruith Is light	56°06'.00N	05°39'.97W
369	**Sound of Luing** - 0.5M WSW of Ardluing SHM	56°11'.00N	05°39'.33W
370	**Sound of Insh** - 1M SSW of Insh Island	56°17'.54N	05°41'.06W
371	**Kerrera Sound** - 0.7M SSW of Rubha Seanach	56°21'.62N	05°33'.97W

Distance Table - South West Scotland

Approximate distances in nautical miles are by the most direct route while avoiding dangers and allowing for Traffic Separation Schemes

	1	2	3	4	5	6	7	8	9	10	11	12	13	14	15	16	17	18	19	20
1. Loch Craignish	1																			
2. Port Ellen (Islay)	42	2																		
3. Crinan	5	39	3																	
4. Ardrishaig	14	48	9	4																
5. East Loch Tarbert	24	58	19	10	5															
6. Campbeltown	55	47	50	39	31	6														
7. Mull of Kintyre	56	27	51	54	45	20	7													
8. Lamlash	48	61	43	34	25	24	34	8												
9. Largs	48	94	43	34	24	39	47	17	9											
10. Rothesay	49	95	44	35	25	43	48	23	9	10										
11. Kip Marina	53	85	48	39	28	50	58	25	10	8	11									
12. Greenock	59	90	54	45	36	53	63	31	16	14	6	12								
13. Rhu (Helensburgh)	62	94	57	48	37	59	67	33	19	17	9	4	13							
14. Troon	54	71	49	40	33	33	44	16	20	25	29	34	38	14						
15. Girvan	67	58	62	53	43	29	31	20	33	40	46	49	51	21	15					
16. Stranraer	89	62	84	75	65	34	35	39	56	63	69	65	74	44	23	16				
17. Portpatrick	88	63	83	74	66	39	36	44	61	67	68	77	77	49	28	23	17			
18. Mull of Galloway	104	78	99	90	82	56	52	60	78	82	84	93	93	65	62	39	16	18		
19. Kirkcudbright	136	111	131	122	114	88	84	92	110	114	116	124	125	97	94	71	48	32	19	
20. Douglas (IoM)	146	120	141	132	124	106	94	102	141	130	126	141	135	107	104	84	60	42	45	20

9

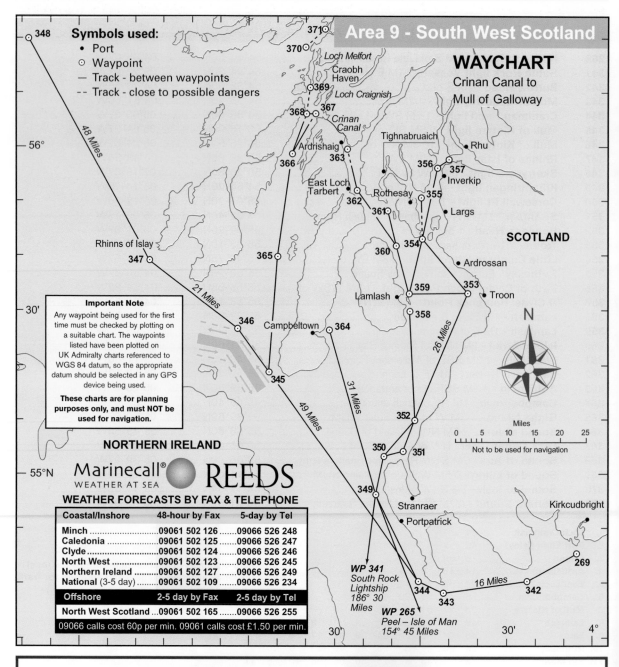

Symbols used:
- • Port
- ⊙ Waypoint
- — Track - between waypoints
- -- Track - close to possible dangers

Area 9 - South West Scotland

WAYCHART
Crinan Canal to
Mull of Galloway

SCOTLAND

NORTHERN IRELAND

Important Note
Any waypoint being used for the first
time must be checked by plotting on
a suitable chart. The waypoints
listed have been plotted on
UK Admiralty charts referenced to
WGS 84 datum, so the appropriate
datum should be selected in any GPS
device being used.

**These charts are for planning
purposes only, and must NOT be
used for navigation.**

WP 341
South Rock
Lightship
186° 30
Miles

WP 265
Peel – Isle of Man
154° 45 Miles

Miles
0 5 10 15 20 25
Not to be used for navigation

Marinecall®
WEATHER AT SEA

REEDS

WEATHER FORECASTS BY FAX & TELEPHONE

Coastal/Inshore	48-hour by Fax	5-day by Tel
Minch	09061 502 126	09066 526 248
Caledonia	09061 502 125	09066 526 247
Clyde	09061 502 124	09066 526 246
North West	09061 502 123	09066 526 245
Northern Ireland	09061 502 127	09066 526 249
National (3-5 day)	09061 502 109	09066 526 234
Offshore	**2-5 day by Fax**	**2-5 day by Tel**
North West Scotland	09061 502 165	09066 526 255
09066 calls cost 60p per min. 09061 calls cost £1.50 per min.		

NW ENGLAND, ISLE OF MAN & N WALES - Mull of Galloway to Bardsey Is

Marinecall® REEDS
WEATHER AT SEA
WEATHER FORECASTS BY FAX & TELEPHONE

Coastal/Inshore	2-day by Fax	5-day by Phone
Northern Ireland	09061 502 127	09066 526 249
Clyde	09061 502 124	09066 526 246
North West	09061 502 123	09066 526 245
Wales	09061 502 122	09066 526 244
National (3-5 day)	09061 502 109	09066 526 234

Offshore	2-5 day by Fax	2-5 day by Phone
Northern North Sea	09061 502 166	09066 526 256
North West Scotland ...	09061 502 165	09066 526 255
Irish Sea	09061 502 163	09066 526 253
English Channel	09061 502 161	09066 526 251

09066 CALLS COST 60P PER MIN. 09061 CALLS COST £1.50 PER MIN.

Key to Marina Plans symbols

Calor Gas		P	Parking
Chandler			Pub/Restaurant
Disabled facilities			Pump out
Electrical supply			Rigging service
Electrical repairs			Sail repairs
Engine repairs			Shipwright
First Aid			Shop/Supermarket
Fresh Water			Showers
Fuel - Diesel			Slipway
Fuel - Petrol		WC	Toilets
Hardstanding/boatyard			Telephone
Laundry facilities			Trolleys
Lift-out facilities		V	Visitors berths

Area 10 - North West England & Wales

MARINAS
Telephone Numbers
VHF Channel
Access Times

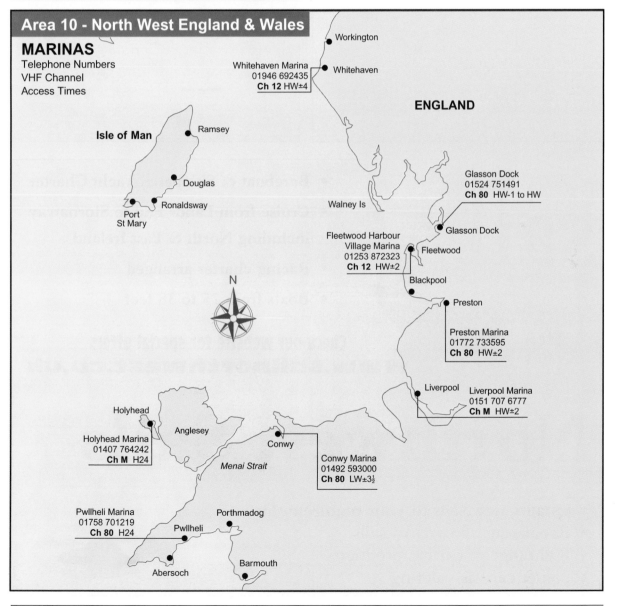

Workington

Whitehaven Marina
01946 692435
Ch 12 HW±4

Whitehaven

ENGLAND

Isle of Man

Ramsey

Douglas

Ronaldsway

Port
St Mary

Walney Is

Glasson Dock
01524 751491
Ch 80 HW-1 to HW

Glasson Dock

Fleetwood Harbour
Village Marina
01253 872323
Ch 12 HW±2

Fleetwood

Blackpool

Preston

Preston Marina
01772 733595
Ch 80 HW±2

Liverpool

Liverpool Marina
0151 707 6777
Ch M HW±2

Holyhead

Anglesey

Conwy

Holyhead Marina
01407 764242
Ch M H24

Menai Strait

Conwy Marina
01492 593000
Ch 80 LW±3½

Pwllheli Marina
01758 701219
Ch 80 H24

Porthmadog

Pwllheli

Abersoch

Barmouth

10

WHITEHAVEN MARINA

Whitehaven Harbour Commissioners, Pears House
1 Duke Street, Whitehaven, Cumbria, CA28 7HW
Tel: 01946 692435 Fax: 01946 691135
email: office@whitehaven-harbour.co.uk
www.whitehaven-harbour.co.uk

VHF	Ch 12
ACCESS	HW±4

Whitehaven Marina can be found at the south-western entrance to the Solway Firth, providing a strategic departure point for those yachts heading for the Isle of Man, Ireland or Southern Scotland. The harbour is one of the more accessible ports of refuge in NW England, affording a safe entry in most weathers. The approach channel across the outer harbour is dredged to about 1.0m above chart datum, allowing entry into the inner harbour via a sea lock at around HW±4.

Conveniently situated for visiting the Lake District, Whitehaven is an attractive Georgian town, renowned in the C18 for its rum and slave imports.

FACILITIES AT A GLANCE

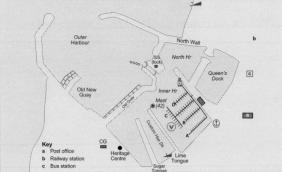

GLASSON DOCK MARINA

Glasson Basin Yacht Company Ltd
Glasson Dock, Lancaster, LA2 0AW
Tel: 01524 751491 Fax: 01524 752626
info@glassonmarina.com
www.glasson-marina.com

VHF	Ch 69
ACCESS	HW-1 to HW

Glasson Dock Marina lies on the River Lune, west of Sunderland at the foot of the Lancaster Canal. It is accessed via an inner lock and lifting bridge, with the sea lock opening just half an hour before HW Liverpool. For those yachts arriving early, it is best to anchor in the River Lune, to the east of the entrance, and contact the marina ahead of time on VHF Ch 69. All the necessary requirements can be found either on site or within easy reach of Glasson Dock, including boat, rigging and sail repair services as well as a launderette, ablution facilities, shops and restaurants.

FACILITIES AT A GLANCE

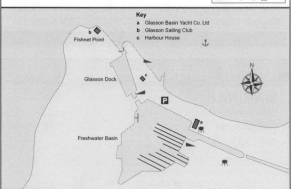

FLEETWOOD HARBOUR MARINA

Fleetwood Harbour Village Marina
The Dock Office, Wyre Dock, Fleetwood, FY7 6PP
Tel: 01253 872323 Fax: 01253 777549
email: fleetwood@abports.co.uk

VHF	Ch 12
ACCESS	HW±1

Fleetwood Harbour Village Marina provides a good location from which to cruise Morecambe Bay and the Irish Sea. To the north west is the Isle of Man, to the north is the Solway Firth and the Clyde Estuary, while to the south west is Conwy, the Menai Straits and Holyhead.

Tucked away in a protected dock which dates back as far as 1835, Fleetwood Harbour Marina has 300 berths and offers extensive facilities. Overlooking the marina is a 15-acre retail and leisure park laid out in a popular American style.

FACILITIES AT A GLANCE

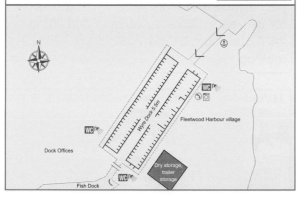

PRESTON MARINA

Preston Marine Services Ltd
The Boathouse, Navigation Way, Preston, PR2 2YP
Tel: 01772 733595 Fax: 01772 731881
email: info@prestonmarina.co.uk www.prestonmarina.co.uk

VHF	Ch 80
ACCESS	HW±2

Preston Marina forms part of the comprehensive Riversway Docklands development, meeting all the demands of modern day boat owners. With the docks' history dating back over 100 years, today the marina comprises 40 acres of fully serviced pontoon berths sheltered behind the refurbished original lock gates. Lying 15 miles up the River Ribble, which itself is an interesting cruising ground with an abundance of wildlife, Preston is well placed for sailing to parts of Scotland, Ireland or Wales. The Docklands development includes a wide choice of restaurants, shops and cinemas as well as being in easy reach of all the cultural and leisure facilities provided by a large town.

FACILITIES AT A GLANCE

Key
a   Riverway control building
b   Marina HQ
c   Pub/restaurant

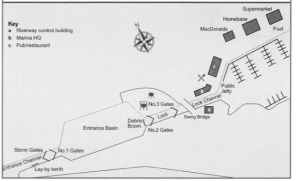

LIVERPOOL MARINA

Liverpool Marina
Coburg Wharf, Sefton Street, Liverpool, L3 4BP
Tel: 0151 707 6888 Fax: 0151 707 6777
email: harbourside@liverpoolmarina.com

VHF	Ch M
ACCESS	HW±2

Liverpool Marina is ideally situated for yachtsmen wishing to cruise the Irish Sea. Access is through a computerised lock that opens two and a half hours either side of high water between 0600 and 2200 daily. Once in the marina, you can enjoy the benefits of the facilities on offer, including a first class club bar and restaurant.

Liverpool itself is now a thriving cosmopolitan city, with attractions ranging from numerous bars and restaurants to museums, art galleries and the Beatles Story.

FACILITIES AT A GLANCE

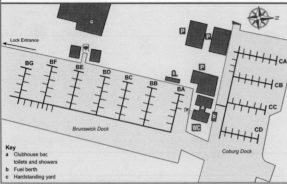

Key
a Clubhouse bar, toilets and showers
b Fuel berth
c Hardstanding yard

CONWY MARINA

Conwy Marina
Conwy, LL32 8EP
Tel: 01492 593000 Fax: 01492 572111
www.crestnicholsonmarinas.co.uk

| VHF | Ch 80 |
| ACCESS | LW=3.5 |

Situated in an area of outstanding natural beauty, with the Mountains of Snowdonia National Park providing a stunning backdrop, Conwy is the first purpose-built marina to be developed on the north coast of Wales. Enjoying a unique site next to the 13th century Conwy Castle, the third of Edward I's great castles, it provides a convenient base from which to explore the cruising grounds of the North Wales coast. The unspoilt coves of Anglesey and the beautiful Menai Straits prove a popular destination, while further afield are the Llyn Peninsula and the Islands of Bardsey and Tudwells.

The marina incorporates about 500 fully serviced berths which are accessible through a barrier gate between half tide and high water.

FACILITIES AT A GLANCE

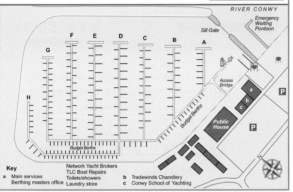

Key
a Main services   Network Yacht Brokers
   Berthing masters office   TLC Boat Repairs   b Tradewinds Chandlery
                          Toilets/showers   c Conwy School of Yachting
                          Laundry store

HOLYHEAD MARINA

Holyhead Marina Ltd
Newry Beach, Holyhead, Gwynedd, LL65 1YA
Tel: 01407 764242

| VHF | Ch M |
| ACCESS | H24 |

One of the few natural deep water harbours on the Welsh coast, Anglesey is conveniently placed as a first port of call if heading to North Wales from the North, South or West. Its marina at Holyhead, accessible at all states of the tide, is sheltered by Holyhead Mountain as well as an enormous harbour breakwater and extensive floating breakwaters, therefore offering good protection from all directions.

Anglesey boasts numerous picturesque anchorages and beaches in addition to striking views over Snowdonia, while only a tide or two away are the Isle of Man and Eire.

FACILITIES AT A GLANCE

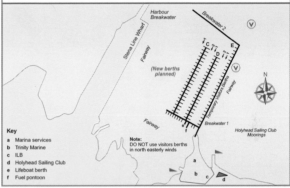

Key
a Marina services   Note:
b Trinity Marine   DO NOT use visitors berths
c ILB   in north easterly winds
d Holyhead Sailing Club
e Lifeboat berth
f Fuel pontoon

10

PWLLHELI MARINA

Pwllheli Marina
Glan Don, Pwllheli, North Wales, LL53 5YT
Tel: 01758 701219 Fax: 01758 701443
email: hafanpwlleli@hafanpwllehi.co.uk

VHF **Ch 80**
ACCESS **H24**

Pwllheli is an old Welsh market town providing the gateway to the Llyn Peninsula, which stretches out as far as Bardsey Island to form an 'Area of Outstanding Natural Beauty'. Enjoying the spectacular backdrop of the Snowdonia Mountains, Pwllheli's numerous attractions include an open-air market every Wednesday, 'Neuadd Dwyfor', offering a mix of live theatre and latest films, and beautiful beaches.

Pwllheli Marina is situated on the south side of the Llyn Peninsula. One of Wales' finest marinas and sailing centres, it has over 400 pontoon berths and excellent onshore facilities.

FACILITIES AT A GLANCE

Key
a Marina offices
  Toilets
  Showers
  Baby change
  Launderette
b Domestic refuse point
c Dinghy park and slipway
d Short stay boat park
e Pwllheli sailing club
f Chandlery

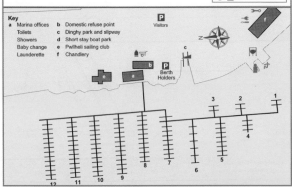

ABC Powermarine Beaumaris
Boat repairs; chandler; moorings;
boat sales   01248 811413

Abersoch Boatyard Ltd Pwllheli
Boat repairs; maintenance; chandler;
storage   01758 712213

Albert Dock Liverpool   0151 709 6558

Aquatech Diving Services
Port of St Mary   01624 833037

Arfon Oceaneering Caernarfon
Boat repairs; chandlery; engine
maintenance   01286 676055

Autosound Marine Bradford
Electronics   01274 688990

Blackpool and Fleetwood YC
                       01253 884205

Blundellsands SC   0151 929 2101

Booth W Kelly Ltd Ramsey
Boatyard services & supplies
                       01624 812322

Bridge House Marina & Caravan Park
Preston
Marina, chandler   01995 603207

Caernarfon Dock (Menai Strait)
Caernarfon   01286 672346

Caernarfon HM   01286 672118

Caernarfon Police   01286 673333

Caernarfon SC (Menai Strait)
Caernarfon   01286 672861

Cambrian Engineering (Cymru) Ltd
Bangor
Mechanical engineers   01248 370248

Castletown Bay HM   01624 823549

Coastline Technology Ltd Addingham
Mooring and anchoring equipment
                       01943 830399

Conwy HM   01492 596253

Conwy Marina Conwy   01492 593000

Conwy Police   01492 517171

Conwy YC Deganwy   01492 583690

Cosalt Perrys Birkenhead
Ship chandler   0151 647 5751

Dawson (Sails), J Port Dinorwic
                       01248 670103

Dickie & Sons Ltd, AM Bangor
Boat repairs; chandler; engines
                       01248 352775

Dickie & Sons Ltd, AM Pwllheli
Boat chandlers; repairs; engine services
                       01758 701828

Dickies of Bangor
Full yard services, chandlery, brokerage
                       01248 363400

Dinas Boat Yard Ltd Y Felinheli
                       01248 671642

Doling & Son, GW Barrow In Furness
Chandler; engines; boat sales
                       01229 823708

Dolphin Maritime Software Ltd
Lancaster
Specialists in navigation, tidal prediction
and other programs for both yachting and
commercial uses   01524 841946

Douglas Bay YC Douglas
                       01624 673965

Douglas Marine Preston
Moorings; storage; repairs; chandlery
                       01772 812462

Douglas HM   01624 686628

Douglas Police   01624 631212

Dubois Phillips & McCallum Ltd
Liverpool
Chart agents & publications
                       0151 236 2776

Elton Boatbuilding Ltd Kirkcudbright
                       01557 330177

Evans Marine Engineering, Tony
Pwllheli   01758 613219

Firmhelm Ltd Pwllheli
Boat repairs; chandlery; boat storage
                       01758 612244

Fleetwood Harbour Village Marina
Fleetwood   01253 872323

Fleetwood HM   01253 872323

Fleetwood Police   01524 63333

**Fleetwood Trawlers' Supply Co Ltd,
The** Fleetwood   01253 873476

Fylde Coast Sailmaking Co Fleetwood
                       01253 873476

Garlieston HM   01988 600274

GJW Direct Liverpool
Marine Insurance   0151 473 8000

Glaslyn Marine Porthmadog
Chandler   01766 513545

Glasson Dock HM   01524 751724

Glasson Dock Marina Lancaster
                       01524 751491

Glasson SC Lancaster 01524 751089

Hafan Pwllheli Pwllheli
Marina; storage   01758 701219

**Hansing & Associates Marine
Surveyors** Caernarfon 01248 671291

Henri Lloyd Manchester
Foul weather gear   0161 799 1212

Holyhead HM   01407 763071

Holyhead Marina Holyhead
                       01407 764242

Holyhead Marine Services Ltd
Holyhead
Boat repairs   01407 760111

Holyhead Marine Yacht Chandlery
Holyhead   01407 760031

Holyhead Police   01286 673333

Holyhead SC Holyhead 01407 762526

Hoylake SC Wirral   0151 632 2616

Hoylake Sailing School Wirral
                       0151 632 4664

Hudson, Dave Trearddur Bay
Diver   01407 860628

Indespension Trailers Horwich, Bolton
                       01204 478500

International Marine Designs Aberdyfi
Boat designer & builder of quality
launches & yachts   01654 767572

Island Boat Services Port St Mary
Boat maintenance & repairs
                       01624 832073

Island Sea School Port Dinorwic
Sailing tuition   01977 680860

Isle of Anglesey County Council
                       01248 752331

Isle of Man YC Port St Mary
                       01624 832088

Jalsea Marine Services Ltd
Weaver Shipyard, Northwich
Repairs, spray painting, storage, moorings
                       01606 77870

JKA Sailmakers Pwllheli 01758 613266

Jones (Boatbuilders), David Chester
Moorings, boat repairs, chandlery; engine
repairs; boat trips   01244 390363

Kirkcudbright Police 01557 330600

Kirkcudbright SC Kirkcudbright
                       01557 331727

Kirkcudbright Scallop Gear Ltd
Kirkcudbright   01557 330399

Lamb & Sons Ltd, JP Liverpool
Ships chandler   0151 709 4861

Liverpool HM   0151 949 6134/5

Liverpool Marina Liverpool
                       0151 707 6888

Liverpool Police   0151 709 6010

Liverpool Power Boats Bootle
Outboard engines   0151 944 1163

Mailspeed Marine Warrington
Mailorder chandlery   01925 838858

10

Mannings Marine Ltd Bootle
Boatbuilders; repairs   0151 933 0820

Manx Marine Ltd Douglas
                        01624 674842

Manx Sailing & CC Ramsey
                        01624 813494

Marina BC Pwllheli   01758 612271

Marine Electronics Pwllheli
                        01758 712845

Maryport Harbour and Marina
Maryport   01900 814431

Maryport HM   01900 814431

Maryport Police   01900 602422

Maryport YC   01228 560865

Martin (Marine) Ltd, Alec Birkenhead
Engine repairs   0151 652 1663

Mayor & Co Ltd, J Preston
Boatbuilders & repairs   01772 812250

Menai Bridge BC Beaumaris
                        01248 810583

Menai Strait HM   01248 712312

Menai Strait Police   01286 673333

Moss (Boatbuilders), David
Thornton-Cleveleys   01253 893830

Mouse Sails Holyhead   01407 763636

**National Marine Correspondence
School** Birkenhead   0151 647 6777

Nationwide Marine Hire Warrington
Liferaft service station; supplier of Zodiac
liferafts, EPIRB's, inflatables and
lifejackets   01925 245788

Network Yacht Brokers Conwy
                        01492 580001

Network Yacht Brokers Pwllheli
                        01758 701170

New Tec Diving Services Blackpool
                        01253 691665

North Wales Boat Centre Conwy
Repairs, engines, electronics, boat sales
                        01492 580740

North Wales CC Conwy 01492 593481

North West Venturers YC (Beaumaris)
                        0161 2921943

Owen Marine, Robert Porthmadog
Marine engineering   01766 513435

Partington Marine Ltd, William
Pwllheli
Boat repairs; chandlery; boat sales
                        01758 612808

Peel HM   01624 842338

Peel Police   01624 631212

Peel Sailing and CC Peel
                        01624 842390

Penrhyn Bangor HM   01248 352525

**Plas Menai National Watersports
Centre** Caernarfon
Boat repairs; chandlery; boat sales
                        01248 670964

Pollard Marine Port St Mary
                        01624 835831

Polymarine Ltd Conwy
Inflatable boat specialists 01492 583322

Port Dinorwic Marina Y Felinheli
                        01248 671500

Port St Mary HM   01624 833205

Port St Mary Police   01624 631212

Porth Dinllaen HM   01758 720276

Premium Liferaft Services Isle of Man
Hire/sale of liferafts and safety equipment
                        01624 674842

Premium Liferaft Services Pwllheli
As above   01758 701886
Preston HM   01772 726711

Preston Marina Preston 01772 733595

Preston Marine Services Ltd Preston
Boat repairs, chandlery   01772 733595

Preston Police   01772 203203

Pwllheli HM   01758 704081

Pwllheli Police   01286 673347

Pwllheli SC Pwllhelli   01758 613343

Ramsey HM   01624 812245

Ramsey Police   01624 631212

Reliance Marine Wirral
Boat repairs; chandlery; engines; boat
sales   0151 625 5219

Ribble CC Lytham St Anne's
                        01253 739983

River Wyre YC   01253 811948

Robbins Marine Electronics Liverpool
Radio navigational equipment
                        0151 709 5431

Roberts Marine Ltd, S Liverpool Marina
Chandlery, boatbuilding, repairs, rigging,
surveying   0151 707 8300

Rowlands Marine Electronics Ltd
Pwllheli   01758 613193

Royal Anglesey YC (Beaumaris)
Anglesey   01248 810295

Royal Mersey YC Birkenhead
                        0151 645 3204

Royal Welsh YC (Caernarfon)
Caernarfon   01286 672599

Salvesen UK Ltd Liverpool
Divers   0151 933 6038

Seahog Boats Preston
Chandlery   01772 633016

Sherlock Foams Ltd Stockport
                        0161 429 9769

Shipsides Marine Ltd Preston
Chandler; electronics   01772 797079

Silloth HM   016973 31358

Solway YC Kirkdudbright 01556 620312

TJ Rigging Conwy
Mobile rigging service   07780 972411

Tradewinds Marine Conwy
Chandlers & boat sales   01492 572777

Trinity Marine Ltd Holyhead
Boat repairs; maintenance 01407 763855

Troop & Co, James Liverpool
Sales; maintenance and parts of inboard
& outboard engines   0151 709 0581

UK Customs Nationwide
                        0845 0109000

UK Epoxy Resins Burscough
Suppliers of Epoxy Resin; adhesives;
fillers; fibreglass tape 01704 892364

V Ships (Isle of Man) Douglas
Ship management; maritime services
including crewing, leisure & financial
                        01624 688886

Virgo Marine Co Wirral
Boatbuilders & repairs   0151 644 1037

Waterfront Marine Bangor
Boatbuilders; repairs; storage
                        01248 352513

West Kirby SC West Kirby
                        0151 625 5579

Westward Ho Sailing Ltd Newport
Bareboat charters; yacht charters;
holidays afloat in the UK and Greece
                        01633 760970

Whitehaven Harbour Marina
Whitehaven   01946 692435

Whitehaven HM   01946 692435

Whitehaven Police   01946 692616

Workington HM   01900 602301

Workington Police   01900 602422

Yacht Haven Management Pwllheli
Pwllheli Marina   01758 701219

Yates Marine, Martin Galgate
New & used outboards; outboard repairs;
services; spares   01524 751750

Waypoint Guide Area 10 – NW England & N Wales - Mull of Galloway to Bardsey Is

254	**Causeway WCM** - 2M SW of	52°39'·95N	04°27'·90W
255	**Abersoch** - 1·2M SE St Tudwal's Is light	52°47'·14N	04°26'·76W
256	**Porthmadog** - 1·1M SW Fairway Buoy	52°52'·72N	04°12'·57W
257	**Bardsey Island light** - 4M NNW	52°48'·63N	04°50'·37W
258	**Menai Strait** - 1·4M SW Llanddwyn Is	53°07'·32N	04°26'·87W
259	**Holyhead** - 1M N of W Breakwater	53°20'·84N	04°37'·17W
260	**Menai Strait** - 1·2M N of Puffin Is	53°20'·50N	04°01'·50W
261	**Liverpool** - 0·7M S of Bar light Vessel	53°31'·30N	03°20'·97W
262	**Fleetwood** - 2M SW Lune Deep SCM	53°54'·04N	03°13'·07W
263	**Douglas** - 1·1M E of Douglas Head	54°08'·60N	04°26'·02W
264	**Ramsey** - 1·3M ENE of S breakwater	54°19'·90N	04°20'·27W
265	**Peel** - 1M NW of entrance	54°14'·50N	04°42'·57W
266	**Pt St Mary** - 1·2M S of Kallow Point	54°02'·90N	04°44'·05W
267	**St Bees Head light** - 2M W of	54°30'·80N	03°41'·67W
268	**Workington** - 1M WNW of breakwater	54°39'·40N	03°36'·40W
269	**Kirkcudbright** -1·5M S of Little Ross light	54°44'·50N	04°05'·07W

Distance Table - NW England & N Wales

Approximate distances in nautical miles are by the most direct route while avoiding dangers and allowing for Traffic Separation Schemes

	1	2	3	4	5	6	7	8	9	10	11	12	13	14	15	16	17	18	19	20
1. Portpatrick	1																			
2. Mull of Galloway	16	2																		
3. Kirkcudbright	48	32	3																	
4. Maryport	65	49	26	4																
5. Workington	63	47	25	6	5															
6. Ravenglass	70	54	40	30	23	6														
7. Point of Ayre	38	22	28	37	31	34	7													
8. Peel	41	26	46	55	49	52	18	8												
9. Port St Mary	56	41	61	63	57	50	35	18	9											
10. Douglas	60	42	46	50	44	39	19	30	13	10										
11. Ramsey	44	28	34	41	35	34	6	24	27	15	11									
12. Glasson Dock	101	85	74	66	60	37	64	85	69	63	61	12								
13. Fleetwood	95	79	68	59	53	30	58	80	63	57	55	10	13							
14. Liverpool	118	102	97	89	83	60	80	86	76	70	77	52	46	14						
15. Conwy	111	95	95	92	86	58	72	72	57	59	68	62	56	46	15					
16. Beaumaris	109	93	94	95	89	72	71	73	58	58	70	66	60	49	12	16				
17. Caernarfon	117	103	104	105	99	82	81	73	68	68	80	76	70	59	22	10	17			
18. Holyhead	93	81	94	96	90	69	68	62	46	50	65	79	73	68	36	32	26	18		
19. Bardsey Island	127	113	129	129	123	114	107	94	80	88	98	107	101	90	53	41	31	43	19	
20. Fishguard	171	158	175	175	169	160	153	140	126	134	144	153	147	136	100	88	78	89	45	20

10

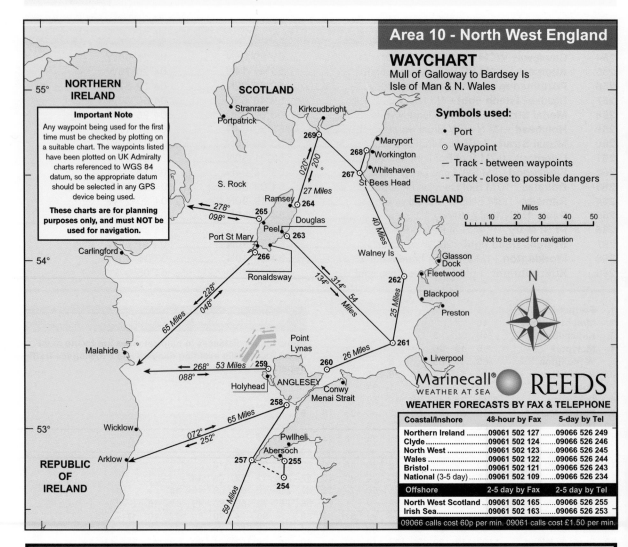

Area 10 - North West England

WAYCHART
Mull of Galloway to Bardsey Is
Isle of Man & N. Wales

Symbols used:
- • Port
- ⊙ Waypoint
- — Track - between waypoints
- -- Track - close to possible dangers

NORTHERN IRELAND

SCOTLAND

ENGLAND

Important Note

Any waypoint being used for the first time must be checked by plotting on a suitable chart. The waypoints listed have been plotted on UK Admiralty charts referenced to WGS 84 datum, so the appropriate datum should be selected in any GPS device being used.

These charts are for planning purposes only, and must NOT be used for navigation.

REPUBLIC OF IRELAND

Miles
0 10 20 30 40 50

Not to be used for navigation

Marinecall® WEATHER AT SEA

REEDS

WEATHER FORECASTS BY FAX & TELEPHONE

Coastal/Inshore	48-hour by Fax	5-day by Tel
Northern Ireland	09061 502 127	09066 526 249
Clyde	09061 502 124	09066 526 246
North West	09061 502 123	09066 526 245
Wales	09061 502 122	09066 526 244
Bristol	09061 502 121	09066 526 243
National (3-5 day)	09061 502 109	09066 526 234
Offshore	**2-5 day by Fax**	**2-5 day by Tel**
North West Scotland	09061 502 165	09066 526 255
Irish Sea	09061 502 163	09066 526 253

09066 calls cost 60p per min. 09061 calls cost £1.50 per min.

SOUTH WALES & BRISTOL CHANNEL - Bardsey Island to Land's End

Marinecall® WEATHER AT SEA — REEDS
WEATHER FORECASTS BY FAX & TELEPHONE

Coastal/Inshore	2-day by Fax	5-day by Phone
North West	09061 502 123	09066 526 245
Wales	09061 502 122	09066 526 244
Bristol	09061 502 121	09066 526 243
South West	09061 502 120	09066 526 242
National (3-5 day)	09061 502 109	09066 526 234

Offshore	2-5 day by Fax	2-5 day by Phone
Irish Sea	09061 502 163	09066 526 253
English Channel	09061 502 161	09066 526 251
Biscay	09061 502 164	09066 526 254
North West Scotland ...	09061 502 165	09066 526 255

09066 CALLS COST 60P PER MIN. 09061 CALLS COST £1.50 PER MIN.

Key to Marina Plans symbols

Calor Gas		P	Parking
Chandler		✗	Pub/Restaurant
Disabled facilities			Pump out
Electrical supply			Rigging service
Electrical repairs			Sail repairs
Engine repairs			Shipwright
First Aid			Shop/Supermarket
Fresh Water			Showers
Fuel - Diesel			Slipway
Fuel - Petrol		WC	Toilets
Hardstanding/boatyard			Telephone
Laundry facilities			Trolleys
Lift-out facilities		V	Visitors berths

Area 11 - South Wales & Bristol Channel

MARINAS
Telephone Numbers
VHF Channel
Access Times

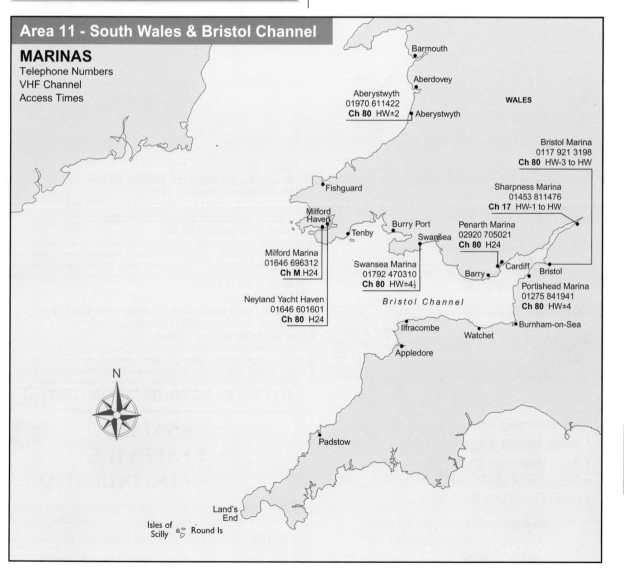

Barmouth

Aberdovey

Aberystwyth
01970 611422
Ch 80 HW±2 • Aberystwyth

WALES

Bristol Marina
0117 921 3198
Ch 80 HW-3 to HW

Sharpness Marina
01453 811476
Ch 17 HW-1 to HW

• Fishguard

Milford
Haven

Burry Port

Milford Marina
01646 696312
Ch M H24

• Tenby

Swansea

Penarth Marina
02920 705021
Ch 80 H24

Cardiff •

Bristol

Swansea Marina
01792 470310
Ch 80 HW±4½

Barry •

Portishead Marina
01275 841941
Ch 80 HW±4

Neyland Yacht Haven
01646 601601
Ch 80 H24

Bristol Channel

• Burnham-on-Sea

Ilfracombe

Watchet

N

• Appledore

• Padstow

Land's
End

Isles of
Scilly   Round Is

ABERYSTWYTH MARINA

Aberystwyth Marina, IMP Developments
Trefechan, Aberystwyth, Ceredigion, SY23 1AS
Tel: 01970 611422 Fax: 01970 624122
www.abermarina.com email: abermarina@aol.com

| VHF | Ch 80 |
| ACCESS | HW±2 |

Aberystwyth is a picturesque university seaside town on the west coast of Wales. Its £9 million marina provides over 100 permanent pontoon berths and welcomes on average between 1,500 and 2,000 visiting yachts per year. Accessible two hours either side of high water, its facilities incorporate the usual marine services as well as an on site pub and restaurant.

A short distance away are several pretty Welsh harbours, including Fishguard, Cardigan, Porthmadog and Abersoch, while the east coast of Ireland can be reached within a day's sail.

FACILITIES AT A GLANCE

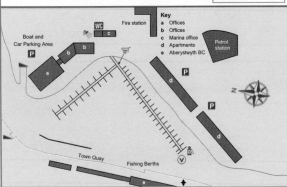

Key
a Offices
b Offices
c Marina office
d Apartments
e Aberystwyth BC

MILFORD MARINA

Milford Marina, Milford Docks
Milford Haven, Pembrokeshire SA73 3AF
Tel: 01646 696312 Fax: 01646 696314
www.milford-docks.co.uk

| VHF | Ch M |
| ACCESS | H24 |

Set within one of the deepest natural harbours in the world, Milford Marina was opened in 1991 by the Duke of York. Since then its facilities have gradually developed to include hard standing areas, secure boat yards, a diesel pump and chandlery as well as various bars and restaurants.

Accessed via an entrance lock (with waiting pontoons both inside and outside the lock), the marina is ideally situated for exploring the picturesque upper reaches of the River Cleddau or cruising out beyond St Ann's Head to the unspoilt islands of Skomer, Skokholm and Grassholm.

FACILITIES AT A GLANCE

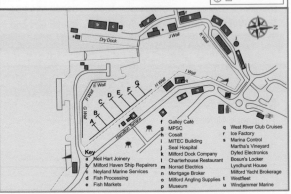

Key
a Neil Hart Joinery
b Milford Haven Ship Repairers
c Neyland Marine Services
d Fish Processing
e Fish Markets
f Galley Café
g MPSC
h Cosalt
i MITEC Building
j Seal Hospital
k Milford Dock Company
l Charterhouse Restaurant
m Norrad Electrics
n Mortgage Broker
o Milford Angling Supplies
p Museum
q West River Club Cruises
r Ice Factory
s Marina Control
  Martha's Vineyard
  Dyfed Electronics
  Bosun's Locker
  Lyndhurst House
  Milford Yacht Brokerage
t Westfleet
u Windjammer Marine

NEYLAND YACHT HAVEN

Neyland Yacht Haven Ltd
Brunel Quay, Neyland, Pembrokeshire, SA73 1PY
Tel: 01646 601601 Fax: 01646 600713
email: neyland@yachthavens.com

VHF	Ch 80, M
ACCESS	H24

Approximately 10 miles from the entrance to Milford Haven lies Neyland Yacht Haven. Tucked away in a well protected inlet just before the Cleddau Bridge, this marina has around 380 berths and

can accommodate yachts up to 25m LOA with draughts of up to 2.5m. The marina is divided into two basins, with the lower one enjoying full tidal access, while entry to the upper one is restricted by a tidal sill.

Offering a comprehensive range of services, Neyland Yacht Haven is within a five minute walk of the town centre where the various shops and takeaways cater for most everyday needs.

FACILITIES AT A GLANCE

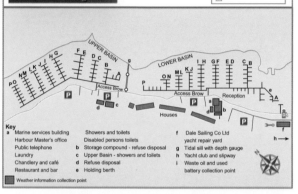

Key
a Marine services building
   Harbour Master's office
   Public telephone
   Laundry
   Chandlery and café
   Restaurant and bar
b Storage compound - refuse disposal
c Upper Basin - showers and toilets
d Refuse disposal
e Holding berth
   Showers and toilets
   Disabled persons toilets
f Dale Sailing Co Ltd
   yacht repair yard
g Tidal sill with depth gauge
h Yacht club and slipway
i Waste oil and used
   battery collection point

■ Weather information collection point

SWANSEA MARINA

Swansea Marina
Lockside, Maritime Quarter, Swansea, SA1 1WG
Tel: 01792 470310 Fax: 01792 463948
www.swansea.gov.uk/swanseamarina
email: swanmar@swansea.gov.uk

VHF	Ch 80
ACCESS	HW±4.5

At the hub of the city's recently redeveloped and award winning Maritime Quarter, Swansea Marina can be accessed HW±4½ hrs via a lock. Surrounded by a plethora of shops, restaurants and marine businesses to cater for most yachtsmen's needs, the marina is in close proximity to the picturesque Gower coast, where there is no shortage of quiet sandy beaches off which to anchor. It also provides the perfect starting point for cruising to Ilfracombe, Lundy Island, the North Cornish coast or West Wales.

Within easy walking distance of the marina is the city centre, boasting a covered shopping centre and market. For those who prefer walking or cycling, take the long promenade to the Mumbles fishing village from where there are plenty of coastal walks.

FACILITIES AT A GLANCE

Key
a Leisure Centre
b Maritime Museum
c Pumphouse Restaurant
d Yacht Club
e Repair shed
f Mariott Hotel

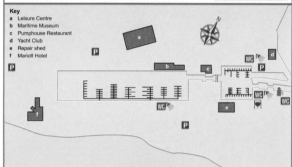

PENARTH MARINA

Penarth Marina
Penarth, Vale of Glamorgan, CF64 1TQ
Tel: 02920 705021 Fax: 02920 712170
www.crestnicholsonmarinas.co.uk
email: penarthmarina@crestnicholson.com

VHF	Ch 80
ACCESS	H24

Constructed around the historic basins of Penarth Dock, which first opened in 1865, Penarth Marina enjoys a prime setting within the sheltered waters of Cardiff Bay. It can be accessed at virtually all states

of the tide through the Cardiff Bay Barrage and has become established as one of the major boating facilities in the area.

Although the marina boasts its own high quality restaurants, both of which are housed in the attractively converted Custom House, Penarth town centre is only a 10-minute stroll away and has a selection of shops and eating places as well as a fully-equipped leisure complex.

FACILITIES AT A GLANCE

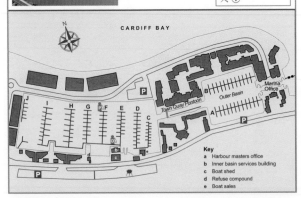

Key
a Harbour masters office
b Inner basin services building
c Boat shed
d Refuse compound
e Boat sales

SHARPNESS MARINA

Sharpness Marina, Sharpness
Berkeley, Gloucestershire GR13 9UN
Tel: 01453 811476

VHF	Ch 17
ACCESS	HW-2

Sharpness is a small port on the River Severn lying at the entrance to the Gloucester and Sharpness Canal. At the time of its completion in 1827, the canal was the largest and deepest ship canal in the world. However, although once an important commercial waterway, it is now primarily used by pleasure boats. Yachts approaching the marina from seaward can do so via a lock two hours before high water, but note that the final arrival should be timed as late as possible to avoid strong tides in the entrance. From the lock, a passage under two swing bridges and a turn to port brings you to the marina, where pontoon berths are equipped with electricity and water supplies.

FACILITIES AT A GLANCE

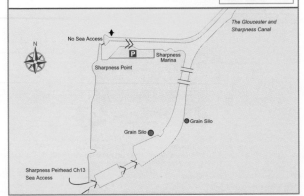

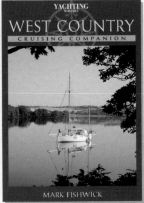

BRISTOL MARINA

Bristol Marina Ltd
Hanover Place, Bristol, BS1 6TZ
Tel: 0117 921 3198 Fax: 0117 929 7672

VHF	Ch 80
ACCESS	HW-3 to HW

Situated in the heart of the city, Bristol is a fully serviced marina providing over 100 pontoon berths for vessels up to 20m LOA. Among the facilities are a new fuelling berth and pump out station as well as an on site chandler and sailmaker. It is situated on the south side of the Floating Harbour, about eight miles from the mouth of the River Avon. Accessible from seaward via the Cumberland Basin, passing through both Entrance Lock and Junction Lock, it can be reached approximately three hours before HW.

Shops, restaurants, theatres and cinemas are all within easy reach of the marina, while local attractions include the SS *Great Britain*, designed by Isambard Kingdom Brunel, and the famous Clifton Suspension Bridge, which has an excellent visitors' centre depicting its fascinating story.

FACILITIES AT A GLANCE

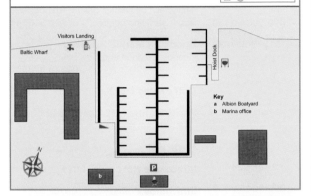

Key
a Albion Boatyard
b Marina office

PORTISHEAD QUAYS MARINA

Portishead Quays Marina
The Docks, Harbour Road, Portishead, Bristol BS20 7DF
Tel: 01275 841941 Fax: 01275 841942
email: portishead@crestnicholson.com
www.crestnicholsonmarinas.co.uk

VHF	Ch 80
ACCESS	HW±4

Opened in May 2001, Portishead Quays Marina, with its excellent facilities and 24 hour security, is becoming increasingly popular with locals and visitors alike. However, visiting yachtsmen should be

aware of the large tidal ranges and strong tidal flows that they are likely to encounter in this part of the Bristol Channel as well as shipping plying to and from the Avonmouth and Portbury Docks. The entrance to the marina is via a lock, with access for a 1.5m yacht being at HW±4½ hrs on neaps and HW±3¾ hrs on springs – contact the marina on VHF Ch 80 ahead of time for the next available lock.

FACILITIES AT A GLANCE

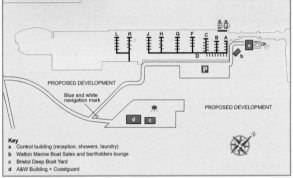

PROPOSED DEVELOPMENT

Blue and white navigation mark

PROPOSED DEVELOPMENT

Key
a Control building (reception, showers, laundry)
b Walton Marine Boat Sales and bertholders lounge
c Bristol Deep Boat Yard
d A&W Building + Coastguard

Aberaeron HM 01545 571645

Aberaeron YC Aberdovey 01545 570077

Aberdovey HM 01654 767626

Aberdovey Police 01286 673333

Abersoch Boatyard Ltd Abersoch
01758 712213

Abersoch Police 01286 673333

Abersoch Power BC 01758 712027

Aberystwyth BC Aberystwyth
01970 624575

Aberystwyth HM 01970 611433

Aberystwyth Marina Aberystwyth
01970 611422

Aberystwyth Police 01970 612791

Appledore HM 01237 474569

Appledore Police 08705 777444

Aquascan International Ltd Newport
Marine electronics 01633 841117

Attfield & Company, GB Dursley
Volt watch – fuel gauge for batteries
01453 547185

Avon Inflatables Llanelli 01554 882000

Barmouth HM 01341 280671

Barmouth Police 01286 673333

Barry HM 01446 732665

Barry Police 01446 734451

Barry YC Barry 01446 735511

Baumbach Bros Boatbuilders Hayle
Boatbuilder; repairs 01736 753228

Bideford HM 01237 346131

Bosun's Locker Chandlery
Milford Haven 01646 697834

Breaksea Sails Barry 01446 730785

Bristol Avon SC Bristol 01225 873472

Bristol Boat Ltd Bristol
Moorings; chandler; boat sales; engine
sales/services/parts 01225 872032

Bristol Channel Marine Cardiff
Insurance 029 2063 1163

Bristol Channel YC Swansea
01792 366000

Bristol Corinthian YC Axbridge
01934 732033

Bristol HM 0117 926 4797

Bristol Marina Bristol 0117 921 3198

Bristol Police 0117 9277777

Bristol Sails Bristol 0117 922 5080

Brunel Chandlery Ltd Neyland
01646 601667

Bude HM 01288 353111

Burnham-on-Sea HM 01278 782180

Burnham-on-Sea Police 01823 337911

Burnham-on-Sea SC Bridgewater
01278 792911

Burry Port Police 01554 772222

Burry Port YC Burry Port 01554 833635

Cabot CC 0117 9514389

Cambrian Boat Centre Swansea
Chandler; electronics and engine supplier
01792 467263

Cambrian Marine Services Ltd Cardiff
Marina; boatyard; marine repairs
029 2034 3459

Canard Sails Swansea 01792 367838

Cardiff Bay YC Cardiff 029 20226575

**Cardiff Commercial Boat Operators
Ltd** Cardiff
Marine charter, surveying, towing, diving,
salvage 02920 377872

Cardiff HM 029 20400500

Cardiff Police 01446 734451

Cardiff YC Cardiff 029 2046 3697

Cardigan Outboards Cardigan
Marine engine repairs 01239 613966

Chapman & Hewitt Boatbuilders
Wadebridge 01208 813487

Craythorne & De Tessier Porthcawl
Marine tools 01656 771700

Crest Nicholson Marinas Ltd Bristol
0117-923 6466

Crest Nicholson Marinas Ltd Penarth
029 2070 5021

Dale Sailing Co Ltd
Neyland Marina, Milford Haven
Sales, repairs, engines, rigging, chandlery,
storage, brokerage 01646 603110

Dale YC Nr Haverfordwest
01646 636362

Diving & Marine Engineering Barry
01446 721553

Dovey Marine Aberdovey 01654 767581

Dovey YC Aberdovey 01654 767607

Dyfed Electronics Ltd Milford Haven
Sales, service and installation
01646 694572

Dudley Marine Milford Haven
Boatbuilders & repairs 01646 692787

East Llanion Marine Ltd Pembroke Dock
Boat repairs 01646 686866

Fishguard Bay YC Lower Fishguard
01348 872866

Fishguard HM 01348 404425

Fishguard (Lower Harbour) HM
01348 874726

Fishguard Police 01437 763355

Force 4 Chandlery Bristol
0117 926 8396

Forum Software Ltd
St Ishmael's, Nr Haverfordwest
Software for marine use 01646 636363

Garland Sails Bristol
Sailmaker 0117 935 3233

Glaslyn Marine Supplies Ltd
Porthmadog
Chandlery; inflatables dealer; RIB centre;
liferaft servicing centre 01766 513545

Goodwick Marine Fishguard
Chandler; marine engine repairs
01348 873955

Griff Chains Ltd Dudley 01384 569415

Harris Marine (1984) Ltd, Ray Barry
Boatbuilders; repairs 01446 740924

Hayle HM 01736 754043

Ilfracombe HM 01271 862108

Ilfracombe Police 08705 777444

Ilfracombe YC Ilfracombe
01271 863969

Instow Marine Services Bideford
Marine engineers 01271 861081

James Marine Yacht Services Bristol
Boat repairs 0117 966 2291

Jones & Teague Saundersfoot
Chandler 01834 813429

Kaymac Diving Services Swansea
01792 793316

Kelpie Boats Pembroke Dock
Chandler; electronic/engine specialist
01646 683661

Lars & Clode Knutsen Swansea
Ship chandler 01792 652412

Lawrenny YC 01646 651212

Lawrenny Yacht Station Kilgetty
Boat repairs; moorings; chandler
01646 651212

Madoc YC Porthmadog 01766 512976

Madog Boatyard Porthmadog
01766 514205/513435

Marine Electronic Services Ltd Bristol
0117 983 0740

Marine Electronic Systems Bideford
01805 622870

Marine Scene Cardiff
Watersports equipment 029 2070 5780

Merioneth YC Barmouth 01341 280000

Milford Haven HM 01646 696100

Milford Haven Police 01437 763355

Milford Marina Milford Haven
  01646 696312/3

Minehead HM 01643 702566

Minehead Police 01823 337911

Monk Optics Brockweir, Chepstow
Marine binocular specialists
  01291 689858

Monkstone Cruising and SC Swansea
  01792 812229

Mumbles YC Swansea 01792 369321

New Quay YC Aberdovey 01545 560516

Newport and Uskmouth SC Cardiff
  01633 271417

Newquay HM 01637 872809

Neyland Marine Services Ltd
Milford Haven
Repair and supply service for electrical
and electronic equipment 01646 698968

Neyland Yacht Haven Neyland
  01646 601601

Neyland YC Neyland 01646 600267

North Devon YC Bideford
  01271 860367

Padstow HM 01841 532239

Padstow Police 08705 777444

Patriot Charters and Sail School
Milford Haven 01437 741202

Pembroke Haven YC 01646 684403

Pembrokeshire Cruising Neyland
Sailing tuition 01646 602500

Pembrokeshire YC Milford Haven
  01646 692799

Penarth Marina Penarth 029 20705021

Penarth YC Penarth 029 20708196

Penrhos Marine Aberdovey
Chandler; electronics; boat repairs
  01654 767478

Picton Boats Ltd Bridgend
Boat sales; boat manufacturer
  01656 724444

Porlock Weir SC Watchet
  01643 862702

Portavon Marina Keynsham
Marina; repairs; chandlery; engine
maintenance; boat sales 0117 986 1626

Porthcawl Harbour BC Swansea
  01656 655935

Porthcawl Insurance Consultants
Porthcawl 01656 784866

Porthmadog & Trawsfynydd SC
Talsarnau 01766 513546

Porthmadog HM 01766 512927

Porthmadog Police 01286 673333

Portishead Police 01934 638272

Portishead Quays Marina Bristol
  01275 841941

Premium Liferaft Services Neyland
Hire/sale of liferafts and safety equipment
  01646 601946

Price & Co Ltd, WF Bristol
Maps & charts 0117 929 2229

**Protective Rubber Coatings
(Limpetite) Ltd** Bristol
Protective coatings 0117 966 1155

Rainbow Sailing School Swansea
Sailing school and yacht charter
  01792 467813

Rat Rigs Water Sports Cardiff
Chandler 029 2062 1309

Reed's Nautical Books
Bradford on Avon 01225 868821

RNS Marine Northam
Chandler 01237 474167

Robbins Timber Bristol
Specialist in teak decking, hardwoods and
softwoods 0117 963 3136

Rock Sailing and Water Ski Club
Wadebridge 01208 862431

Rudders Boatyard & Moorings
Milford Haven
Boat repairs 01646 600288

Sail Loft Bideford
Chandler 01271 860001

Saltford Marina Ltd Saltford
Marina; boat and engine maintenance
  01225 872226

Saundersfoot Auto Marine
Saundersfoot
Boat covers; spray hoods 01834 812115

Seaguard Marine Engineering Ltd
Goodwick 01348 872976

Secumar Swansea
Buoyancy aids; liferafts 01792 280545

Severn Valley Boat Centre
Stourport-on-Severn 01299 871165

Severn Valley Cruisers Ltd (Boatyard)
Stourport-on-Severn 01299 871165

Sharpness HM 01453 811862/64

Sharpness Marine Berkeley
  01453 811476

Sharpness Police 01452 521201

Solva Boat Owners Association
Fishguard 01437 721538

South Caernavonshire YC Abersoch
  01758 712338

St Ives HM 01736 795018

Steel-kit Borth
Flat pack kits for steel & aluminium boats
  01970 871713

Stephen Ratsey Sailmakers Neyland
  01646 601561

Swansea HM 01792 653787

Swansea Marina Swansea
  01792 470310

Swansea Police 01792 456999

Swansea Yacht & Sub-Aqua Club
Swansea 01792 469096

Teifi BC – Cardigan Bay Fishguard
  01239 613846

Tenby HM 01834 842717

Tenby Police 01834 842303

Tenby SC Tenby 01834 842762

Tenby YC 01834 842762

Towy BC, R Tenby 01267 241755

Underwater Services Dyffryn Arbwy
  01341 247702

United Kingdom Hydrographic Office
Taunton
Range of Admiralty Navigational Products
  01823 337900

Walton Marine Sales Portishead
Boat sales 01275 840132

Watchet Boat Owner Association
Watchet 01984 633736

Watchet HM 01984 631264

Watermouth YC Watchet
  01271 865048

Wema (UK) Bristol 01454 316103
Electronics

Weston Bay YC Portishead
  01275 620772

Wigmore Wright Marine Services
Penarth
Boatbuilders & repairs 029 2070 9983

Williams Ltd, TJ Cardiff
Marine engineers 029 20 487676

Worcester Yacht Chandlers Ltd
Barbourne 01905 22522

11

Marinecall®

WEATHER AT SEA

NEW SERVICES

Revised Content and New Services for even better Boating

Coastal/Inshore Area	BY TELEPHONE Localised 6-Hour Forecasts plus 5-Day Outlook 09066 526 + Area No.	BY FAX Localised 6-Hour Forecasts plus 48-Hour Outlook 09061 502 + Area No.
Cape Wrath - Rattray Head	235	110
Rattray Head - Berwick	236	114
Berwick - Whitby	237	115
Whitby - The Wash	238	116
The Wash - North Foreland	239	117
North Foreland - Selsey Bill	240	118
Selsey Bill - Lyme Regis	241	119
Lyme Regis - Hartland Point	242	120
Hartland Point - St. Davids Head	243	121
St. Davids Head - Colwyn Bay	244	122
Colwyn Bay - Mull of Galloway	245	123
Mull of Galloway - Mull of Kintyre	246	124
Mull of Kintyre - Ardnamurchan	247	125
Ardnamurchan - Cape Wrath	248	126
Lough Foyle - Carlingford Lough	249	127
Channel Islands	250	-
National Inshore Waters	234	-

Offshore Area	2-5 Day Planning Forecasts 09066 526 + Area No.	2-5 Day Planning Forecasts plus Wave Height Contour Graph 09061 502 + Area No.
English Channel	251	161
Southern North Sea	252	162
Irish Sea	253	163
Biscay	254	164
North West Scotland	255	165
Northern North Sea	256	166

09066 calls cost 60p/min.   09061 calls cost £1.50p/min.   * Localised 6-Hour Forecasts are not available for these Inshore/Coastal areas.
Marinecall is a brand of iTouch UK Ltd and produced in partnership with Met Office. Customer Helpdesk 0870 600 4219 (Mon-Fri)
E-mail: Marinecall@itouch.co.uk Website: www.marinecall.co.uk
Met Office and the Met Office logo are registered trademarks

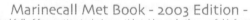

Marinecall Met Book - 2003 Edition -
Packed full of forecasting techniques, tide tables and other useful information.

To reserve your copy call: 09065 22 33 12.   Calls cost £1.50p/min. Max call length is one minute.

Met Office

Waypoint Guide Area 11 – South Wales & Bristol Channel - Bardsey Is to Land's End

129	**Runnel Stone SCM** - 0·3M S of	50°00'·88N	05°40'·36W
130	**Wolf Rock light** - 2M S of	49°54'·70N	05°48'·54W
131	**St Mary's, Scilly** - 2M E of St Mary's	49°54'·04N	06°15'·06W
233	**Padstow** - 2M NW of Stepper Point	50°35'·70N	04°59'·16W
234	**Hartland Point** - 2·5M NW of	51°02'·83N	04°34'·47W
235	**River Taw** - 1·6M NW of Bideford Fairway Buoy	51°06'·23N	04°18'·27W
236	**Morte Point** - 2·5M NNW of	51°13'·63N	04°15'·87W
237	**Ilfracombe** - 1·5M N of	51°14'·20N	04°06'·87W
238	**Foreland Point** - 1·5M N of	51°16'·20N	03°47'·25W
239	**Burnham on Sea** - 4·75M WNW of Burnham-on-Sea	51°15'·30N	03°07'·80W
240	**Barry & R Severn** - 2·9M SSW entrance	51°21'·03N	03°17'·37W
241	**Ledge SCM By** - 2M S of	51°28'·00N	03°58'·84W
242	**Swansea** - 1M SE of Mumbles Head	51°33'·40N	03°57'·00W
243	**Caldey Island** - 7M SE of	51°32'·20N	04°35'·25W
244	**Tenby** - 1M SE of Caldey Island	51°37'·22N	04°39'·68W
245	**Crow Rock** - 1·3M S of	51°35'·45N	05°03'·30W
246	**Milford Haven** - 1·1M S of St Ann's Head	51°39'·74N	05°10'·68W
247	**Skokholm Island light** - 1·6M W of	51°41'·62N	05°19'·78W
248	**South Bishop Is light** - 3M NW of	51°53'·35N	05°27'·90W
249	**Fishguard** - 1·5M N of Strumble Head	52°03'·25N	05°04'·42W
250	**Aberystwyth** - 1·5M W of entrance	52°24'·40N	04°08'·00W
251	**Aberdovey** - 1·5M W of harbour bar	52°31'·80N	04°07'·15W
252	**Sarn-y-Bwch WCM** - 1·1M W of	52°34'·82N	04°15'·42W
253	**Barmouth** - 1·2M W of harbour bar	52°42'·62N	04°05'·67W
254	**Causeway WCM** - 2M SW of	52°39'·92N	04°28'·07W
255	**Abersoch** - 1·2M SE of St Tudwal's Is light	52°47'·20N	04°26'·80W
256	**Porthmadog** - 1·1M SW Fairway Buoy	52°52'·65N	04°13'·05W
257	**Bardsey Island light** - 4M NNW	52°48'·70N	04°50'·38W

Distance Table - South Wales & Bristol Channel

Approximate distances in nautical miles are by the most direct route while avoiding dangers and allowing for Traffic Separation Schemes

	1	2	3	4	5	6	7	8	9	10	11	12	13	14	15	16	17	18	19	20
1. Bardsey Island	1																			
2. Abersoch	14	2																		
3. Pwllheli	18	5	3																	
4. Barmouth	27	18	18	4																
5. Aberdovey	31	26	25	14	5															
6. Aberystwyth	33	30	30	20	10	6														
7. Fishguard	45	54	58	56	47	40	7													
8. South Bishop	60	70	74	74	67	61	25	8												
9. Milford Haven	83	93	97	97	90	84	48	23	9											
10. Tenby	106	116	120	120	113	107	71	46	28	10										
11. Swansea	129	139	143	143	136	130	94	69	55	36	11									
12. Barry	151	161	165	165	158	152	116	91	77	57	37	12								
13. Cardiff	160	170	174	174	167	161	125	100	86	66	46	9	13							
14. Sharpness	191	201	205	205	198	192	156	131	117	106	75	39	33	14						
15. Avonmouth	174	184	188	188	181	175	139	114	100	89	58	22	20	18	15					
16. Burnham-on-Sea	168	178	182	182	175	169	133	108	94	70	48	18	53	50	33	16				
17. Ilfracombe	127	137	141	141	134	128	92	67	53	35	25	35	44	74	57	45	17			
18. Lundy Island	110	120	124	124	117	111	75	50	38	30	37	54	63	95	78	66	22	18		
19. Padstow	141	151	155	155	148	142	106	81	70	70	76	88	97	127	110	98	55	39	19	
20. Longships	168	178	182	182	175	169	133	108	105	110	120	130	139	169	152	140	95	82	50	20

11

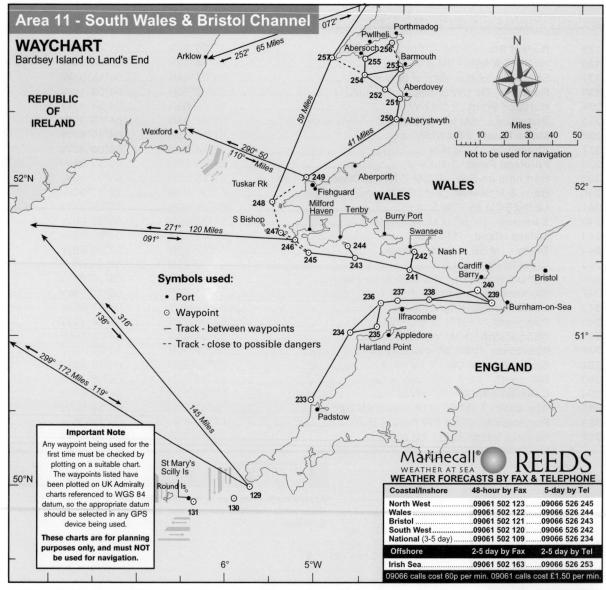

Area 11 - South Wales & Bristol Channel

WAYCHART
Bardsey Island to Land's End

REPUBLIC
OF
IRELAND

Arklow ← 252° 65 Miles

Wexford •

52°N

Tuskar Rk

248

S Bishop

247

246

245

271° 120 Miles
091° →

290° 50
110° → Miles

41 Miles

59 Miles

072° →

Porthmadog
Pwllheli •
Abersoch 256
257 255 Barmouth
254 253
252 251 Aberdovey
250 • Aberystwyth

Aberporth

249
Fishguard

Milford
Haven
Tenby

Burry Port
Swansea

244
243

242 Nash Pt

241

Cardiff
Barry
240
239
Burnham-on-Sea

Bristol

N

Miles
0 10 20 30 40 50
Not to be used for navigation

WALES

WALES

WALES

52°

Symbols used:

- • Port
- ⊙ Waypoint
- — Track - between waypoints
- -- Track - close to possible dangers

136° 316°

299° 172 Miles 119° →

145 Miles

236
237 238
235 • Appledore
234 Ilfracombe
Hartland Point

233
Padstow

ENGLAND

51°

50°N

Important Note
Any waypoint being used for the first time must be checked by plotting on a suitable chart. The waypoints listed have been plotted on UK Admiralty charts referenced to WGS 84 datum, so the appropriate datum should be selected in any GPS device being used.

These charts are for planning purposes only, and must NOT be used for navigation.

St Mary's
Scilly Is
Round Is
131

130

129

6°   5°W

Marinecall® ⊙ **REEDS**
WEATHER AT SEA
WEATHER FORECASTS BY FAX & TELEPHONE

Coastal/Inshore	48-hour by Fax	5-day by Tel
North West	09061 502 123	09066 526 245
Wales	09061 502 122	09066 526 244
Bristol	09061 502 121	09066 526 243
South West	09061 502 120	09066 526 242
National (3-5 day)	09061 502 109	09066 526 234

Offshore	2-5 day by Fax	2-5 day by Tel
Irish Sea	09061 502 163	09066 526 253

09066 calls cost 60p per min. 09061 calls cost £1.50 per min.

Marinecall® REEDS
WEATHER AT SEA

WEATHER FORECASTS BY FAX & TELEPHONE

Coastal/Inshore	2-day by Fax	5-day by Phone
Northern Ireland	09061 502 127	09066 526 249
Wales	09061 502 122	09066 526 244
Bristol	09061 502 121	09066 526 243
South West	09061 502 120	09066 526 242
National (3-5 day)	09061 502 109	09066 526 234

Offshore	2-5 day by Fax	2-5 day by Phone
Irish Sea	09061 502 163	09066 526 253
English Channel	09061 502 161	09066 526 251
Biscay	09061 502 164	09066 526 254
North West Scotland	09061 502 165	09066 526 255

09066 CALLS COST 60P PER MIN. 09061 CALLS COST £1.50 PER MIN.

Key to Marina Plans symbols

Calor Gas		P	Parking
Chandler			Pub/Restaurant
Disabled facilities			Pump out
Electrical supply			Rigging service
Electrical repairs			Sail repairs
Engine repairs			Shipwright
First Aid			Shop/Supermarket
Fresh Water			Showers
Fuel - Diesel			Slipway
Fuel - Petrol		WC	Toilets
Hardstanding/boatyard			Telephone
Laundry facilities			Trolleys
Lift-out facilities		V	Visitors berths

Area 12 - South Ireland

MARINAS
Telephone Numbers
VHF Channel
Access Times

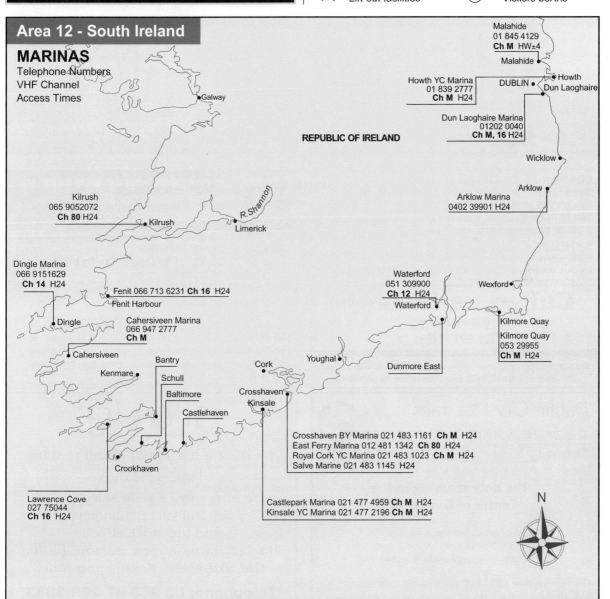

REPUBLIC OF IRELAND

Malahide
01 845 4129
Ch M HW±4
Malahide

Howth YC Marina
01 839 2777
Ch M H24

DUBLIN • Howth
Dun Laoghaire

Dun Laoghaire Marina
01202 0040
Ch M, 16 H24

Wicklow

Arklow

Arklow Marina
0402 39901 H24

Galway

Kilrush
065 9052072
Ch 80 H24
Kilrush

R.Shannon
Limerick

Dingle Marina
066 9151629
Ch 14 H24

Fenit 066 713 6231 **Ch 16** H24
Fenit Harbour

Dingle

Cahersiveen Marina
066 947 2777
Ch M

Cahersiveen

Kenmare

Bantry

Schull

Baltimore

Castlehaven

Crookhaven

Cork

Youghal

Crosshaven
Kinsale

Waterford
051 309900
Ch 12 H24
Waterford

Wexford

Kilmore Quay
Kilmore Quay
053 29955
Ch M H24

Dunmore East

Lawrence Cove
027 75044
Ch 16 H24

Crosshaven BY Marina 021 483 1161 **Ch M** H24
East Ferry Marina 012 481 1342 **Ch 80** H24
Royal Cork YC Marina 021 483 1023 **Ch M** H24
Salve Marine 021 483 1145 H24

Castlepark Marina 021 477 4959 **Ch M** H24
Kinsale YC Marina 021 477 2196 **Ch M** H24

N

12

MALAHIDE MARINA

Malahide Marina
Malahide, Co. Dublin
Tel: 00353 1 845 4129 Fax: 00353 1 845 4255
www.malahidemarina.net

| VHF | Ch M |
| ACCESS | HW±4 |

Malahide Marina, situated just 10 minutes from Dublin Airport and 20 minutes north of Dublin's city centre, is a fully serviced marina accommodating up to 350 yachts. Capable of taking vessels of up to 75m in length, its first class facilities include a boatyard with hard standing for approximately 170 boats and a 30-ton mobile hoist. Its on site restaurant, Cruzzo, provides a large seating area in convivial surroundings. The village of Malahide has plenty to offer the visiting yachtsmen, with a wide variety of eating places, nearby golf courses and tennis courts as well as a historic castle and botanical gardens.

FACILITIES AT A GLANCE

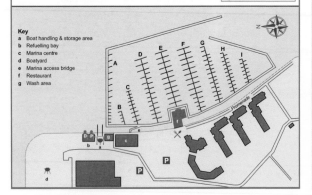

Key
a Boat handling & storage area
b Refuelling bay
c Marina centre
d Boatyard
e Marina access bridge
f Restaurant
g Wash area

HOWTH MARINA

Howth Marina
Howth Marina Harbour Road, Howth, Co. Dublin
Tel: 00353 1 8392777 Fax: 00353 1 8392430
Email: marina@hyc.ie
www.hyc.ie

| VHF | Ch 80, M |
| ACCESS | H24 |

Based on the north coast of the rugged peninsula that forms the northern side of Dublin Bay, Howth Marina is ideally situated for north or south-bound traffic in the Irish Sea. Well sheltered in all winds, it can be entered at any state of the tide. Overlooking the marina is Howth Yacht Club, which has in recent years been expanded and is now said to be the largest yacht club in Ireland. With good road and rail links, Howth is in easy reach of Dublin's airport and ferry terminal, making it an obvious choice for crew changeovers.

FACILITIES AT A GLANCE

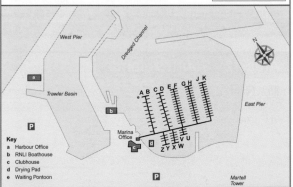

Key
a Harbour Office
b RNLI Boathouse
c Clubhouse
d Drying Pad
e Waiting Pontoon

CREST NICHOLSON MARINAS LTD
Avon House, Newbrick Road, Stokegifford,
Bristol BS34 8RA
Tel: (01179) 236466 Fax: (01179) 236508
e-mail: sriggs@crestnicholson.com
A wholly owned subsidiary of Crest Nicholson plc, operate comprehensive yachting facilities at 5 locations in the UK and are marketing agents for Malahide Marina in Dublin Bay.

Cullen Sailmakers
Galway City
Tel: 091 771991

We make Gleoireog and Folkboat sails for the west coast.
Also any repairs of sails and covers for todays boats

2004/M&WD34/d

Dublin City Moorings
Custom House Quay
Dublin 1

DUBLIN DOCKLANDS
DEVELOPMENT AUTHORITY

**the only mooring in the
Centre of Dublin City**

Beside the Custom House and IFSC.
Opened in 1999 with berthing for 25 boats.
Electricity/water. Showers/toilets. 24 hour security.
Swipe card access.
Telephone +353 1 8183300 Fax: +353 1 8183399
Email: info@dublindocklands.ie Website: http://www.dublindocklands.ie

2004/M&WC2/d

When responding to adverts please mention Marina & Waypoint Guide 2004

DUN LAOGHAIRE MARINA
Harbour Road, Dun Laoghaire, Co. Dublin
Tel: ++353 1 2020040
Fax: ++353 1 2020043
e-mail: dlmarina@indigo.ie
www.dlharbour.ie
Located within Dun Laoghaire Harbour - 8 miles from Dublin City centre adjacent suburban rail station and all amenities. Facilities include shore power, potable water, showers/toilet incl. disabled, laundry, fuel - petrol & diesel, gaz, pump out, boatyard, hoist.

SAFETY ○ MARINE ○ ARCHITECTURAL

We offer a full standing and running
rigging service.

We also carry a wide selection of
general yacht chandlery
and are stockists of:
*Harken, Liros Ropes, Barton, Baltic,
Gul, Polyform, Bostic, and Rule.*

Telephone: 00 353 87 298 3333

2004/M&WC56/d

DUN LAOGHAIRE MARINA

Dun Laoghaire Marina
Harbour Road, Dun Laoghaire, Co Dublin, Eire
Tel: +353 1 202 0040 Fax: +353 1 202 0043
dlmarina@indigo.ie

VHF	Ch M1, M2, 16
ACCESS	H24

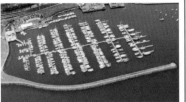

Dun Laoghaire Harbour, at the time of its completion in 1847, was one of the largest man-made harbours in the world. The marina, opened in March 2001, sits on the south side of Dublin Bay within about seven miles of the city centre. Accommodating boats up to 25m LOA, it incorporates over 400 berths, all of which have been designed to allow for easy manoeuvring.

Within a stone's throw of the marina is Dun Laoghaire Shopping Centre, comprising shops, restaurants and chandlers to suit most yachtsmen's needs.

FACILITIES AT A GLANCE

Key
a Royal Irish Yacht Club
b Marina office
c WC
d Royal St George Yacht Club

ARKLOW MARINA

Arklow Marina
North Quay, Arklow, Co. Wicklow, Ireland
Tel: 00353 402 39901/32610 Fax: 00353 402 39902
Mobiles: 087 2375189 or 087 2515699
www.arklowmarina.com

VHF	
ACCESS	H24

Arklow is a popular fishing port and seaside town situated at the mouth of the River Avoca, just 16 miles south of Wicklow and 11 miles north east of Gorey. Historically noted for building small wooden boats, the town now has a flourishing pottery industry and is also ideally placed for visiting the many beauty spots of County Wicklow including Glenmalure, Glendalough and Clara Lara.

Lying on the north bank of the river, just upstream of the commercial quays, is Arklow Marina, which provides 42 berths in an inner harbour and 30 berths on pontoons outside the marina entrance. Note that vessels over 14m LOA should moor on the river pontoons. Just a five-minute walk from the town, the marina is within easy reach of as many as 19 pubs and several restaurants.

FACILITIES AT A GLANCE

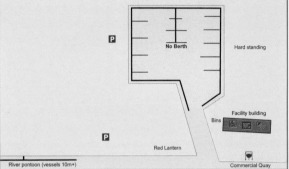

12

KILMORE QUAY

Kilmore Quay
Wexford, Ireland
Tel: 00353 53 29955 Fax: 00353 53 29915
email: hmkilmore@ercom.net

VHF	Ch 80
ACCESS	H24

Located in the SE corner of Ireland, Kilmore Quay is a small rural fishing village situated approximately 14 miles from the town of Wexford and 12 miles from Rosslare ferry port.

Its 55-berthed marina, offering shelter from the elements as well as various on shore facilities, has become a regular port of call for many cruising yachtsmen. Kilmore's fishing industry dates back over the last hundred years and among the species of fresh fish available are bass, shark, skate and whiting. With several nearby areas of either historical or natural significance, Kilmore is renowned for its 'green' approach to the environment.

FACILITIES AT A GLANCE

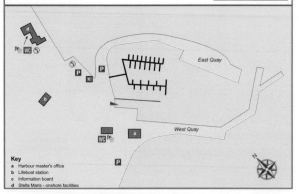

Key
a Harbour master's office
b Lifeboat station
c Information board
d Stella Maris - onshore facilities

CROSSHAVEN BOATYARD MARINA

Crosshaven Boatyard Marina
Crosshaven, Co Cork, Ireland
Tel: 00353 21 4831161 Fax: 00353 21 4831603
e-mail: cby@eircom.net

VHF	Ch M
ACCESS	H24

One of three marinas at Crosshaven, Crosshaven Boatyard was founded in 1950 and originally made its name from the construction of some of the most world-renowned yachts, including *Gypsy Moth* and Denis Doyle's *Moonduster*. Nowadays, however, the yard has diversified to provide a wide range of services to both the marine leisure and professional industries. Situated on a safe and sheltered river only 12 miles from Cork City Centre, the marina boasts 100 fully-serviced berths along with the capacity to accommodate yachts up to 35m LOA with a 4m draught. In addition, it is ideally situated for cruising the stunning south west coast of Ireland.

FACILITIES AT A GLANCE

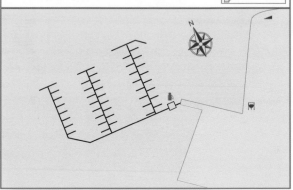

WATERFORD MARINA

Waterford City Marina
Waterford City, Ireland
Tel: 00353 (0)51 309900 Fax: 00353 (0)51 870813

VHF	Ch 12
ACCESS	H24

Famous for its connections with Waterford Crystal, now manufactured on the outskirts of the city, Waterford is the capital of the south east region of Ireland. As a major city, it benefits from good rail links with Dublin, Limerick and Rosslare, a regional airport with daily flights to Britain and an extensive bus service to surrounding towns and villages. The marina can be located on the banks of the River Suir, in the heart of this historic Viking city dating back to the ninth century. Yachtsmen can therefore make the most of Waterford's wide range of shops, restaurants and bars without having to walk too far from their boats. Facilities include 100 fully serviced berths and first rate security, with showers available in the nearby Tower Hotel.

FACILITIES AT A GLANCE

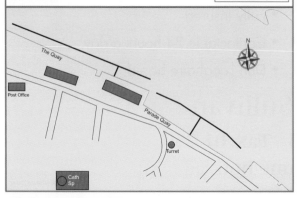

C.J. DEEVY & CO LTD
48 Pomoell St, Waterford, Ireland.
Tel: 00 353 (51) 855717
Fax: 00 353 (51) 855710
e-mail: sales@deevys.com
www.deevys.com
Motor & marine supplies for the South East region of Ireland. Est 1935. Offering a comprehensive range of products to both marine enthusiasts and motor enthusiasts. Branches in Waterford and Clonmell.

K P O MAHONY & CO LTD
Survey House, Upton, County Cork, Ireland
Tel: +353 21 477 6150
Fax: +353 21 477 6152
e-mail: kpom@indigo.ie
Providing fully comprehensive range of marine surveys - Hull, machinery, cargo condition/damage for underwriters, P & I clubs, fishing vessels/small craft condition/damage/sale/purchase. Expert Witness services. Members of Yacht Brokers, Designers & Surveyors Association.

WEATHER FORECASTS BY FAX & TELEPHONE

Coastal/Inshore	2-day by Fax	5-day by Phone
Northern Ireland	09061 502 127	09066 526 249
Wales	09061 502 122	09066 526 244
Bristol	09061 502 121	09066 526 243
South West	09061 502 120	09066 526 242
National (3-5 day)	09061 502 109	09066 526 234

Offshore	2-5 day by Fax	2-5 day by Phone
Irish Sea	09061 502 163	09066 526 253

SALVE MARINE

Salve Marine
Crosshaven, Co Cork, Ireland
Tel: 00353 21 483 1145 Fax: 00353 21 483 1747
e-mail: salvemarine@eircom.net

VHF
ACCESS H24

Crosshaven is a picturesque seaside resort providing a gateway to Ireland's south and south west coasts. Offering a variety of activities to suit all types, its rocky coves and quiet sandy beaches stretch from Graball to Church Bay and from

Fennell's Bay to nearby Myrtleville. Besides a selection of craft shops selling locally produced arts and crafts, there are plenty of pubs, restaurants and takeaways to suit even the most discerning of tastes. Lying within a few hundred metres of the village centre is Salve Marine, accommodating yachts up to 43m LOA with draughts of up to 4m. Its comprehensive services range from engineering and welding facilities to hull and rigging repairs.

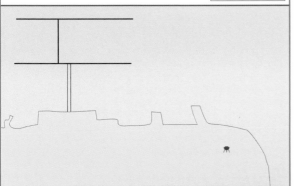

ROYAL CORK YACHT CLUB

Royal Cork Yacht Club Marina
Crosshaven, Co Cork, Ireland
Tel: 00353 21 483 1023 Fax: 00353 21 483 1586
email: office@royalcork.com   www.royalcork.com

VHF Ch M
ACCESS H24

Founded in 1720, the Royal Cork Yacht Club is one of the oldest and most prominent yacht clubs in the world. Organising, among many other events, the prestigious biennial Ford Cork Week, it boasts a number of World, European and National sailors among its membership.

The Yacht Club's marina is situated at Crosshaven, which nestles on the hillside at the mouth of the Owenabue River just inside the entrance to Cork Harbour. The harbour is popular with yachtsmen as it is accessible and well sheltered in all weather conditions. It also benefits from the Gulf Stream producing a temperate climate practically all year round.

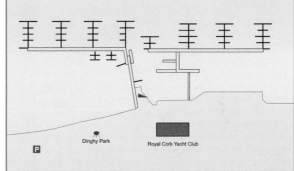

Dinghy Park   Royal Cork Yacht Club

EAST FERRY MARINA

East Ferry Marina
Cobh, Co Cork, Ireland
Tel: 00353 21 481 1342 Fax: 00353 21 481 1342

VHF Ch 80
ACCESS H24

East Ferry Marina lies on the east side of Great Island, one of three large islands in Cork Harbour which are now all joined by roads and bridges. Despite its remote, tranquil setting, it offers all the fundamental facilities including showers, water, fuel, electricity and that all important pub. The

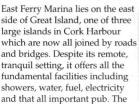

nearest town is Cobh, which is a good five mile walk away, albeit a pleasant one.

Formerly known as Queenstown, Cobh (pronounced 'cove') reverted back to its original Irish name in 1922 and is renowned for being the place from where thousands of Irish men and women set off to America to build a new life for themselves, particularly during the famine years of 1844–48.

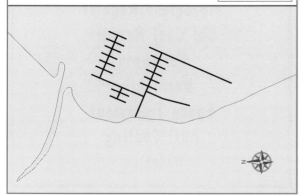

KINSALE YACHT CLUB MARINA

Kinsale Yacht Club Marina
Kinsale, Co Cork, Ireland
Tel: 00353 21 4772196 Fax: 00353 21 4774455
email: kyc@iol.ie

VHF Ch M
ACCESS H24

Kinsale is a natural, virtually land-locked harbour on the estuary of the Bandon River, approximately 12 miles south west of Cork harbour entrance. Home to a thriving fishing fleet as well as frequented by commercial shipping, it boasts two fully serviced marinas, with the Kinsale Yacht Club & Marina being the closest to the town. Visitors to this marina automatically become temporary members of the club and are therefore entitled to make full use of the facilities, which include a fully licensed bar and restaurant serving evening meals on Wednesdays, Thursdays and Saturdays. Fuel, water and repairs services are also readily available.

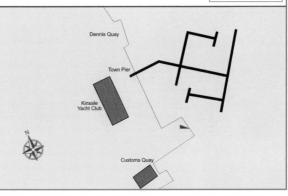

Dennis Quay

Town Pier

Kinsale
Yacht Club

Customs Quay

12

CASTLEPARK MARINA

Castlepark Marina Centre
Kinsale, Co Cork, Ireland
Tel: 00353 21 4774959 Fax: 00353 21 4774958
email: maritime@indigo.ie

| VHF | Ch 16 |
| ACCESS | H24 |

Situated on the south side of Kinsale Harbour, Castlepark is a small marina with deep water pontoon berths that are accessible at all states of the tide. Surrounded by rolling hills, it boasts its own beach as well as being in close proximity to the parklands of James Fort and a traditional Irish pub. The attractive town of Kinsale, with its narrow streets and slate-clad houses, lies just 1.5 miles away by road or five minutes away by ferry. Known as Ireland's 'fine food centre', it incorporates a number of gourmet food shops and high quality restaurants as well as a wine museum.

FACILITIES AT A GLANCE

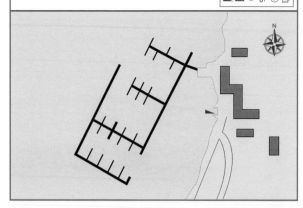

LAWRENCE COVE MARINA

Lawrence Cove Marina
Lawrence Cove, Bere Island, Co Cork, Ireland
Tel: 00 353 27 75044 Fax: 00 353 27 75044
email: lcm@i.ol.ie
www.lawrencecovemarina.com

| VHF | Ch 16 |
| ACCESS | H24 |

Lawrence Cove enjoys a peaceful location on an island at the entrance to Bantry Bay. Privately owned and run, it offers sheltered and secluded waters as well as excellent facilities and fully serviced pontoon berths. A few hundred yards from the marina you will find a shop, pub and restaurant, while the mainland, with its various attractions, can be easily reached by ferry. Lawrence Cove lies at the heart of the wonderful cruising grounds of Ireland's south west coast and, just two hours from Cork airport, is an ideal place to leave your boat for long or short periods.

FACILITIES AT A GLANCE

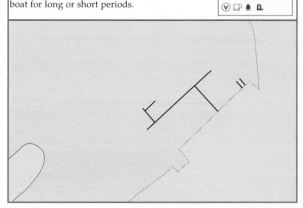

CAHERSIVEEN MARINA

Cahersiveen Marina
The Pier, Cahersiveen, Co. Kerry, Ireland
Tel: 00 353 66 9472777 Fax: 00 353 66 9472993
email: info@cahersiveenmarina.ie
www.cahersiveenmarina.ie

| VHF | Ch M |
| ACCESS | H24 |

Situated two miles up Valentia River from Valentia Harbour, Cahersiveen Marina is well protected in all wind directions and is convenient for sailing to Valentia Island and Dingle Bay as well as for visiting some of the spectacular uninhabited islands in the surrounding area. Boasting a host of sheltered sandy beaches, the region is renowned for salt and fresh water fishing as well as being good for scuba diving.

Within easy walking distance of the marina lies the historic town of Cahersiveen, incorporating an array of convivial pubs and restaurants.

FACILITIES AT A GLANCE

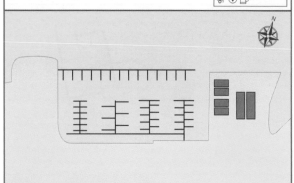

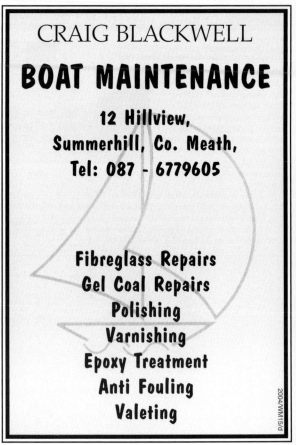

DINGLE MARINA

Dingle Marina
Strand Street, Dingle, Co Kerry, Ireland
Tel: 353 66 9151629 Fax: 353 66 9152629
www.dinglemarina.com email:dinglemarina@eircom.net

VHF	Ch 14
ACCESS	H24

Dingle is Ireland's most
westerly marina, lying at
the heart of the sheltered
Dingle Harbour, and is easily
reached both day and night
via a well buoyed approach
channel. The surrounding
area is an interesting and
unfrequented cruising
ground, with several islands,
bays and beaches for the yachtsman to explore.

The marina lies in the heart of the old market town, renowned for
its hospitality and traditional Irish pub music.
Besides enjoying the excellent seafood restaurants
and 52 pubs, other recreational pastimes include
horse riding, golf, climbing and diving.

FACILITIES AT A GLANCE

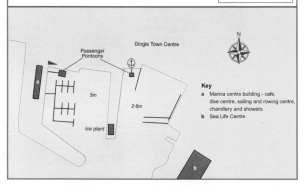

Passenger Pontoons
Dingle Town Centre

Key
a Marina centre building - cafe,
   dive centre, sailing and rowing centre,
   chandlery and showers
b Sea Life Centre

5m
2·6m
Ice plant

FENIT HARBOUR MARINA

Fenit Harbour
Fenit, Tralee, Co. Kerry, Republic of Ireland
Tel: 00353 66 7136231 Fax: 00353 66 7136473
email: fenitmarina@eircom.net

VHF	Ch 16
ACCESS	H24

Fenit Harbour Marina is
tucked away in Tralee Bay,
not far south of the
Shannon Estuary. Besides
offering a superb cruising
ground, being within a
day's sail of Dingle and
Kilrush, the marina also
provides a convenient base from which to visit inland attractions such
as the picturesque tourist towns of Tralee and Killarney. This 120-berth
marina accommodates boats up to 15m LOA and benefits from deep
water at all states of the tide.

The small village of Fenit incorporates a grocery
shop as well a several pubs and restaurants, while
among the local activities are horse riding, swimming
from one of the nearby sandy beaches and golfing.

FACILITIES AT A GLANCE

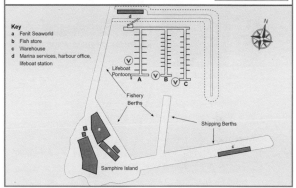

Key
a Fenit Seaworld
b Fish store
c Warehouse
d Marina services, harbour office,
   lifeboat station

Lifeboat Pontoon
A B C
Fishery Berths
Shipping Berths
Samphire Island

KILRUSH CREEK MARINA

Kilrush Creek Marina Ltd
Kilrush, Co. Clare, Ireland
Tel: 00353 (0)65 9052072 Fax: 00353 (0)65 9051692

VHF	Ch 80
ACCESS	H24

Kilrush Creek Marina, situated
in the picturesque Shannon
Estuary, is strategically placed
for exploring the unspoilt west
coast of Ireland, including
Galway Bay, Dingle, West Cork
and Kerry. It also provides a
gateway to over 150 miles of
cruising on Lough Derg, the River Shannon and the Irish canal
system. Accessed via lock gates, the marina lies at one end of the
main street in Kilrush, a vibrant market town with a long maritime
history. A 15-minute ferry ride from the marina takes you to Scattery
Island, once a sixth century monastic settlement but now uninhabited
except by wildlife. The Shannon Estuary is reputed for being
the country's first marine Special Area of
Conservation (SAC) and is home to Ireland's only
known resident group of bottlenose dolphins.

FACILITIES AT A GLANCE

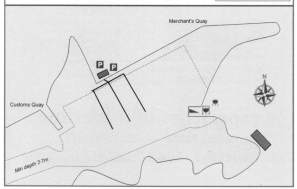

Merchant's Quay
Customs Quay
Min depth 2·7m

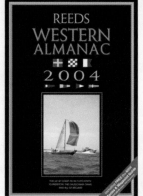
12

Arklow Customs	00353 402 32553
Arklow HM	00353 402 32466
Arklow Marina Arklow	
	00353 402 39901
Arklow Police	00353 402 32304/5
Arklow SC Arklow	00353 402 33100
Arklow Slipway Arklow	
	00353 402 33233

Baltimore Boatyard Baltimore
00353 28 20444

**Baltimore Diving and Watersports
Centre** West Cork   00353 28 20300

Baltimore HM	00353 28 22145
Baltimore Police	00353 28 20102
Baltimore SC Baltimore	
	00353 28 20426
Bantry Bay HM	00353 27 53277
Bantry Bay Police	00353 27 50045
Bantry Bay SC Bantry	00353 27 50081
Bantry Customs	00353 27 50061

Blackwell, Craig County Meath
Repairs, valeting   00353 87 6779605

Brennan, John Dun Laoghaire
Boatbuilders; repairs; maintenance
00353 1 280 5308

Cahersiveen Marina Cahersiveen
00353 669 473214

Carlingford Lough Customs
00353 42 34248

Carroll's Ballyhack Boatyard
New Ross
Boat repairs; boat sales
00353 51 389164

Castle Haven Police   00353 28 36144

Castlepark Marina Kinsale
00353 21 4774959

Castlepoint Boatyard Crosshaven
00353 21 4832154

CH Marine (Cork) Cork
Boatyard supplies; sea safety equipment;
leisure & boat accessories; commercial
fishing gear   00353 21 4315700

CH Marine Skibbereen
As above   00353 28 23190

Cork Customs	00353 21 311024
Cork HM	00353 21 4273125

Cotters Marine & General Supplies
Baltimore
Gas; marine diesel; limited chandlery
00353 28 20106

Courtmacsherry HM
00353 23 46311/46600

Crookhaven HM   00353 28 35319

Crookhaven SC Crookhaven
087 2379997 mobile

Crosshaven Boatyard Co Ltd
Crosshaven
Boat repairs; boat sales
00353 21 831161

Crosshaven Boatyard Marina
Crosshaven   00353 21 4831161

Deevy and Co Ltd, CJ Waterford
Chandlery   00353 51 855719

**Dinghy Supplies Ltd/Sutton Marine
Ltd** Sutton   00353 1 832 2312

Dingle Customs	00353 66 7121480
Dingle HM	00353 66 915 1629
Dingle Marina Dingle	
	00353 66 915 1629
Dingle Police	00353 66 9151522
Dingle SC Dingle	00353 66 51984

**Downer International Sails &
Chandlery**
Dun Laoghaire   00353 1 280 0231

Dublin City Moorings Dublin Docklands
Berthing for 25 boats   00353 1 8183300

Dublin Customs	00353 1 679 2777
Dublin HM	00353 1 855779/874871
Dublin Police	00353 1 666 5000

Dun Laoghaire Customs
00353 1 280 3992

Dun Laoghaire HM
00353 1280 1130/8074

Dun Laoghaire Marina Dun Laoghaire
00353 1 202 0040

Dun Laoghaire MYC   00353 1 288 938

Dunmore East Customs
00353 51 875391

Dunmore East HM   00353 51 383166

Dunmore East Police
00353 51 383112

East Ferry Marina Cobh
00353 21 481 1342

Fenit Harbour Customs
00353 66 36115

Fenit Harbour Marina Fenit
00353 66 7136231

Ferguson Engineering Wexford
00353 65 66822133

Ferrypoint Boat Co Youghal
Boat repairs; chandler; electronics;
engines; boat sales   00353 24 94232

Foynes YC Foynes   00353 69 91201

Galway Customs   00353 91 567191

Galway Marine Chandlers Ltd Galway
Chandler   00353 91 566568

Glenans Irish Sailing School
00353 1 6611481

Hardware and Marine Supplies
Kilmore Quay   00353 53 29791

Howth HM	00353 1 832 2252
Howth Marina Howth	00353 1839 2777
Howth YC Howth	00353 1 832 2141
Hunt, Kevin Tralee	00353 6671 25979

Iniscealtra SC Limerick
00353 61 338347

Irish CC   00353 214870031

Kearon Ltd, George Arklow
Hardware; yacht equipment ranging from
antifouling to lifejackets 00353 402 32319

Kenmare River Police 00353 64 41177

Kilkee Diving Centre Kilkee
00353 6590 56707

Killybegs Customs	00353 73 31070
Kilmore Customs	00353 53 33741
Kilmore Quay HM	00353 53 29955

Kilmore Quay Marina Kilmore Quay
00353 53 29955

Kilmore Quay Police 00353 53 29642

Kilrush Customs   00353 61 415366

Kilrush Marina & Boatyard Kilrush
00353 65 9052072

Kilrush Police   00353 65 51057

Kinsale Boatyard Kinsale
00353 21 4774774

Kinsale Customs	00353 21 311044
Kinsale HM	00353 21 4772503
Kinsale Police	00353 21 4772302

Kinsale Yacht Club Marina Kinsale
00353 21 4772196

Lawrence Cove Marina Bear Island
00353 27 75044

Lencraft Boats Ltd Dungarvan
Boat repairs; chandlery; electronics;
engines; boat sales   00353 58 68220

Lough Swilly Customs
00353 74 21611

Malahide Customs   00353 1 874 6571

Malahide Marina Malahide
00353 1 8454129

Malahide Police   00353 1 6664600

Malahide YC Malahide
00353 1 845 3372

Marindus Engineering Kilmore Quay
00353 53 29794

Matthews Ltd, D Cork
Waterproofs; clothing 00353 214 277633

**McWilliam Sailmaker Ltd
(Crosshaven)**   00353 21 4831505

Murphy, Nicholas Dunmore East
Fisherman; general marine supplies
00353 51 383259

12

National YC Dun Laoghaire
00353 1 280 5725

O'Sullivans Marine Ltd Tralee
GRP boatbuilding company
00353 66 7124524

Poolbeg YC 00353 1 660 4681

Prest Customs 00353 94 21131

Rathmullan Customs 00353 74 26324

Rossbrin Boatyard Schull
00353 28 37352

Rosslare Customs 00353 53 33116

Rosslare Harbour HM 00353 53 57921

Royal Cork Yacht Club Marina
Crosshaven 00353 21 4831023

Royal Cork YC Crosshaven
00353 21 831023

Royal Irish YC Dun Laoghaire
00353 1 280 9452

Royal St George YC Dun Laoghaire
00353 1 280 1811

Ryan & Roberts Marine Services
Askeaton
Marine engineers 00353 61 392198

Salve Marine Ltd Crosshaven
Marine engineers 00353 21 4831145

Schull Customs 00353 27 51562

Schull Police 00353 28 28111

Schull SC Schull 00353 28 37352

Schull Watersports Centre Schull
00353 28 28554

Shannon Customs 00353 61 471076

Shannon Estuary Customs
00353 69 415366

Skinners Boat Yard Baltimore
00353 28 20114

Sligo Customs 00353 71 61064

South Cork SC 00353 28 36383

Sutton Marine (Dublin) Sutton
00353 1 832 2312

Tralee SC Tralee 00353 66 36119

Tuskar Rock Marine Rosslare
Commercial diving company
00353 53 33376

UK/McWilliam Sailmakers (Irl) Ltd
Crosshaven 00353 21 831505

Union Chandlery Cork
00353 21 4554334

Viking Marine Ltd Dun Laoghaire
Chandlery 00353 1 280 6654

Waterford City Marina Waterford
00353 51 309900

Waterford Customs 00353 51 875391

Waterford Harbour SC Dunmore East
00353 51 383230

Waterford HM 00353 51 874907

Watson Sails Dublin
00353 1 832 6466

Western Marine Dublin
Boat repairs; chandlers; electronic and
engine supplier; boat sales
00353 1280 0321

Western YC Kilrush 00353 87 2262885

Wexford Customs 00353 532 2889

Wexford HBC Wexford 00353 53 22039

Wexford Police 00353 404 67107

Wicklow Customs 00353 404 67222

Wicklow HM 00353 404 67455

Wicklow Police 00353 404 67107

Wicklow SC Wicklow 00353 404 67526

Youghal HM 00353 24 92626

Youghal Police 00353 24 92200

Youghal SC Youghal 00353 24 92447

Waypoint Guide Area 12 – South Ireland - Malahide south to Liscanor Bay

299	Loop Head light - 1·6M W of	52°33'·65N	09°58'·55W
300	Loop Head light - 1·4M S of	52°32'·25N	09°55'·92W
301	Kilrush - 0·9M S of Kilcredaun light	52°33'·85N	09°42'·57W
302	Tearaght Island light - 2·5M NW of	52°06'·22N	10°42'·53W
303	Great Foze Rock - 1·8M SW of	52°00'·02N	10°43'·23W
304	Dingle - 1·2M S of Reenbeg Point	52°05'·62N	10°15'·80W
305	Bray Head - 1·4M W of	51°52'·83N	10°28'·05W
306	The Bull Island light - 1·7M SW of	51°34'·32N	10°20'·13W
307	Crow Head - 1·9M S of	51°32'·92N	10°09'·44W
308	Bantry - 0·8M SW of Whiddy Island	51°40'·03N	09°32'·83W
309	Sheep's Head light - 1·5M W of	51°32'·56N	09°53'·30W
310	Mizen Head light (SW) - 2M SSW of	51°25'·02N	09°50'·34W
311	Crookhaven - 1M ESE of Streek Head	51°27'·83N	09°40'·34W
312	Schull - 1M S of Long Island light	51°29'·22N	09°32'·03W
313	The Fastnet Rock light	51°23'·36N	09°36'·18W
314	Cape Clear - 1·6M SW of	51°24'·23N	09°32'·93W
315	Baltimore - 1·5M S of harbour entrance	51°26'·85N	09°23'·50W
316	Toe Head - 1·5M S of	51°27'·33N	09°13'·65W
317	Castle Haven - 1M SE of entrance	51°30'·10N	09°09'·94W
318	Galley Head - 1·4M S of	51°30'·40N	08°57'·20W
319	Old Head of Kinsale light - 1·5M SSE of	51°34'·92N	08°30'·84W
320	Cork Landfall By - 0·4M E of	51°43'·03N	08°14'·84W
321	Roche's Point light - 1·2M S of	51°46'·35N	08°15'·28W
322	Ballycotton Island light - 1·5M S of	51°47'·95N	07°59'·17W
323	Youghal, S - IM SE of Capel Island	51°52'·26N	07°50'·08W
324	Youghal, SE - 2M SE of Blackball ECM	51°54'·77N	07°45'·28W
325	Waterford - 1·35M SSE of Dunmore E	52°07'·42N	06°58'·85W
326	Coningbeg light vessel - 0·4M N of	52°02'·80N	06°39'·45W
327	Carnsore Point - 3·2M ESE of	52°09'·42N	06°16'·45W
328	Greenore Point - 1·8M E of	52°14'·43N	06°15'·90W
329	Wexford - 1·6M E of entrance	52°20'·52N	06°19'·30W
330	W Blackwater SHM - 0·4M W of	52°25'·82N	06°14'·06W
331	Cahore Point - 1·7M SE of	52°32'·52N	06°09'·96W
332	Arklow - 1·2M E by S of	52°47'·42N	06°06'·36W
333	Mizen Head (E coast) -1M ESE of	52°51'·02N	06°01'·96W
334	Wicklow - 2·6M E of	52°58'·92N	05°57'·86W
335	Dun Laoghaire - 2·2M NE of	53°19'·62N	06°04'·66W
336	Ben of Howth - 1·4M E of	53°22'·42N	06°00'·56W
337	Malahide - 1·5M E of Bar	53°27'·03N	06°04'·86W
338	Rockabill light - 1·2M WSW of	53°35'·32N	06°02'·06W

Distance Table - South Ireland

Approximate distances in nautical miles are by the most direct route while avoiding dangers and allowing for Traffic Separation Schemes

		1	2	3	4	5	6	7	8	9	10	11	12	13	14	15	16	17	18	19	20
1.	Carlingford Lough	1																			
2.	Howth	39	2																		
3.	Dun Laoghaire	48	8	3																	
4.	Wicklow	63	25	21	4																
5.	Arklow	75	37	36	15	5															
6.	Tuskar Rock	113	73	70	52	37	6														
7.	Rosslare	108	70	66	47	34	8	7													
8.	Dunmore East	139	101	102	84	69	32	32	8												
9.	Youghal	172	134	133	115	100	63	65	34	9											
10.	Crosshaven	192	154	155	137	122	85	85	59	25	10										
11.	Kinsale	202	164	168	150	135	98	95	69	35	17	11									
12.	Baltimore	239	201	196	177	164	128	132	102	70	54	42	12								
13.	Fastnet Rock	250	212	207	189	174	137	144	112	78	60	49	10	13							
14.	Bantry	281	243	241	223	208	171	174	146	112	94	83	42	34	14						
15.	Darrynane	283	245	240	221	208	172	176	146	114	98	86	44	39	38	15					
16.	Valentia	295	257	252	242	227	184	188	165	131	113	102	56	48	55	16	16				
17.	Dingle	308	270	265	246	233	197	201	171	139	123	111	69	61	63	29	13	17			
18.	Kilrush	361	323	318	299	286	250	254	224	192	176	164	122	114	116	82	66	64	18		
19.	Galway	366	362	357	339	324	287	291	262	228	210	199	159	150	155	119	103	101	76	19	
20.	Slyne Head	317	351	346	328	313	276	283	251	217	199	188	153	139	144	113	97	95	75	49	20

12

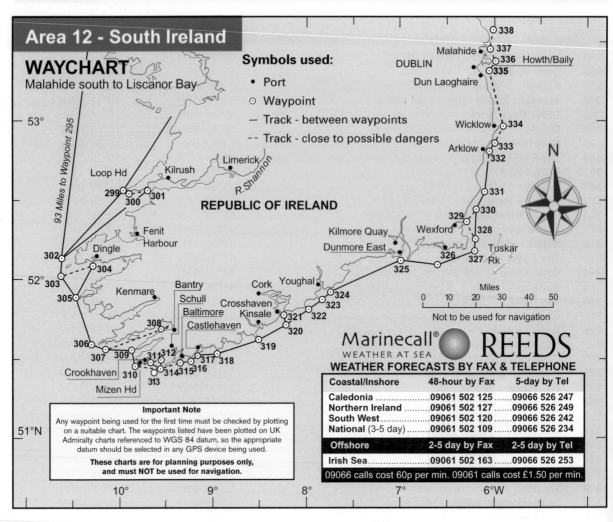

Area 12 - South Ireland

WAYCHART
Malahide south to Liscanor Bay

Symbols used:
- • Port
- ⊙ Waypoint
- — Track - between waypoints
- -- Track - close to possible dangers

Important Note
Any waypoint being used for the first time must be checked by plotting on a suitable chart. The waypoints listed have been plotted on UK Admiralty charts referenced to WGS 84 datum, so the appropriate datum should be selected in any GPS device being used.

These charts are for planning purposes only, and must NOT be used for navigation.

Marinecall WEATHER AT SEA **REEDS**

WEATHER FORECASTS BY FAX & TELEPHONE

Coastal/Inshore	48-hour by Fax	5-day by Tel
Caledonia	09061 502 125	09066 526 247
Northern Ireland	09061 502 127	09066 526 249
South West	09061 502 120	09066 526 242
National (3-5 day)	09061 502 109	09066 526 234
Offshore	**2-5 day by Fax**	**2-5 day by Tel**
Irish Sea	09061 502 163	09066 526 253

09066 calls cost 60p per min. 09061 calls cost £1.50 per min.

IRELAND AFLOAT
IRELAND'S ONLY BOATING MAGAZINE

www.afloat.ie

Irish Marine Press Publications Ltd
2 Lower Glenageary Road, Dun Laoghaire, Co.Dublin, Ireland
Tel: +353 (0)1 2846161 Fax: +353 (0)1 2846192 Email: info@afloat.ie

SAILING • MOTORBOATING WATERSPORTS

€40 FOR 10 ISSUES **SUBSCRIBE NOW!** CALL OUR HOTLINE TEL: +353 (0)1 2846161

NORTH IRELAND - Lambay Island, north to Liscanor Bay

Marinecall® REEDS
WEATHER AT SEA

WEATHER FORECASTS BY FAX & TELEPHONE

Coastal/Inshore	2-day by Fax	5-day by Phone
Caledonia	09061 502 125	09066 526 247
Northern Ireland	09061 502 127	09066 526 249
Clyde	09061 502 124	09066 526 246
North West	09061 502 123	09066 526 245
National (3-5 day)	09061 502 109	09066 526 234

Offshore	2-5 day by Fax	2-5 day by Phone
Irish Sea	09061 502 163	09066 526 253
English Channel	09061 502 161	09066 526 251
Biscay	09061 502 164	09066 526 254
North West Scotland ...	09061 502 165	09066 526 255

09066 CALLS COST 60P PER MIN. 09061 CALLS COST £1.50 PER MIN.

Key to Marina Plans symbols

Calor Gas		P	Parking
Chandler			Pub/Restaurant
Disabled facilities			Pump out
Electrical supply			Rigging service
Electrical repairs			Sail repairs
Engine repairs			Shipwright
First Aid			Shop/Supermarket
Fresh Water			Showers
Fuel - Diesel			Slipway
Fuel - Petrol		WC	Toilets
Hardstanding/boatyard			Telephone
Laundry facilities			Trolleys
Lift-out facilities		V	Visitors berths

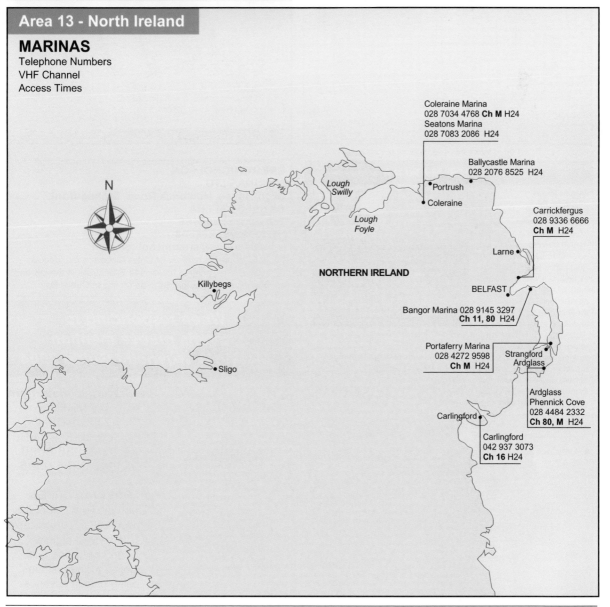

Area 13 - North Ireland

MARINAS
Telephone Numbers
VHF Channel
Access Times

Coleraine Marina
028 7034 4768 **Ch M** H24
Seatons Marina
028 7083 2086 H24

Ballycastle Marina
028 2076 8525 H24

Carrickfergus
028 9336 6666
Ch M H24

Portrush
Coleraine

Larne

NORTHERN IRELAND

BELFAST

Bangor Marina 028 9145 3297
Ch 11, 80 H24

Portaferry Marina
028 4272 9598
Ch M H24

Strangford
Ardglass

Ardglass
Phennick Cove
028 4484 2332
Ch 80, M H24

Carlingford

Carlingford
042 937 3073
Ch 16 H24

Killybegs

Sligo

Lough Swilly

Lough Foyle

COLERAINE MARINA

Coleraine Marina
64 Portstewart Road, Coleraine, Co Londonderry, BT52 1RS
Tel: 028 7034 4768

VHF **Ch M**
ACCESS **H24**

Coleraine Marina and Caravan complex enjoys a superb location in sheltered waters just one mile north of the town of Coleraine and four and a half miles south of the River Bann Estuary and the open sea. Besides accommodating vessels up to 18m LOA, this modern marina offers hard standing, fuel, a chandlery and shower facilities.

Among one of the oldest known settlements in Ireland, Coleraine is renowned for its linen, whiskey and salmon. Its thriving commercial centre includes numerous shops, a four-screen cinema and ice rink as well as a state-of-the-art leisure complex.

FACILITIES AT A GLANCE

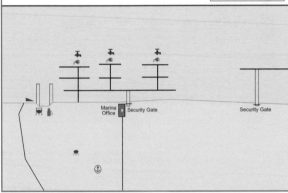

BALLYCASTLE MARINA

Ballycastle Marina
Bayview Road, Ballycastle, Northern Ireland
Tel: 028 2076 8525   Fax: 028 2076 6215

VHF **Ch 80**
ACCESS **H24**

Ballycastle is a traditional seaside town situated on Northern Ireland's North Antrim coast. The 74-berthed, sheltered marina provides a perfect base from which to explore the well known local attractions such as the Giant's Causeway world heritage site, the spectacular

Nine Glens of Antrim, and Rathlin, the only inhabited island in Northern Ireland. The most northern coastal marina in Ireland, Ballycastle is accessible at all states of the tide, although yachts are required to contact the marina on VHF Ch 80 before entering the harbour. Along the seafront are a selection of restaurants, bars and shops, while the town centre is only about a five-minute walk away.

FACILITIES AT A GLANCE

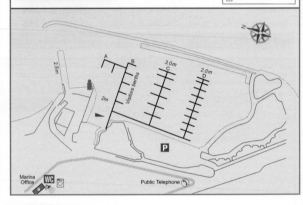

SEATONS MARINA

Seatons Marina
Drumslade Rd, Coleraine, Londonderry, BT52 1SE
Tel: 028 7083 2086   email: ssp@seatonsmarina.co.uk
www.seatonsmarina.co.uk

VHF
ACCESS **H24**

Seatons Marina is a privately owned business on the north coast of Ireland, which was established by Eric Seaton in 1962. It lies on the east bank of the River Bann, approximately two miles downstream from Coleraine and three miles from the sea.

Although facilities are currently rather limited, plans are underway to improve the services available to yachtsmen. The pontoon berths are suitable for yachts up to 13.5m, with a minimum depth of 2.4m on the outer berths, although some of the inner berths do occasionally dry out. Seatons is also able to provide swinging moorings, all of which come with a galvanised chain riser passed over the stem roller.

FACILITIES AT A GLANCE

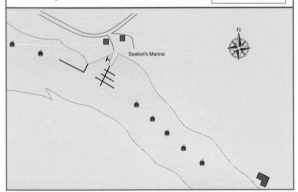

CARRICKFERGUS WATERFRONT

Carrickferus Waterfront
3 Quayside, Carrickfergus, Co. Antrim, BT38 8BE
Tel: 028 9336 6666 Fax: 028 9335 0505
email: waterfront@carrickfergus.org
www.carrickferguswaterfront.co.uk

VHF	Ch M
ACCESS	H24

Located on the north shore of Belfast Lough, Carrickfergus Waterfront incorporates two sheltered areas suitable for leisure craft. The harbour is dominated by a magnificent 12th century Norman Castle which, recently renovated, includes a film theatre, banqueting room and outdoor models depicting the castle's chequered history.

The marina is located 250 metres west of the harbour and has become increasingly popular since its opening in 1985. A range of shops and restaurants along the Waterfront caters for most yachtsmen's needs.

FACILITIES AT A GLANCE

Key
a Office space
b Development site
c Waterfront Administration Building
d Cinema/restaurant
e Retail superstore

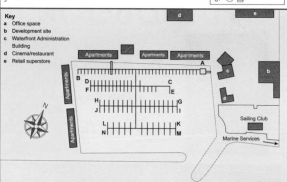

BANGOR MARINA

Crest Nicholson Marinas Ltd
Bangor Marina, Bangor, Co. Down, BT20 5ED
Tel: 028 9145 3297 Fax: 028 9145 3450
email: bangormarina@crestnicholson.com
www.crestnicholsonmarinas.co.uk

| VHF | Ch 11, 80 |
| ACCESS | H24 |

Situated on the south shore of Belfast Lough, Bangor Marina is part of a £20 million seafront development which also includes landscaped gardens, a promenade leading to a £3 million children's play park and an array of top class hotels, restaurants and shops. Within easy walking distance of the marina are numerous attractions including a leisure centre, golf courses, tennis courts and cinemas, as well as places of local interest such as the Ulster Folk and Transport Museum and the Heritage Centre at Bangor Castle.

FACILITIES AT A GLANCE

Key
a   Boat hoist - BJ Marine
b   Boat yard - BJ Marine
c   Bregenz House
d   Chandlery/brokerage BJ Marine
e   Dinghy berths
f   Access bridge
g   Lifeboat slipway
h   Domestic waste facilities
i   Waste oil tank
j   Disabled berthing
k   Flare disposal

TODD CHART AGENCY LTD
Navigation House, 85 High Street, Bangor, County Down, Northern Ireland BT20 5BD
Tel: 028 9146 6640
Fax: 028 9147 1070
e-mail:admiralty@toddchart.co.uk
www.nautical-charts.com
International Admiralty Chart Agent, chart correction service and nautical booksellers. Programming Centre for C-MAP NT and Navionics electronic charts. Stockist of Imray charts and books, navigation and chartroom instruments, binoculars, clocks etc. UK agent for Icelandic Hydrographic Service. Mail order - Visa, Mastercard, American Express and Switch/Delta accepted.

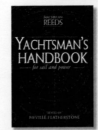

PORTAFERRY MARINA

Portaferry Marina
11 The Strand, Portaferry, BT22 1PF
Tel: 028 4272 9598 Mobile: 07703 209 780 Fax: 028 4272 9784
email: barholm.portaferry@virgin.net

VHF	Ch M
ACCESS	H24

Portaferry Marina lies on the east shore of the Narrows, the gateway to Strangford Lough on the north east coast of Ireland. A marine nature reserve of outstanding natural beauty, the Lough offers plenty of recreational activities. The marina, which caters for draughts of up to 2.5m, is fairly small, at present accommodating around 30 yachts. The office is situated about 200m from the marina itself, where you will find ablution facilities along with a launderette.

Portaferry incorporates several pubs and restaurants as well as a few convenience stores, while one of its prime attractions is the Exploris Aquarium. Places of historic interest in the vicinity include Castleward, an 18th century mansion in Strangford, and Mount Stewart House & Garden in Newtownards, both of which are owned by the National Trust.

FACILITIES AT A GLANCE

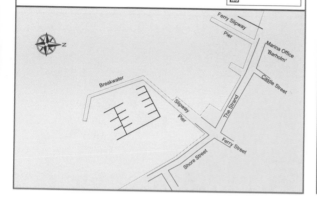

PHENNICK COVE MARINA

Phennick Cove Marina
19 Quay Street, Ardglass
N. Ireland, BT30 7SA
Tel: 028 4484 2332 Fax: 028 4484 2332
www.ardglassmarina.co.uk

VHF	Ch 80, M
ACCESS	H24

Situated just south of Strangford, Phennick Cove has the capacity to accommodate up to 55 yachts as well as space for small craft. Despite being relatively small in size, the marina boasts an extensive array of facilities, either on site or close at hand. Most of the necessary shops, including grocery stores, a post office, chemist and off-licence, are all within a five-minute walk from the marina. Among the local onshore activities are golf, mountain climbing in Newcastle, which is 18 miles south, as well as scenic walks at Ardglass and Delamont Park.

FACILITIES AT A GLANCE

North Dock

Key
a   Administration building
b   Boat storage

Additional Facilities
Reception car park - 60 vehicles
Waste oil tanks
Local charts for Strangford Lough
Heavy duty battery charging
High pressure water washing
Internet and email access
Barbeque facilities
Car hire

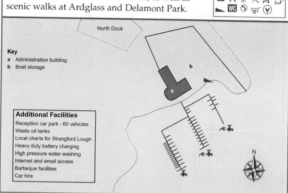

2004/M&WM51/d

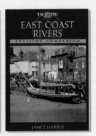
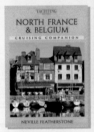

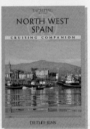
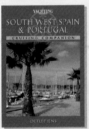

CARLINGFORD MARINA

Carlingford Marina
Co. Louth, Ireland
Tel: 00353 (0)42 937 3073
Fax: 00353 (0)42 937 3075
www.carlingfordmarina.ie

VHF   Ch 16
ACCESS   H24

Carlingford Lough is an eight-mile sheltered haven between the Cooley Mountains to the south and the Mourne Mountains to the north. The marina is situated on the southern shore, about four miles from Haulbowline Lighthouse, and can be easily reached via a deep water shipping channel. Among the most attractive destinations in the Irish Sea, Carlingford is only 60 miles from the Isle of Man and within a day's sail from Strangford Lough and Ardglass. Full facilities in the marina include a first class bar and restaurant offering superb views across the water.

FACILITIES AT A GLANCE

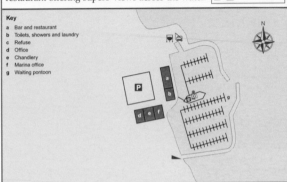

Key
a Bar and restaurant
b Toilets, showers and laundry
c Refuse
d Office
e Chandlery
f Marina office
g Waiting pontoon

Abco Divers Belfast   028 90610492

Albert Clarke Newtownards
Chandler   028 9187 2325

Ardglass HM   028 4484 1291

Ardglass Marina   028 4484 2332

Ardglass Police   028 4461501

Ballycastle Marina Ballycastle
    028 2076 8525

Ballyholme YC Bangor   028 91271467

Bangor Marina Bangor   028 91 453297

Belfast Lough HM   028 90 553012

Belfast Lough Police   028 91 454444

Belfast River Manager 028 90 328507

BJ Marine Ltd Bangor
Chandlery; sales, full boatyard services;
engine and electrical repairs; emergency
call out   028 9127 1434

Burtonport HM   00353 075 42155

Carlingford Lough Police 042 9373102

Carlingford Lough YC Rostrevor
    028 4173 8604

Carlingford Marina Carlingford
    00353 42 937073

Carnlough Harbour HM 07703 606763

Carrick Marine Projects Co Antrim
Marina services; boat storage; repairs;
brokerage   02893 355884

Carrickfergus Marina Carrickgergus
    028 93 366666

Carrickfergus SC Whitehead
    028 93 351402

Caters Carrick Ltd Carrickfergus
Chandler   028 93351919

Co Antrim YC Carrickfergus
    028 9337 2322

Coleraine Marina Coleraine
    028 7034 4768

Coleraine YC Coleraine 028 703 44503

Corrib Rowing & YC Galway City
    00353 91 564560

Courtmacsherry Police
    00353 23 46122

Docksafe Ltd Bangor
Fender supplier   028 9147 0453

Down Marine Co Ltd Belfast
Chandlery; surveys   028 90480247

DV Diving   028 91 464671

East Antrim BC Antrim   028 28 277204

East Belfast YC Belfast 028 9065 6283

Exploris Aquarium Portaferry
    028 4272 8062

Galway Bay HM   00353 91 561874

Galway Bay Police   00353 91 538000

Galway Bay SC   00353 91 794527

Galway Maritime Galway
    00353 91 566568

Gaw, EA Belfast
Sailmaker   028 9045 1905

Glandore Police   00353 23 48162

Glénans Irish SC (Westport)
    00353 98 26046

Groomsport Bay HM   028 91 278040

Holywood YC Holywood 028 90423355

Howth Police   00353 1 6664900

Jamison and Green Ltd Belfast
Chandler   028 90322444

Keller, Hilary Buncrana
Diver   00353 77 62146

Killybegs HM   00353 73 31032

Killybegs Police   00353 73 31002

Killyleagh YC Killyleagh 028 4482 8250

Kirkcubbin SC Kirkcubbin
    028 4273 8422

KTS Seasafety Kilkeel
Liferafts & marine safety equipment
    028 918 28405

Larne HM   028 2887 2100

Larne Police   028 2827 2266

Larne Rowing & SC Larne
    028 2827 4573

Lomax Boatbuilders Cliffony
    00353 71 66124

Lough Foyle HM   028 7186 0555

Lough Foyle Police   028 7776 6797

Lough Swilly Police   00353 72 51102

Lough Swilly YC Fahn   00353 74 22377

Marina Upholstery Carrickfergus
    028 9336 6655

Mayo SC (Rosmoney) Rosmoney
    00353 98 27772

McCready & Co Ltd, James Belfast
Chandler   028 9023 2842

McCready Sailboats Ltd Holywood
    028 9042 1821

McWilliam Sailmaker (Killinchy)
Killinchy   028 97542345

Mooney Boats Killybegs
Boatbuilding & repairs
    00353 73 31152/31388

Morrison, A Killyleagh
Boat repairs   028 44828215

Nautical World (Bangor) Bangor
Chandler   028 91460330

Newtownards SC Newtownards
    028 9181 3426

Parkinson (Sinbad Marine Services), J
Killybegs
Shipping agency   00353 73 31417

Phennick Cove Marina Ardglass
    028 44842332

Portaferry Marina Portaferry
    028 4272 9598

Portrush HM   028 7082 2307

Portrush Police   028 7034 4122

Portrush YC Portrush   028 70 823932

Quoile YC Downpatrick 028 44 612266

Red Bay Boats Ltd Cushendall
Builder of fishing boats and ribs
    028 2177 1331

River Bann & Coleraine HM
    028 7034 2012

River Bann and Coleraine Police
    028 70344122

Rossreagh Boatyard Rathmullan
    00353 74 51082

Royal North of Ireland YC
    028 90 428041

Royal Ulster YC Bangor 028 91 270568

Rynn Engineering, Pat Galway
    00353 91 562568

Seaton Marina Coleraine
    028 7083 2086

Skerries SC Carlingdford Lough
    00353 1 849 1233

Sketrick Sailmakers Ltd Killinchy
    028 9754 1400

Sligo HM   00353 71 61197

Sligo Police   00353 71 57000

Sligo YC Sligo   00353 71 77168

Strangford Lough HM 028 44 881637

Strangford Lough Marina Portaferry
    00353 1247 729598

Strangford Lough Police
    028 44615011

Strangford Lough YC Newtownards
    028 97 541883

Strangford SC Downpatrick
    028 4488 1404

Sunset Marine & Watersports Sligo
    00353 71 62792

Sunset Sails Sligo   00353 71 62792

Todd Chart Agency Ltd Bangor
Chart agent, chart corrections; nautical
booksellers   028 9146 6640

UK Customs Nationwide
    0845 0109000

Warrenpoint BC Warrenpoint
    028 4175 2137

Westport Police   00353 98 25555

Whale Water Systems Bangor
On-board water management
    028 9127 0531

Wilson, Alan c/o Portrush YC Portrush
    028 2076 2225

open your eyes to the world.

BAREBOAT • LUXURY CHARTER • CREWED • FLOTILLA • MEDITERRANEAN • CARIBBEAN • INDIAN OCEAN • ASIA PACIFIC • CANADA AND NORTH AMERICA

With 39 of the world's most mesmerizing cruising areas to choose from, you can let your imagination run wild. Discover the rugged beauty of the Corsican coast with its pine-clad hills and bustling harbours. Or cruise the exotic islands of French Polynesia where lapis-blue waters lick sugar-white sand. As for the boats, you're free to choose from an unrivalled fleet of new and modern yachts including our luxurious Platinum bareboats - all superbly kitted out and supported by great service. Ready to expand your horizons? Give us a call, we'll help you find your personal paradise.

CALL 0870 777 0210 (24HRS) OR CLICK WWW.SUNSAIL.COM FOR E-NEWS AND SPECIAL OFFERS

Sunsail®

Waypoint Guide Area 13 – North Ireland - Lambay Island north to Liscanor Bay

270	**Mew Is Lt** - 1·5M ENE of	54°42'·73N	05°28'·56W
271	**Belfast** - 0·7M ENE of No 1 Fairway Buoy	54°42'·00N	05°45'·13W
272	**Black Hd Lt** -1·3M ENE of	54°46'·50N	05°39'·26W
273	**Isle of Muck** - 1·1M NE of	54°51'·70N	05°41'·91W
274	**Larne Lough** - 1M N of Barr's Point	54°52'·53N	05°46'·81W
275	**E Maiden Lt** - 1·7M SW of	54°54'·50N	05°45'·57W
276	**Torr Head** - 0·6M ENE of	55°12'·20N	06°02'·87W
277	**Fair Head** - 0·9M N of	55°14'·60N	06°09'·00W
278	**L Foyle 4·1M NNE of Inishowen Lt**	55°17'·90N	06°52'·27W
279	**Malin Head** - 3M NNE of	55°25'·00N	07°21'·26W
280	**Lough Swilly** -1M N of ent	55°18'·20N	07°34'·36W
281	**Tory Island** - 1·25M SE of	55°14'·00N	08°11'·04W
282	**Rinrawros Pt Lt, Aran** - 1·3M NW of	55°01'·75N	08°35'·44W
283	**Rathlin O'Birne Is Lt** -1·9M WSW of	54°39'·20N	08°52'·94W
284	**Killibegs** - 2·5M WNW of St John's Point Lt	54°34'·70N	08°31'·84W
285	**Sligo** - 2·7M N of Aughris Hd	54°19'·50N	08°45'·36W
286	**The Stags rocks** - 1·3M N of	54°23'·30N	09°47'·18W
287	**Broadhaven** - 1M N of the bay	54°20'·40N	09°56'·04W
288	**Eagle Island** -1·4M NW of	54°17'·81N	10°07'·43W
289	**Black Rock** - 2·7M NE by N of	54°06'·20N	10°16'·63W
290	**Achill Head** - 1·8M SW of	53°57'·30N	10°17'·93W
291	**Clew Bay** - 1M SW of Achillbeg Is Lt	53°50'·80N	09°57'·93W
292	**Westport** - 1·5M WSW of Inishgort Lt	53°49'·00N	09°42'·63W
293	**Clew Bay** - 1·5M NW of Roonah Head	53°46'·95N	09°55'·70W
294	**Inishturk Island** - 1·2M NW of	53°43'·60N	10°08'·85W
295	**Inishshark Island** - 1·8M W of	53°36'·50N	10°21'·05W
296	**Slyne Head Lt** -1·6M SW of	53°22'·90N	10°16'·05W
297	**Rock Is Lt** - 5·3M NW by W of	53°11'·80N	09°58'·65W
298	**Galway** - 2·3M N of Black Head Lt	53°11'·55N	09°15'·84W
333	**Mizen Head (E coast)** - 1M ESE of	52°51'·02N	06°01'·96W
334	**Wicklow** - 2·6M E of	52°58'·92N	05°57'·86W
335	**Dun Laoghaire** - 2·2M NE of	53°19'·62N	06°04'·66W
336	**Ben of Howth** - 1·4M E of	53°22'·42N	06°00'·56W
337	**Malahide** - 1·5M E of Bar	53°27'·03N	06°04'·86W
338	**Rockabill** - 1·2M WSW of	53°35'·32N	06°02'·06W
339	**Carlingford Lough SWM**	53°58'·70N	06°01'·12W
340	**Strangford Lough SWM**	54°18'·62N	05°28'·69W
341	**South Rock light vessel** - 1·1M E of	54°24'·52N	05°20'·13W

Distance Table - North Ireland

Approximate distances in nautical miles are by the most direct route while avoiding dangers and allowing for Traffic Separation Schemes

	1	2	3	4	5	6	7	8	9	10	11	12	13	14	15	16	17	18	19	20
1. Dun Laoghaire	1																			
2. Carlingford Lough	50	2																		
3. Strangford Lough	71	36	3																	
4. Bangor	96	61	34	4																
5. Carrickfergus	101	66	39	6	5															
6. Larne	108	73	45	16	16	6														
7. Carnlough	118	78	50	25	26	11	7													
8. Altacarry Head	135	102	74	45	45	31	21	8												
9. Portrush	150	115	87	58	60	48	35	19	9											
10. Lough Foyle	157	121	92	72	73	55	47	30	11	10										
11. L Swilly (Fahan)	200	166	138	109	104	96	81	65	48	42	11									
12. Tory Island	209	174	146	117	113	105	90	74	57	51	35	12								
13. Burtonport	218	182	153	130	130	116	108	90	74	68	49	18	13							
14. Killybegs	267	232	204	175	171	163	148	132	115	109	93	58	43	14						
15. Sligo	281	246	218	189	179	177	156	146	123	117	107	72	51	30	15					
16. Eagle Island	297	262	234	205	198	193	175	162	147	136	123	88	72	62	59	16				
17. Westport	337	323	295	266	249	240	226	207	193	187	168	137	120	108	100	57	17			
18. Slyne Head	352	317	289	260	257	248	234	217	201	195	178	143	128	117	114	55	44	18		
19. Galway	348	366	338	309	307	297	284	266	253	245	227	192	178	166	163	104	94	49	19	
20. Kilrush	318	361	364	335	332	323	309	291	276	270	251	220	203	191	183	142	119	75	76	20

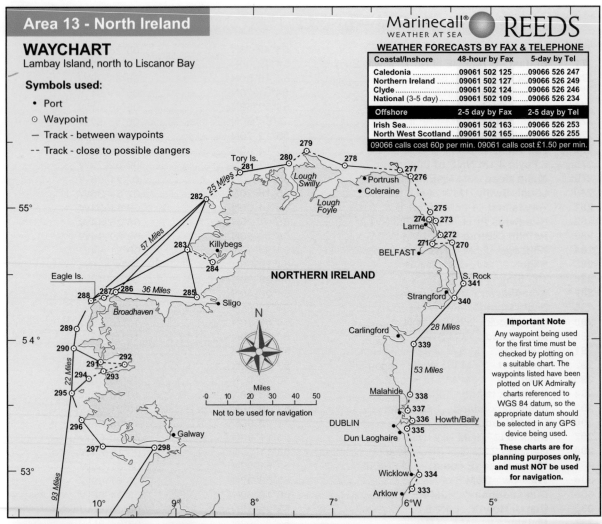

Area 13 - North Ireland

WAYCHART
Lambay Island, north to Liscanor Bay

Symbols used:

- • Port
- ⊙ Waypoint
- — Track - between waypoints
- -- Track - close to possible dangers

Marinecall® WEATHER AT SEA · **REEDS**

WEATHER FORECASTS BY FAX & TELEPHONE

Coastal/Inshore	48-hour by Fax	5-day by Tel
Caledonia	09061 502 125	09066 526 247
Northern Ireland	09061 502 127	09066 526 249
Clyde	09061 502 124	09066 526 246
National (3-5 day)	09061 502 109	09066 526 234

Offshore	2-5 day by Fax	2-5 day by Tel
Irish Sea	09061 502 163	09066 526 253
North West Scotland	09061 502 165	09066 526 255

09066 calls cost 60p per min. 09061 calls cost £1.50 per min.

Important Note

Any waypoint being used for the first time must be checked by plotting on a suitable chart. The waypoints listed have been plotted on UK Admiralty charts referenced to WGS 84 datum, so the appropriate datum should be selected in any GPS device being used.

These charts are for planning purposes only, and must NOT be used for navigation.

CHANNEL ISLANDS - Guernsey, Jersey & Alderney

Marinecall® REEDS
WEATHER AT SEA
WEATHER FORECASTS BY FAX & TELEPHONE

Coastal/Inshore	2-day by Fax	5-day by Phone
Bristol	09061 502 121	09066 526 243
South West	09061 502 120	09066 526 242
Mid Channel	09061 502 119	09066 526 241
Channel Islands	-	09066 526 250
National (3-5 day)	09061 502 109	09066 526 234

Offshore	2-5 day by Fax	2-5 day by Phone
English Channel	09061 502 161	09066 526 251
Southern North Sea	09061 502 162	09066 526 252
Irish Sea	09061 502 163	09066 526 253
Biscay	09061 502 164	09066 526 254

09066 CALLS COST 60P PER MIN. 09061 CALLS COST £1.50 PER MIN.

Key to Marina Plans symbols

Calor Gas		P Parking	
Chandler		Pub/Restaurant	
Disabled facilities		Pump out	
Electrical supply		Rigging service	
Electrical repairs		Sail repairs	
Engine repairs		Shipwright	
First Aid		Shop/Supermarket	
Fresh Water		Showers	
Fuel - Diesel		Slipway	
Fuel - Petrol		WC Toilets	
Hardstanding/boatyard		Telephone	
Laundry facilities		Trolleys	
Lift-out facilities		V Visitors berths	

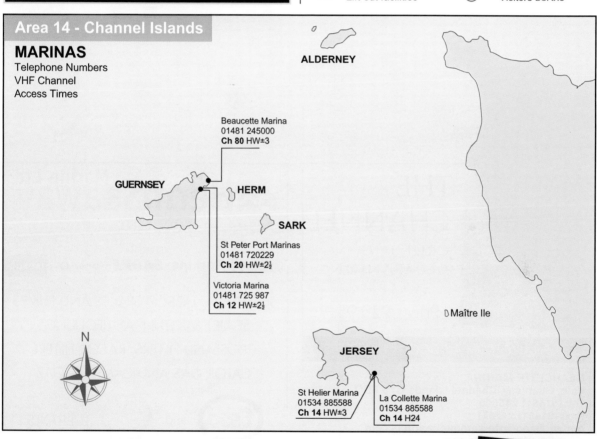

Area 14 - Channel Islands

MARINAS
Telephone Numbers
VHF Channel
Access Times

ALDERNEY

Beaucette Marina
01481 245000
Ch 80 HW±3

GUERNSEY

HERM

SARK

St Peter Port Marinas
01481 720229
Ch 20 HW±2½

Victoria Marina
01481 725 987
Ch 12 HW±2½

ⁱ Maître Ile

JERSEY

St Helier Marina
01534 885588
Ch 14 HW±3

La Collette Marina
01534 885588
Ch 14 H24

N

BEAUCETTE MARINA

Beaucette Marina
Vale, Guernsey, GY3 5BQ
Tel: 01481 245000 Fax: 01481 247071
Mobile: 07781 102302
email: beaucette@premiermarinas.com

VHF Ch 80
ACCESS HW±3

Situated on the north east tip of Guernsey, Beaucette enjoys a peaceful, rural setting in contrast to the more vibrant atmosphere of Victoria Marina. Now owned by Premier Marinas and offering a high standard of service, the site was originally formed from an old quarry.

The marina office incorporates a small shop for basic provisions, or alternatively there is a general store close by, while the bustling town of St Peter Port is only 20 minutes away by bus.

FACILITIES AT A GLANCE

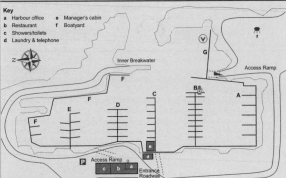

Key
a Harbour office
b Restaurant
c Showers/toilets
d Laundry & telephone
e Manager's cabin
f Boatyard

GUERNSEY VICTORIA MARINA

Guernsey Victoria Marina
Harbour Masters Office, St Peter Port
Guernsey
Tel: 01481 725987 Fax: 01481 714177

VHF Ch 12
ACCESS HW±2.5

Victoria Marina in St Peter Port accommodates approximately 300 visiting yachts. In the height of the season it gets extremely busy, but when the marina is full the overspill can be berthed in other local marinas or moored in the outer harbour. Depending on draught, the marina is accessible approximately two and a half hours either side of HW, with yachts crossing over a sill drying to 4.2m. The marina dory will direct you to a berth on arrival or else will instruct you to moor up on one of the waiting pontoons just outside.

Once in the marina, you can benefit from its superb facilities as well as from its central location to St Peter Port's shops and restaurants.

Guernsey is well placed for exploring the rest of the Channel Islands, including the quiet anchorages off Herm and Sark, or making a short hop to one of the French ports such as St Malo, Carteret and Le Dielette.

FACILITIES AT A GLANCE

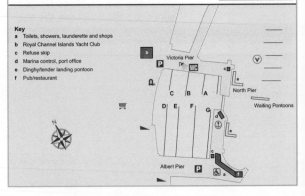

Key
a Toilets, showers, launderette and shops
b Royal Channel Islands Yacht Club
c Refuse skip
d Marina control, port office
e Dinghy/tender landing pontoon
f Pub/restaurant

ST PETER PORT

Harbour Master Office
St Julians Emplacement
St Peter Port, GY1 2LW
Tel: 01481 720229 Fax: 01481 714177

VHF	Ch 20
ACCESS	HW±2.5

The harbour of St Peter Port comprises the Queen Elizabeth II Marina to the N and Victoria and Albert Marinas to the S, with visiting yachtsmen usually accommodated in Victoria Marina.

Renowned for being an international financial centre and tax haven, St Peter Port is the capital of Guernsey. Its regency architecture and picturesque cobbled streets filled with restaurants and boutiques help to make it one of the most attractive harbours in Europe. Among the places of interest are Hauteville House, home of the writer Victor Hugo, and Castle Cornet.

FACILITIES AT A GLANCE

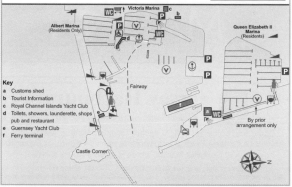

Key
a Customs shed
b Tourist Information
c Royal Channel Islands Yacht Club
d Toilets, showers, launderette, shops pub and restaurant
e Guernsey Yacht Club
f Ferry terminal

A B MARINE LTD
Castle Walk, St Peter Port, Guernsey,
Channel Islands GY1 1AU.
Tel: (01481) 722378
Fax: (01481) 711080

We specialise in safety and survival equipment and are a M.C.A. approved service station for liferafts including R.F.D., Beaufort/Dunlop, Zodiac, Avon, Plastimo and Lifeguard. We also carry a full range of new liferafts, dinghies and lifejackets and distress flares.

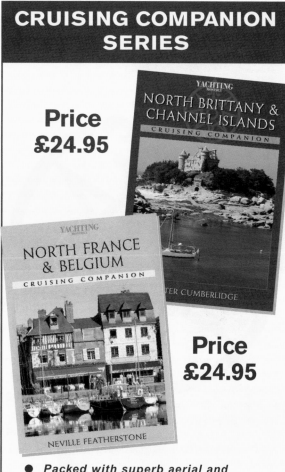

ST HELIER HARBOUR

St Helier Harbour, Maritime House, La Route du Port Elizabeth
St Helier, Jersey, JE1 1HB
Tel: 01534 885588 Fax: 01534 885599
www.jersey-harbours.com
email: moorings@jersey-harbours.com

| VHF | Ch 14 |
| ACCESS | HW±3 |

Jersey is the largest of the Channel Islands, attracting the most number of tourists per year. Although St Helier can get very crowded in the height of the summer, if you hire a car and head out to the north coast in particular you will soon find isolated bays and pretty little fishing villages.

St Helier comprises three marinas, the first of which is La Collette Yacht Basin, accessible at any state of the tide. St Helier Marina enjoys a central position to the town, but can only be entered three hours either side of HW via a sill, while Elizabeth Marina tends to be designated for longer term craft.

FACILITIES AT A GLANCE

Key
a Marina office
b Water/toilets/public phone
c Tourism
d Harbour office and Customs
e Maritime house
f Waiting pontoon
g Passenger Terminal
h Trailer park
i Port control
j Marina shop
k Cafe

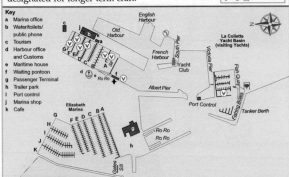

An introduction to Jersey, its harbours and waters

States of Jersey

Tel: 01534 885588   Fax: 01534 885599
Email: jsyhbr@itl.net

This is Jersey - an island with an independent history which has kept many of it's ancient traditions alive - an island which has also taken what the world can offer so that it can support a buoyant economy with high employment while seeking to preserve all that is best. An island with it's own laws and currency - an island of traditional agriculture and modern finance - an island, above all, at which a welcome is assured whether you stop off for a couple of nights on your passage back from St Malo and the Brittany coast or whether you take several days off to explore Jersey - and why not? It is well worth it.

"You may only want to laze on your boat or you may wish to explore and enjoy what Jersey has to offer, whatever your preference we are here to welcome you and ensure you have a pleasant and enjoyable holiday in Jersey's five gold anchor marinas."

Brian Nibbs

**Captain Brian Nibbs
Chief Executive
Jersey Harbours**

2004/M&WM58/d

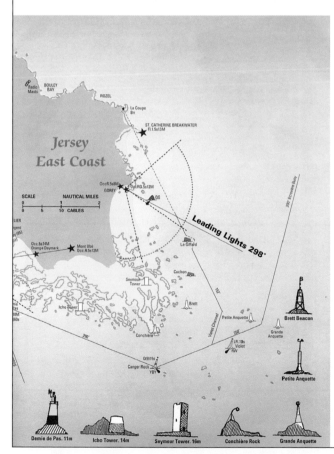

AB Marine Ltd St Peter Port
Safety and survival equipment; inflatables
01481 722378

Alderney & Burhou HM 01481 822620

Alderney and Burhou Police
01481 725111

Alderney Boating Centre
Chandlery 01481 823725

Alderney SC Alderney 01481 822959

Aqua-Star Ltd St Sampsons
Motor boat builder 01481 244550

Battrick, Lee St Helier
Surveyor 01534 611143

Battricks Boatyard St Aubin
Boat repairs; chandler 01534 743412

Beaucette HM Vale 1481 245000

Beaucette Marina Vale 01481 245000

Boatworks + Ltd St Peter Port
Boat repairs; chandler; boat sales
01481 726071

Castlemain Ltd St Peter Port
Boat sales; marine insurance
01481 721319

Channel Islands Marine Ltd Guernsey
Boat sales; marine engineers
01481 716880

Channel Islands Marine Ltd Jersey
Boat sales; marine engineers
01534 767595

Chicks Marine Ltd Guernsey
Boat repairs; electronics; engines
01481 724536

Collins Marine St Helier
Mechanical engineers 01534 732415

Elizabeth Marina St Helier
01534 885530

Fox Marine Services Ltd Jersey
Mechanical engineer 01534 721312

Freeport Marine Jersey
Chandlery; boatyard; engineer
01534 888100

Gallichan Marine Ltd Jersey
Boat repairs; chandler; electronics;
boat sales 01534 746387

Gorey HM 01534 853616

Gorey Marine Supplies Gorey
Fuel 07797 742384

Guernsey Police 01481 725111

Guernsey Tourist Board St Peter Port
01481 723552

Guernsey YC St Peter Port
01481 722838

Herm Seaway Marine Ltd St Peter Port
Antifouling; marine engineers; inflatables
01481 726829

Interseals (Guernsey) Ltd Guernsey
Gaskets; oil seals; hydraulic packing
01481 246364

Iron Stores Marine St Helier
Chandlery 01534 877755

Island Yachts St Helier
Sailmaker 01534 725048

Jackson Yacht Services Jersey
Boat repairs; chandler; electronics; boat
sales; sailmaker/repairs 01534 743819

**Jersey Cruising School & Yacht
Charters**
Jersey 01534 888100

Jersey Harbours Dept St Helier
01534 885588

Jersey Marine Electronics Ltd Jersey
01534 721603

Keating Marine Engineering Ltd, Bill
Jersey 01534 733977

La Collette Yacht Basin St Helier
01534 885588

Mainbrayce Marine Alderney
Boat repairs; chandlery; engine repairs
01481 822772

Marine Services Jersey
Chandlery 01534 626930

Maritime International Ltd Guernsey
Distributor for Honda outboards;
marine products 01481 723716

Marquand Brothers
St Peter Port, Guernsey
Chandlery 01481 720962

New Horizon Yacht Agency Guernsey
Boat sales 01481 726335

North Quay Marine St Sampson's
Chandler 01481 246561

Premium Liferaft Services
Channel Islands
Hire/sale of liferafts and safety equipment
01481 720485

Radio & Electronic Services Ltd
St Peter Port
Marine electronics & radio systems
01481 728837

Royal Channel Islands YC (Guernsey)
01481 723154

Royal Channel Islands YC (Jersey)
St Aubin 01534 745783

Sark HM 01481 832323

Scott & Co, Graham St Peter Port
Sailmaker 01481 728989

Seaquest Marine Ltd St Peter Port
Chandler; electronics 01481 721773

South Pier Shipyard St Helier
Boat repairs; chandler; electronics;
boat sales 01534 519700

St Helier HM 01534 885588

St Helier Marina St Helier
01534 885588

St Helier Police 01534 612612

St Helier YC St Helier
01534 721307/32229

St Peter Port HM 01481 720229

St Peter Port Marinas St Peter Port
01481 720229

UK Customs Nationwide
0845 0109000

Victoria Marina St Peter Port
01481 725987

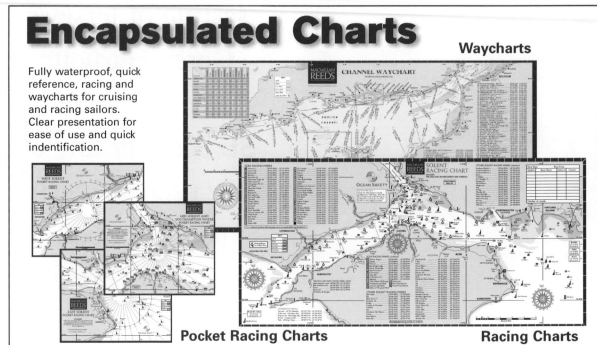

Waypoint Guide Area 14 – Channel Islands - Guernsey, Jersey, Alderney

35	**Alderney - Bray Harbour** - 1M NNE	49°46'·60N	02°10'·63W
36	**The Swinge** - turning waypoint	49°43'·44N	02°14'·48W
37	**Casquets** -1M W of	49°43'·32N	02°24'·15W
38	**Guernsey NE** - 1·2M E of Beaucette	49°30'·07N	02°28'·38W
39	**St Peter Port** - 0·5M E of entrance	49°27'·37N	02°30'·72W
40	**Big Russel** - midway S	49°25'·24N	02°26'·08W
41	**Guernsey** - 1M SE of St Martin's Pt	49°24'·60N	02°30'·60W
42	**Guernsey** - 1·5M S of Pleinmont Pt	49°24'·00N	02°40'·08W
43	**Guernsey** - 1·8M W of Les Hanois	49°26'·10N	02°45'·08W
44	**Sark** - 0·3M S of Brecou	49°25'·41N	02°23'·32W
45	**Sark** - 1M E of Creux Harbour	49°25'·80N	02°19'·08W
46	**Jersey** - 1·75M NW of Grosnez Pt	49°16'·56N	02°16'·84W
47	**Jersey** - 1M WSW of La Corbiere	49°10'·40N	02°16'·40W
48	**Jersey** - 0·15M S of Noirmant Pt	49°09'·75N	02°10'·08W
49	**St Helier** - 0·3M S of Breakwater	49°09'·91N	02°07'·38W
50	**St Helier** - 0·3M S of Demie de Ras	49°08'·71N	02°06'·12W
51	**SE Jersey** - 1st turning pt going E	49°08'·00N	02°03'·43W
52	**SE Jersey** - 2nd turning pt to Gorey	49°07'·54N	01°57'·98W
53	**SE Jersey** - 3rd turning pt to Gorey	49°08'·64N	01°57'·28W
54	**Gorey Entrance** - 298°, 1·6M SE of	49°11'·04N	01°59'·20W
55	**St Catherine, Jersey** - 0·5M SE of anchorage	49°13'·04N	02°00'·08W
56	**Les Écrehou** - 1·4M S of Maitre Ile Bn	49°15'·64N	01°55'·58W
57	**NW Minquiers NCM** - 0·1M W of	48°59'·64N	02°20'·74W
58	**SW Minquiers WCM** - 0·1M SW of	48°54'·28N	02°19'·51W
59	**Roches Douvres Lt** - 3M NW of	49°08'·54N	02°52'·18W
60	**Roches Douvres Lt** - 2·4M NE of	49°08'·04N	02°46'·28W
61	**Lezardrieux** - 1·5M N of La Horaire Bn	48°55'·01N	02°55'·23W
62	**Lezardrieux approach** - 1·7M NNE	48°53'·54N	02°58'·27W
63	**Les Héaux de Brehat** - 3M N of	48°57'·54N	03°05'·18W
81	**Iles Chausey** - 1M S of entrance	48°51'·04N	01°49'·08W
82	**Granville** - 0·7M SW of Granville Lt	48°49'·56N	01°37'·63W
83	**Iles Chausey** - 0·5M E of Anvers ECM	48°53'·94N	01°40'·08W
84	**SE Minquiers ECM** - 1M SE of	48°52'·74N	01°58'·98W
85	**Les Ardentes ECM Buoy** - 0·2M E of	48°57'·84N	01°51'·23W
86	**NE Minquiers ECM** - 0·1M NE of	49°00'·91N	01°55'·19W
87	**Les Écrehou SE** - 0·4M SE of Écrevière SCM	49°15'·04N	01°51'·73W
88	**Carteret** - 1·75M SW of	49°20'·84N	01°49'·28W
89	**Carteret** - 0·3M SW of Trois Grunes WCM	49°21'·59N	01°55'·53W
90	**Cap de Flamanville** - 2M W of	49°31'·59N	01°56'·38W
91	**Diélette** - 1M NW of on transit	49°33'·87N	01°52'·90W
92	**Cap de La Hague** - 4·4M SSW of	49°40'·48N	02°01'·63W
93	**Cap de La Hague** - 2·5M W of	49°43'·44N	02°00'·36W
94	**Cap de La Hague** - 1·5M N of La Plate Lt	49°45'·44N	01°55'·78W
95	**Omonville** - 1M E of, in white sector	49°42'·50N	01°48'·33W

Distance Table - Channel Islands

Approximate distances in nautical miles are by the most direct route while avoiding dangers and allowing for Traffic Separation Schemes

		1	2	3	4	5	6	7	8	9	10	11	12	13	14	15	16	17	18	19	20
1.	Cherbourg	1																			
2.	Cap de la Hague	14	2																		
3.	Carteret	41	23	3																	
4.	Granville	75	61	38	4																
5.	St Malo	87	73	49	23	5															
6.	Casquets	31	17	32	63	70	6														
7.	Braye (Alderney)	23	9	26	66	73	8	7													
8.	Beaucette	39	25	34	59	58	15	19	8												
9.	St Peter Port	42	28	31	55	54	18	23	4	9											
10.	Les Hanois	49	35	37	58	56	23	29	14	10	10										
11.	Creux (Sark)	37	23	23	50	52	18	22	11	10	16	11									
12.	St Helier	59	45	28	30	38	43	46	33	29	32	24	12								
13.	Gorey (Jersey)	47	33	16	29	38	36	35	32	29	35	20	13	13							
14.	Dahouet	88	74	62	44	28	70	72	62	58	57	53	41	47	14						
15.	St Quay-Portrieux	88	74	64	54	35	71	73	55	56	48	51	46	52	12	15					
16.	Paimpol	91	77	65	56	42	67	70	54	50	45	50	45	53	24	24	16				
17.	Lézardrieux	88	74	68	54	49	65	68	52	48	42	38	47	55	33	21	14	17			
18.	Tréguier	94	80	72	72	60	66	72	56	52	42	58	53	63	58	46	29	22	18		
19.	Roscoff	117	103	95	96	84	87	94	77	73	63	79	80	93	71	59	58	54	41	19	
20.	L'Aberwrac'h	145	131	126	128	116	115	122	107	103	93	109	110	123	103	91	88	84	72	32	20

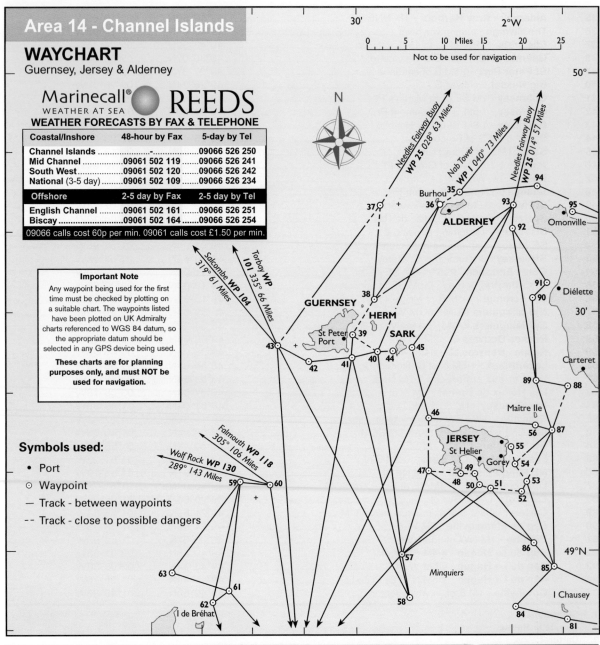

Area 14 - Channel Islands

WAYCHART
Guernsey, Jersey & Alderney

Marinecall® REEDS
WEATHER AT SEA
WEATHER FORECASTS BY FAX & TELEPHONE

Coastal/Inshore	48-hour by Fax	5-day by Tel
Channel Islands	-	09066 526 250
Mid Channel	09061 502 119	09066 526 241
South West	09061 502 120	09066 526 242
National (3-5 day)	09061 502 109	09066 526 234
Offshore	**2-5 day by Fax**	**2-5 day by Tel**
English Channel	09061 502 161	09066 526 251
Biscay	09061 502 164	09066 526 254

09066 calls cost 60p per min. 09061 calls cost £1.50 per min.

Important Note
Any waypoint being used for the first time must be checked by plotting on a suitable chart. The waypoints listed have been plotted on UK Admiralty charts referenced to WGS 84 datum, so the appropriate datum should be selected in any GPS device being used.

These charts are for planning purposes only, and must NOT be used for navigation.

Symbols used:

- • Port
- ⊙ Waypoint
- — Track - between waypoints
- -- Track - close to possible dangers

Not to be used for navigation

GUERNSEY · St Peter Port · HERM · SARK · **ALDERNEY** · Burhou · Omonville · Diélette · Carteret · Maître Ile · **JERSEY** St Helier · Gorey · Minquiers · I Chausey · I de Bréhat

Needles Fairway Buoy **WP 25** 028° 63 Miles
Nab Tower **WP 1** 040° 73 Miles
Needles Fairway Buoy **WP 25** 014° 57 Miles
Salcombe **WP 104** 319° 61 Miles
Torbay **WP 101** 335° 66 Miles
Falmouth **WP 118** 305° 106 Miles
Wolf Rock **WP 130** 289° 143 Miles

THE CHANNEL
CRUISING COMPANION

The English Channel can be a challenge, a lot of fun and occasionally a pig, but if you do master your trade here, you are probably good enough to sail the world. You are in safe hands with this new Cruising Companion that covers Scilly to Ramsgate, Dunkerque to Finistère and includes the Channel Islands.

Packed with superb aerial and surface photographs it provides a description of every harbour and takes you ashore to decent restaurants, the nearest supermarket, glorious beaches for the kids or just a launderette or bank. Suggestions for interesting visits on foot, bike or four wheels are all within.

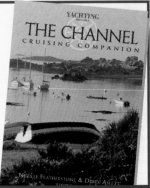

YACHTING
THE CHANNEL
CRUISING COMPANION

NEVILLE FEATHERSTONE & DEREK AGLETT

NAUTICAL DATA ORDER HOTLINE: 01243 389898

SECTION 2
MARINE SUPPLIES AND SERVICES GUIDE

ADHESIVES

Adhesive Technologies
Braintree   01376 346511

Bettabond Adhesives
Leeds   0113 278 5088

Casco Products Industrial Adhesives
St Neots   01480 476777

CC Marine (Rubbaweld) Ltd
Chichester   01243 672606

Industrial Self Adhesives Ltd
Nottingham   0115 9681895

Sika Ltd Garden City   01707 394444

Technix Rubber & Plastics Ltd
Southampton   023 8063 5523

Tiflex Liskeard   01579 320808

Trade Grade Products Ltd
Poole   01202 820177

UK Epoxy Resins
Burscough   01704 892364

Wessex Resins & Adhesives Ltd
Romsey   01794 521111

3M United Kingdom plc
Bracknell   01344 858315

ASSOCIATIONS/ AGENCIES

Cruising Association
London   020 7537 2828

Fishermans Mutual Association (Eyemouth) Ltd
Eyemouth   01890 750373

Maritime and Coastguard Agency
Swansea   0870 6006505

Radiocommunications Agency
London   020 7211 0211

Royal Institute of Navigation
London   020 7591 3130

Royal National Lifeboat Institution
Poole   01202 663000

Royal Yachting Association (RYA)
Southampton   0845 345 0400

BERTHS & MOORINGS

ABC Powermarine
Beaumaris   01248 811413

Aqua Bell Ltd Norwich   01603 713013

Ardfern Yacht Centre
Lochgilphead   01852 500247/500636

Ardmair Boat Centre
Ullapool   01854 612054

Arisaig Marine Ltd
Inverness-shire   01687 450224

Bristol Boat Ltd Bristol   01225 872032

British Waterways Argyll
    01546 603210

Burgh Castle Marine
Norfolk   01493 780331

Cambrian Marine Services Ltd
Cardiff   029 2034 3459

Chelsea Harbour Ltd
London   020 7225 9108

Clapson & Son (Shipbuilders) Ltd
Barton-on-Humber   01652 635620

Crinan Boatyard
Crinan   01546 830232

Dartside Quay Brixham   01803 845445

DEAN & REDDYHOFF LTD - HASLAR MARINA
Haslar Road, Gosport, Hampshire PO12 1NU
Tel: (023) 9260 1201
Fax: (023) 9260 2201
e-mail:
sales@haslarmarina.co.uk
www.haslarmarina.co.uk
Ideally situated only minutes from open water, Haslar caters for 600 annual berths together with up to 150 visiting berths. Facilities include: Floating Bar/Clubhouse, Riggers, Chandlery, Brokers, Engineers, Maintenance, Electronics, Divers, Valeting, Charters, Wine Bar/Bistro, 24hr security and more.

Douglas Marine Preston
    01772 812462

Dublin City Moorings
Dublin   00353 1 8183300

Emsworth Yacht Harbour
Emsworth   01243 377727

HAFAN PWLLHELI
Glan Don, Pwllheli, Gwynedd LL53 5YT
Tel: (01758) 701219
Fax: (01758) 701443 VHF Ch80
Hafan Pwllheli has over 400 pontoon berths and offers access at virtually all states of the tide. Ashore, its modern purpose-built facilities include luxury toilets, showers, launderette, a secure boat park for winter storage, 40-ton travel hoist, mobile crane and plenty of space for car parking. Open 24-hours a day, 7 days a week.

Highway Marine
Sandwich   01304 613925

Iron Wharf Boatyard
Faversham   01795 537122

Jalsea Marine Services Ltd
Northwich   01606 77870

Jersey Harbours
St Helier   01534 885588

Jones (Boatbuilders), David
Chester   01244 390363

KG McColl Oban   01852 200248

Lawrenny Yacht Station
Kilgetty   01646 651212

MacFarlane & Son
Glasgow   01360 870214

Maramarine
Helensburgh   01436 810971

Melfort Pier & Harbour
Kilmelford   01852 200333

NEPTUNE MARINA LTD
Neptune Quay, Ipswich, Suffolk IP4 1AX
Tel: (01473) 215204
Fax: (01473) 215206
e-mail:
enquiries@neptune-marina.com
www.neptune-marina.com
Accessible through continuously operating lockgates (VHF Channel 68) Neptune Marina (VHF Channels 80 or 37) is located on the north side of Ipswich wet dock immediately adjacent to the town centre and integrated into the rapidly regenerating northern quays.

Orkney Marinas Ltd
Kirkwall   01856 872292

PADSTOW HARBOUR COMMISSIONERS
Harbour House, Padstow, Cornwall PL28 8AQ
Tel: (01841) 532239
Fax: (01841) 533346
e-mail:
padstowharbour@compuserve.com
www.padstow-harbour.co.uk
Inner harbour controlled by tidal gate - opens HW±2 hours. Minimum depth 3 metres at all times. Yachtsmen must be friendly as vessels raft together. Services include showers, toilets, diesel, water and ice. Security by CCTV.

Pearn and Co, Norman
Looe   01503 262244

Peterhead Bay Authority
Peterhead   01779 474020

Philip Leisure Group
Dartmouth   01803 833351

Priors Boatyard
Burnham-on-Crouch   01621 782160

Rossiter Yachts Ltd
Christchurch   01202 483250

Sark Moorings
Channel Islands   01481 832260

Surry Boatyard
Shoreham-by-Sea   01273 461491

Sutton Harbour Marina Plymouth
    01752 204186

Wicor Marine Fareham   01329 237112

Winters Marine Ltd
Salcombe   01548 843580

Yarmouth Marine Service
Yarmouth   01983 760521

Youngboats Faversham   01795 536176

BOAT STORAGE

Abersoch Boatyard Ltd
Pwllheli   01758 712213

Ambrisbeg Ltd
Port Bannatyne   01700 502719

Arisaig Marine
Inverness-shire   01687 450224

Bedwell and Co
Walton-on-the-Naze   01255 675873

Bembridge Boatyard Marine Works
Bembridge   01983 872911

British Waterways Scotland

WELCOME

TO SCOTLAND'S CANALS

Marina and Yachting Facilities

- Superb value Marina Berthing
- Winter Lay-up at keen prices
- Skipper's Guides and Passage Information
- A network of Waterways linking Scotland's cruising waters
- A comprehensive range of licence options to suit your needs

Shoreside

- Experience the unique Falkirk Wheel
- Cycle or walk the canal banks
- Magnificent scenery rich in wildlife
- There is so much to see and do – the ideal family experience

Website

- Everything you need to know Online!

www.scottishcanals.co.uk

2004/NM1/j

Berthon Boat Company
Lymington   01590 673312

Bluewater Horizons
Weymouth   01305 782080

Bure Marine Ltd
Great Yarmouth   01493 656996

C & J Marine Services
Newcastle upon Tyne   0191 295 0072

Caley Marine
Inverness   01463 233437

Carrick Marine Projects
Co Antrim   02893 355884

Challenger Marine
Penryn   01326 377222

Coates Marine Ltd
Whitby   01947 604486

Creekside Boatyard (Old Mill Creek)
Dartmouth   01803 832649

Crinan Boatyard Ltd
Crinan   01546 830232

Dale Sailing Co Ltd
Neyland   01646 603110

Dartside Quay
Brixham   01803 845445

Dauntless Boatyard Ltd
Canvey Island   01268 793782

Dex-Tamar Marine
Plymouth   01752 491454

Douglas Marine Preston 01772 812462

East & Co, Robin
Kingsbridge   01548 531257

Emsworth Yacht Harbour
Emsworth   01243 377727

Fairlie Quay Fairlie   01475 568267

FAIRLIE QUAY —

Main Road
Fairlie
North Ayrshire KA29 0AS

The new and exciting facility just South of Largs
Marina • 80 ton hoist • 64,000sq.ft undercover
storage • 240v power available throughout shed
• on-site contractors for all your maintenance
needs • clean concrete outside storage yard
• call VHF 80 call sign Fairlie Quay.

Visitors are welcome at this developing facility.

Tel: 01475 568267 Fax: 01475 568267
enquire@kipmarina.co.uk

website: www.kipmarina.co.uk

2004/M&WMD23/b

Firmhelm Ltd Pwllheli   01758 612244

Fowey Boatyard Fowey   01726 832194

Freshwater Boatyard
Truro   01326 270443

Hafan Pwllheli Pwllheli 01758 701219

Iron Wharf Boatyard
Faversham   01795 537122

Jalsea Marine Services Ltd
Northwich   01606 77870

KG McColl Oban   01852 200248

Latham's Boatyard
Poole   01202 748029

Lavis & Son, CH
Exmouth   01395 263095

Lincombe Boat Yard
Salcombe   01548 843580

Marine Resource Centre Ltd
Oban   01631 720291

Milford Marina
Milford Haven   01646 696312/3

Northshore Yachts
Chichester   01243 512611

Pasco's Boatyard
Truro   01326 270269

Pearn and Co, Norman
Looe   01503 262244

Pepe Boatyard
Hayling Island   023 9246 1968

Philip Leisure Group
Dartmouth   01803 833351

Ponsharden Boatyard
Penryn   01326 372215

Portsmouth Marine Engineering
Fareham   01329 232854

Priors Boatyard
Burnham-on-Crouch   01621 782160

Qweek Quay Boatyard
Helston   01326 221657

Rossiter Yachts
Christchurch   01202 483250

Shepards Wharf Boatyard Ltd
Cowes   01983 297821

Silvers Marina Ltd
Helensburgh   01436 831222

Waterfront Marine
Bangor   01248 352513

Wicor Marine Fareham   01329 237112

Winters Marine Ltd
Salcombe   01548 843580

Yacht Solutions Ltd
Portsmouth   023 9220 0670

Yarmouth Marine Service
Yarmouth   01983 760521

Youngboats Faversham   01795 536176

BOAT BUILDERS & REPAIRS

ABC Powermarine
Beaumaris   01248 811413

Aqua-Star Ltd
St Sampsons   01481 244550

Ardoran Marine
Oban   01631 566123

Baumbach Bros Boatbuilders
Hayle   01736 753228

Blackwell, Craig
Co Meath   00353 87 677 9605

Bluewater Horizons
Weymouth   01305 782080

BOATWORKS + LTD
**Castle Emplacement,
St Peter Port,
Guernsey, Channel Islands
GY1 1AU.
Tel: (01481) 726071
Fax: (01481) 714224**

Boatworks + provides a comprehensive
range of services including boatbuilding
and repairs, chandlery, clothing and fuel
supplies.

Bowman Yachts Penryn 01326 376107

Brennan, John
Dun Laoghaire   00353 1 280 5308

Burghead Boat Centre
Findhorn   01309 690099

Camper & Nicholsons Yachting
Portsmouth   023 9258 0221

Carrick Marine Projects
Co Antrim   02893 355884

Chicks Marine Ltd
Guernsey   01481 724536

Creekside Boatyard (Old Mill Creek)
Dartmouth   01803 832649

CTC Marine & Leisure
Middlesbrough   01642 230123

Davies Marine Services
Ramsgate   01843 586172

Dex-Tamar Marine
Plymouth   01752 491454

Dickie & Sons Ltd, AM
Bangor   01248 352775

Dickie & Sons Ltd, AM
Pwllheli   01758 701828

Dudley Marine
Milford Haven   01646 692787

East & Co, Robin
Kingsbridge   01548 531257

East Llanion Marine Ltd
Pembroke Dock   01646 686866

Emblem Enterprises
East Cowes   01983 294243

Exe Leisure Exeter   01392 879055

Fairlie Quay Fairlie   01475 568267

Fairweather Marine
Fareham   01329 283500

Fergulsea Engineering
Ayr   01292 262978

Ferrypoint Boat Co
Youghal   00353 24 94232

Floetree Ltd (Loch Lomond Marina)
Balloch   01389 752069

Freshwater Boatyard
Truro   01326 270443

Gallichan Marine Ltd
Jersey   01534 746387

Goodchild Marine Services
Great Yarmouth   01493 782301

Gweek Quay Boatyard
Helston   01326 221657

Hardway Marine Store
Gosport   023 9258 0420

Harris Marine (1984) Ltd, Ray
Barry   01446 740924

Hayling Yacht Company
Hayling Island   023 9246 3592

Holyhead Marine Services Ltd
Holyhead   01407 760111

International Marine Designs
Aberdyfi   01654 767572

Jackson Yacht Services
Jersey   01534 743819

James Marine Yacht Services
Bristol   0117 966 2291

Jones (Boatbuilders), David
Chester 01244 390363

KG McColl Oban 01852 200248

Kingfisher Marine
Weymouth 01305 766595

Kippford Slipway Ltd
Dalbeattie 01556 620249

Langley Marine Services Ltd
Eastbourne 01323 470244

Lavis & Son, CH
Exmouth 01395 263095

Lawrenny Yacht Station
Lawrenny 01646 651212

Lencraft Boats Ltd
Dungarvan 00353 58 682220

Lifeline Marine Services
Poole 01202 669676

Mannings Marine Ltd
Bootle 0151 933 0820

Maritime Workshop
Gosport 023 9252 7805

Mashford Brothers
Torpoint 01752 822232

Mayor & Co Ltd, J
Preston 01772 812250

McKellar's Slipway Ltd
Helensburgh 01436 842334

Mears, HJ Axmouth 01297 23344

Medusa Marina
Woolverstone 01473 780090

Moody Yachts International Ltd
Swanwick 01489 885000

Morrison, A Killyleagh 028 44828215

Moss (Boatbuilders), David
Thornton-Cleveleys 01253 893830

Multi Marine Composites Ltd
Torpoint 01752 823513

Newing, Roy E
Canterbury 01227 860345

Noble and Sons, Alexander
Girvan 01465 712223

Northney Marine Services
Hayling Island 023 9246 9246

Northshore King's Lynn 01485 210236

O'Sullivans Marine Ltd
Tralee 00353 66 7124524

Oyster Marine Ltd
Ipswich 01473 688888

Partington Marine Ltd, William
Pwllheli 01758 612808

Pasco's Boatyard
Truro 01326 270269

Penrhos Marine
Aberdovey 01654 767478

Penzance Marine Services
Penzance 01736 361081

Preston Marine Services Ltd
Preston 01772 733595

Rampart Yachts
Southampton 023 8023 4777

Red Bay Boats Ltd
Cushendall 028 2177 1331

Reliance Marine
Wirral 0151 625 5219

Richards, Eddie
East Cowes 01983 299740

Richardson Boatbuilders, Ian
Stromness 01856 850321

Richardsons Boatbuilders
Newport 01983 821095

Riley Marine Dover 01304 214544

River Tees Engineering & Welding Ltd
Middlesbrough 01642 226226

Roberts Marine Ltd, S
Liverpool 0151 707 8300

Rustler Yachts Ltd
Penryn 01326 376107

Sea & Shore Ship Chandler
Dundee 01832 202666

SEAFIT MARINE SERVICES
Falmouth Marina, North Parade,
Falmouth, Cornwall TR11 2TD

Tel: (01326) 313713
Fax: (01326) 211521
Mobile: (07971) 196175
All repair and service work undertaken.

Seamark-Nunn & Co
Felixstowe 01394 275327

Seaquest Yachts
Penryn 01326 377006

SEAWARD MARINE LTD
Prospect Road, Cowes,
Isle of Wight PO31 7AD
Tel: 01983 280333
Fax: 01983 295095
e-mail: sales@seawardboat.com
www.seawardboat.com
Builders of the Seaward brand of Nelson semi-displacement motor cruisers, renowned for their good seakeeping and traditional style. Custom building and repairs. Used Seaward craft also available.

Spencer Sailing Services, Jim
Brightlingsea 01206 302911

Spicer Boatbuilder, Nick
Weymouth Marina 01305 767118

Starlight Yachts Penryn 01326 376107

Sterling Yacht Services
Port Bannatyne 01700 502716

Stone Pier Yacht Services
Warsash 01489 885400

Tarquin Boat Co
Emsworth 01243 375211

TT Marine Eastbourne 01323 472009

Virgo Marine Co
Wirral 0151 644 1037

WA Simpson Marine Ltd
Dundee 01382 566670

Waterfront Marine
Bangor 01248 352513

Western Marine
Dublin 00353 1 280 0321

Wigmore Wright Marine Services
Penarth 029 2070 9983

Yarmouth Marine Service
01983 760521

Youngboats Faversham 01795 536176

BOATYARD SERVICES & SUPPLIES

A & P Ship Care
Ramsgate 01843 593140

Abersoch Boatyard Ltd
Abersoch 01758 712213

Amble Boat Co Ltd
Amble 01665 710267

Amsbrisbeg Ltd
Port Bannatyne 01700 502719

ARDORAN MARINE
Lerags, Oban, Argyll,
Scotland PA34 4SE

Tel: 01631 566123
Fax: 01631 566611
e-mail: colin@ardoran.co.uk
www.ardoran.co.uk
West coast Scotland. All marine facilities.

Ardmair Boat Centre
Ullapool 01854 612054

Ardmaleish Boat Building Co
Rothesay 01700 502007

Ardrishaig Boatyard
Lochgilphead 01546 603280

Arfon Oceaneering
Caernarfon 01286 676055

Arklow Slipway
Arklow 00353 402 33233

B & G Marine
Maylandsea 01621 743546

Baltic Wharf Boatyard
Totnes 01803 867922

Baltimore Boatyard
Baltimore 00353 28 20444

Battricks Boatyard
St Aubin 01534 743412

Bedwell and Co
Walton-on-the-Naze 01255 675873

Berthon Boat Co
Lymington 01590 673312

Birch Boatbuilders, ER 01268 696094

Birdham Shipyard
Chichester 01243 512310

BJ Marine Ltd Bangor 028 91271434

Blagdon, A Plymouth 01752 561830

Boatworks + Ltd
St Peter Port 01481 726071

Booth W Kelly Ltd
Ramsey 01624 812322

Brennan, John
Dun Laoghaire 00353 1 280 5308

Brightlingsea Boatyard
Brightlingsea 01206 302003/8

Brighton Marina Boatyard
Brighton 01273 819919

Bristol Marina (Yard)
Bristol 0117 921 3198

Buchan & Son Ltd, J
Peterhead 01779 475395

Buckie Shipyard Ltd
Buckie 01542 831245

Bucklers Hard Boat Builders Ltd
Brockenhurst 01590 616214

Bure Marine Ltd
Great Yarmouth 01493 656996

C & J Marine Services
Newcastle Upon Tyne 0191 295 0072

Caley Marina Inverness 01463 233437

Cambrian Boat Centre
Swansea 01792 467263

Cambrian Marine Services Ltd
Cardiff 029 20343459

Cantell and Son Ltd
Newhaven 01273 514118

Carroll's Ballyhack Boatyard
New Ross 00353 51 389164

Castlepoint Boatyard
Crosshaven 00353 21 4832154

Chabot, Gary Newhaven 01273 611076

Chapman & Hewitt Boatbuilders
Wadebridge 01208 813487

Chippendale Craft Rye 01797 227707

Clapson & Son (Shipbuilders) Ltd
Barton on Humber 01652 635620

Coastal Marine Boatbuilders
(Berwick upon Tweed)
Eyemouth 01890 750328

Coastcraft Ltd
Cockenzie 01875 812150

Coates Marine Ltd
Whitby 01947 604486

Cook Boatbuilders and Repairers, S
Whitby 01947 820521

Coombes, AA
Bembridge 01983 872296

Corpach Boatbuilding Company
Fort William 01397 772861

Craobh Marina
By Lochgilphead 01852 500222

Creekside Boatyard (Old Mill Creek)
Dartmouth 01803 832649

Crinan Boatyard
By Lochgilphead 01546 830232

Crosshaven Boatyard Co Ltd
Crosshaven 00353 21 831161

Dale Sailing Co Ltd
Neyland 01646 603110

Darthaven Marina Ltd
Kingswear 01803 752242

Dartside Quay Brixham 01803 845445

Dauntless Boatyard Ltd
Canvey Island 01268 793782

Davis's Boatyard Poole 01202 674349

DICKIES OF BANGOR
36 Garth Road, Bangor,
Gwynedd LL57 2SE
Tel: (01248) 363400
Fax: (01248) 354169
e-mail: info@dickies.co.uk
www.dickies.co.uk
Full yard services, chandlery, brokerage
and new boat dealers for Beneteau Sail
and power boats and Lagoon power
catamarans.

Dinas Boat Yard Ltd
Y Felinheli 01248 671642

Dorset Yachts Poole 01202 674531

Douglas Boatyard
Preston 01772 812462

Dover Yacht Co Dover 01304 201073

Dun Laoghaire Marina
Dun Laoghaire +353 1 2020040

Elephant Boatyard
Southampton 023 80403268

Elton Boatbuilding Ltd
Kirkcudbright 01557 330177

Fairways Marine Engineers
Maldon 01621 852866

Farrow & Chambers Yacht Builders
Humberston 01472 632424

Felixstowe Ferry Boatyard
Felixstowe 01394 282173

Ferguson Engineering
Wexford 00353 6566822133

Ferry Marine South
Queensferry 0131 331 1233

Ferrybridge Marine Services Ltd
Weymouth 01305 781518

Findhorn Boatyard
Findhorn 01309 690099

Firmhelm Ltd Pwllheli 01758 612251

Fishbourne Quay Boatyard
Ryde 01983 882200

Fleming Engineering, J
Stornoway 01851 703488

Forrest Marine Ltd
Exeter 01392 833504

Fowey Boatyard Fowey 01726 832194

Fox's Marina Ipswich 01473 689111

Frank Halls & Son
Walton on the Naze 01255 675596

Freeport Marine Jersey 01534 888100

Goodchild Marine Services
Great Yarmouth 01493 782301

Gweek Quay Boatyard
Helston 01326 221657

Haines Boatyard
Chichester 01243 512228

Harbour Marine
Plymouth 01752 204690/1

Harbour Marine Services Ltd
Southwold 01502 724721

Harris Marine Barry 01446 740924

Hartlepool Marine Engineering
Hartlepool 01429 867883

Hayles, Harold Yarmouth 01983 760373

Henderson, J Shiskine 01770 860259

Heron Marine
Whitstable 01227 361255

Hewitt, George Binham 01328 830078

Hillyard, David
Littlehampton 01903 713327

Holyhead Marina & Trinity Marine Ltd
Holyhead 01407 764242

Instow Marine Services
Bideford 01271 861081

Ipswich Haven Marina
Ipswich 01473 236644

Iron Wharf Boatyard
Faversham 01795 537122

Island Boat Services
Port of St Mary 01624 832073

Jalsea Marine Services Ltd Weaver
Shipyard, Northwich 01606 77870

J B Timber Ltd
North Ferriby 01482 631765

Jersey Harbours Dept
St Helier 01534 885588

Jones & Teague
Saundersfoot 01834 813429

Kilnsale Boatyard
Kinsale 00353 21 4774774

Kilrush Marina & Boatyard – Ireland
00353 65 9052072

Lake Yard Poole 01202 674531

Lallow, C Isle of Wight 01983 292112

Latham's Boatyard
Poole 01202 748029

Leonard Marine, Peter
Newhaven 01273 515987

Lincombe Boat Yard
Salcombe 01548 843580

Lomax Boatbuilders
Cliffony 00353 71 66124

Lucas Yachting, Mike
Torquay 01803 212840

Lymington Yacht Haven
Lymington 01590 677071

MacDougalls Marine Services
Isle of Mull 01681 700294

Macduff Shipyard Ltd
Macduff 01261 832234

Madog Boatyard
Porthmadog 01766 514205/513435

Mainbrayce Marine
Alderney   01481 822772

Malakoff and Moore
Lerwick   01595 695544

**Mallaig Boat Building and
Engineering** Mallaig   01687 462304

Maramarine
Helensburgh   01436 810971

Marindus Engineering
Kilmore Quay   00353 53 29794

Marine Gleam
Lymington   0800 074 4672

Mariners Farm Boatyard
Gillingham   01634 233179

McCallum & Co Boat Builders, A
Tarbert   01880 820209

McCaughty (Boatbuilders), J
Wick   01955 602858

McGruar and Co Ltd
Helensburgh   01436 831313

Mitchell's Boatyard
Poole   01202 747857

Mooney Boats
Killybegs   00353 73 31152/31388

Moore & Son, J
St Austell   01726 842964

Morrison, A Killyleagh   028 44828215

Moss (Boatbuilders), David
Thornton-Cleveleys   01253 893830

Noble and Sons, Alexander
Girvan   01465 712223

North Pier (Oban) Oban 01631 562892

North Wales Boat Centre
Conwy   01492 580740

Northshore Yacht Yard
Chichester   01243 512611

Oban Yachts and Marine Services
By Oban   01631 565333

Parker Yachts and Dinghys Ltd
Nr Boston   01205 722697

Pearn and Co, Norman
Looe   01503 262244

Penrhos Marine
Aberdovey   01654 767478

**Penzance Dry Dock and Engineering
Co Ltd** Penzance   01736 363838

Philip & Son Dartmouth 01803 833351

Phillips, HJ Rye   01797 223234

Ponsharden Boatyard
Penryn   01326 372215

Powersail and Island Chandlers Ltd
East Cowes Marina   01983 299800

Pratt and Son, VJ
King's Lynn   01553 764058

Priors Boatyard
Burnham-on-Crouch   01621 782160

R K Marine Ltd
Swanwick   01489 583572

Rat Island Sailboat Company (Yard)
St Mary's   01720 423399

Retreat Boatyard Ltd
Exeter   01392 874720/875934

Rice and Cole Ltd
Burnham-on-Crouch   01621 782063

Richardson Boatbuilders, Ian
Stromness   01856 850321

Richardsons Boatbuilders
Binfield   01983 821095

Riverside Yard
Shoreham Beach   01273 592456

RJ Prior (Burnham) Ltd
Burnham-on-Crouch   01621 782160

Robertsons Boatyard
Woodbridge   01394 382305

Rossbrin Boatyard
Schull   00353 28 37352

Rossiter Yachts Ltd
Christchurch   01202 483250

Rossreagh Boatyard
Rathmullan   00353 74 51082

Rudders Boatyard & Moorings
Milford Haven   01646 600288

Ryan & Roberts Marine Services
Askeaton   00353 61 392198

Rye Harbour Marina Rye
     01797 227667

Rynn Engineering, Pat
Galway   00353 91 562568

Sandbanks Yacht Company
Poole   01202 707500

Sandy Morrison Engineering
Uig   01470 542300

Scarborough Marine Engineering Ltd
Scarborough   01723 375199

Severn Valley Cruisers Ltd (Boatyard)
Stourport-on-Severn   01299 871165

Shepards Wharf Boatyard Ltd
Cowes   01983 297821

Shotley Marina Ltd
Ipswich   01473 788982

Shotley Marine Services Ltd
Ipswich   01473 788913

Silvers Marina Ltd
Helensburgh   01436 831222

Skinners Boat Yard
Baltimore   00353 28 20114

Sleat Marina Services
Ardvasar   01471 844216

Smith & Gibbs
Eastbourne   01323 734656

**South Dock (Seaham Harbour Dock
Co)** Seaham   0191 581 3877

Sparkes Boatyard
Hayling Island   023 92463572

Spencer Sailing Services, Jim
Brightlingsea   01206 302911

Standard House Boatyard
Wells-next-the-Sea   01328 710593

Strand Shipyard Rye   01797 222070

Stratton Boatyard, Ken
Bembridge   01983 873185

Surry Boatyard
Shoreham-by-Sea   01273 461491

Titchmarsh Marina
Walton-on-the-Naze   01255 672185

Tollesbury Marina
Tollesbury   01621 869202

Toms and Son Ltd, C
Fowey   01726 870232

T J Rigging Conwy 07780 972411

Trinity Marine Holyhead 01407 763855

Trouts Boatyard (River Exe)
Topsham 01392 873044

Upson and Co, RF
Aldeburgh 01728 453047

Versatility Workboats
Rye 01797 224422

Weir Quay Boatyard
Bere Alston 01822 840474

West Solent Boatbuilders
Lymington 01590 642080

Wicor Marine Fareham 01329 237112

WINTERS MARINE LIMITED
(Lincombe Boatyard)
Lincombe, Salcombe,
Devon TQ8 8NQ.
Tel: (01548) 843580
e-mail:
lincombeboatyard@eclipse.co.uk
Deep water pontoon moorings. Winter storage for 150 boats. All maintenance and repair facilities. Slipway capacity 30 tonnes. Short and long-term lifecraft hire.

Woodrolfe Boatyard
Maldon 01621 869202

BOOKS, CHARTS & PUBLISHERS

Adlard Coles Nautical
London 0207 7580200

Brown Son & Ferguson Ltd
Glasgow 0141 429 1234

Chattan Security Ltd
Edinburgh 0131 555 3155

Cooke & Son Ltd, B Hull 01482 223454

Dubois Phillips & McCallum Ltd
Liverpool 0151 236 2776

Fernhurst Books
Arundel 01903 882277

Imray, Laurie, Norie & Wilson
Huntingdon 01480 462114

Kelvin Hughes
Southampton 023 8063 4911

Lilley & Gillie Ltd, John 0191 257 2217

Marine Chart Services
Wellingborough 01933 441629

Price & Co Ltd, WF
Bristol 0117 929 2229

REED'S NAUTICAL
The Barn, Ford Farm, Bradford
Leigh, Bradford-on-Avon, Wilts.
BA15 2RP
Tel: (01225) 868821
Fax: (01225) 868831
e-mail:
sales@abreed.demon.co.uk
www.reedsnautical.com
Specialists in worldwide mail order of nautical books, charts and prints for boating people everywhere - book & chart catalogues available.

SEA CHEST, THE
Admiralty Chart Agent
Queen Anne's Battery Marina,
Plymouth PL4 0LP
Tel: 01752 222012
Fax: 01752 252679
www.seachest.co.uk
Admiralty and Imray Chart Agent, Huge stocks of Books and Charts, Rapid dispatch.

Smith AM (Marine) Ltd
London 020 8529 6988

Stanford Charts
West Mersea 01206 381580

TODD CHART AGENCY LTD
Navigation House, 85 High
Street, Bangor, County Down,
Northern Ireland BT20 5BD
Tel: 028 9146 6640
Fax: 028 9147 1070
e-mail:admiralty@toddchart.co.uk
www.nautical-charts.com
International Admiralty Chart Agent, chart

correction service and nautical booksellers. Programming Centre for C-MAP NT and Navionics electronic charts. Stockist of Imray charts and books, navigation and chartroom instruments, binoculars, clocks etc. UK agent for Icelandic Hydrographic Service. Mail order - Visa, Mastercard, American Express and Switch/Delta accepted.

Warsash Nautical Bookshop
Warsash 01489 572384

YachtingBooks.Com
London 020 8776 8682

UK Hydrographics Office
Taunton 01823 337900

BOW THRUSTERS

ARS Anglian Diesels Ltd
Norfolk 01508 520555

Buckler's Hard Boat Builders Ltd
Beaulieu 01590 616214

JS Mouldings International
Bursledon 023 8040 3220

WESTERN MARINE POWER LTD
Western Hangar, Mount Batten,
Plymouth, Devon PL9 9SJ.
Tel: (01752) 408804
Fax: (01752) 408807
e-mail: info@wmp.co.uk
www.wmp.co.uk
Suppliers and installers of:- Watermakers, Air Conditioning, Generators, Electrical Systems, Electronic Engine Controls, Bow and Stern Thrusters, Teak Decks, Davits, Passarelles and Cranes, Galley and Sanitation Equipment. ISO 9002 Quality Assurance.

BREAKDOWN

BJ Marine Ltd
Bangor, Ireland 028 9127 1434

Seafit Marine Services
Falmouth 01326 313713

SEA START LIMITED
Unit 13, Hamble Point Marina,
Hamble, Southampton SO31 4JD
Tel: (023) 8045 8000
Fax: (023) 8045 2666
e-mail: sales@seastart.co.uk
www.seastart.co.uk
24 hours a day, 365 days a year - marine breakdown assistance.

CHANDLERS

ABC Powermarine
Beaumaris   01248 811413

Absolute Marine
Littlehampton   01903 734411

Acamar Marine Services/Sirius Yacht Training Christchurch   01202 488030

Aladdin's Cave Chandlery Ltd
(Deacons) Bursledon   023 8040 2182

Aladdin's Cave Chandlery Ltd (Camper Nicholsons) Gosport   023 8040 2182

Aladdin's Cave Chandlery Ltd (Hamble Point) Southampton   023 80455 058

Aladdin's Cave Chandlery Ltd (Mercury) Southampton   023 8045 4849

Aladdin's Cave Chandlery Ltd (Port Hamble) Southampton   023 8045 4858

Aladdin's Cave Chandlery Ltd (Swanwick) Swanwick   01489 575828

Alderney Boating Centre
Alderney   01481 823725

Aqua Togs/Shipmates Group
Cowes   01983 295071

Arbroath Fishermen's Association
Arbroath   01241 873132

Ardfern Yacht Centre Ltd
Argyll   01852 500247

Ardoran Marine Oban   01631 566123

Arfon Oceaneering
Caernarfon   01286 676055

Arthurs Chandlery
Gosport   023 9252 6522

Arun Aquasports
Littlehampton   01903 713553

Arun Canvas and Rigging Ltd
Littlehampton   01903 732561

Arun Nautique
Littlehampton   01903 730558

Aruncraft Chandlers
Littlehampton   01903 723667

ASAP Supplies – Equipment & Spares Worldwide
Beccles   0845 1300870

Auto Marine Sales
Southsea   023 9281 2263

Bedwell and Co
Walton on the Naze   01255 675873

BJ Marine Ltd Bangor   028 9127 1434

Bluecastle Chandlers
Portland   01305 822298

Bluewater Horizons
Weymouth   01305 782080

Boatshop Chandlery
Brixham   01803 882055

Boatacs
Westcliffe on Sea   01702 475057

BOATWORKS + LTD
Castle Emplacement,
St Peter Port,
Guernsey, Channel Islands
GY1 1AU.
Tel: (01481) 726071
Fax: (01481) 714224
Boatworks + provides a comprehensive range of services including boatbuilding and repairs, chandlery, clothing and fuel supplies.

Bosun's Locker, The
Milford Haven   01646 697834

Bosun's Locker, The
Ramsgate   01843 597158

Bosuns Locker, The
South Queensferry 0131 331 3875/4496

Bradwell Chandlery
Bradwell-on-Sea   01621 776147

Brancaster Sailing and Sailboard Centre Kings Lynn   01485 210236

Bridger Marine, John
Exeter   01392 216420

Brigantine Teignmouth   01626 872400

Bristol Boat Ltd Bristol   01225 872032

Brixham Chandlers
Brixham   01803 882055

Brixham Yacht Supplies Ltd
Brixham   01803 882290

Brunel Chandlery Ltd
Neyland   01646 601667

Bucklers Hard Boat Builders
Beaulieu   01590 616214

Burghead Boat Centre
Findhorn   01309 690099

Bussell & Co, WL
Weymouth   01305 785633

Buzzard Marine
Yarmouth   01983 760707

C & M Marine Bridlington
                             01262 672212

Cabin Yacht Stores
Rochester   01634 718020

Caley Marina Inverness   01463 233437

Cambrian Boat Centre
Swansea   01792 467263

Captain O M Watts
London   020 7493 4633

Carne (Sales) Ltd, David
Falmouth   01326 318314

Carne (Sales) Ltd, David
Penryn   01326 374177

Caters Carrick Ltd
Carrickfergus   028 93351919

CH Marine (Cork)
Cork   00353 21 4315700

CH Marine Skibbereen 00353 28 23190

Charity & Taylor Ltd
Lowestoft   01502 581529

Chertsey Marine Ltd
Penton Hook Marina   01932 565195

Chicks Marine Ltd
Guernsey   01481 724536

Christchurch Boat Shop
Christchurch   01202 482751

Churcher Marine
Worthing   01903 230523

Clapson & Son (Shipbuilders) Ltd
Barton-on-Humber   01652 635620

Clarke, Albert
Newtownards   01247 872325

Coastal Marine Boatbuilders Ltd (Dunbar) Eyemouth   01890 750328

Coates Marine Ltd/Northern Spar Services Whitby   01947 604486

Collins Marine St Helier 01534 732415

Compass Marine
Lancing   01903 761773

Compass Point Chandlery
Southampton   023 80452388

Cosalt International Ltd
Aberdeen   01224 588327

Cotter, Kieran
Baltimore   00353 28 20106

Cox Yacht Charter Ltd, Nick
Lymington   01590 673489

C Q Chandlers Ltd
Poole   01202 682095

Crinan Boats Ltd
Lochgilphead   01546 830232

CTC Marine & Leisure
Middlesbrough   01642 230123

Dale Sailing Co Ltd
Milford Haven   01646 603110

Danson Marine Sidcup 0208 304 5678

Dart Chandlers
Dartmouth   01803 833772

Dartside Quay
Brixham   01803 845445

Dauntless Boatyard Ltd
Canvey Island   01268 793782

Davis Marine, Ron
Portland   01305 821175

Davis's Yacht Chandler
Littlehampton   01903 722778

DEEVY & CO LTD, C. J.
48 Pomoell St, Waterford,
Ireland.
Tel: 00 353 (51) 855717
Fax: 00 353 (51) 855710
e-mail: sales@deevys.com
www.deevys.com
Motor & marine supplies for the South East
region of Ireland. Est 1935. Offering a
comprehensive range of products to both
marine enthusiasts and motor enthusiasts.
Branches in Waterford and Clonmell.

Denholm Fishselling
Scrabster   01847 896968

Denney & Son, EL
Redcar   01642 483507

Dickie & Sons Ltd, AM
Bangor   01248 352775

Dickie & Sons Ltd, AM
Pwllheli   01758 701828

DINGHY STORE, THE
The Sea Wall, Whitstable, Kent
CT5 1BX
Tel: (01227) 274168
Fax: (01227) 772750
e-mail:
sales@thedinghystore.co.uk
www.thedinghystore.co.uk
One of the largest marine chandlers in
Kent. 1st floor: Harken, Holt, RWO,
Marlow, International Paints, charts,
books. 2nd floor: Musto, Henri Lloyd, Gill,
Crewsaver, Chatham, Icom radios. Open
seven days a week in summer months.

**Dinghy Supplies Ltd/Sutton Marine
Ltd** Sutton   00353 1 832 2312

Diverse Yacht Services
Hamble   023 80453399

Dixon Chandlery, Peter
Exmouth   01395 273248

Dixons Exmouth   01392 273248

Doling & Son, GW
Barrow In Furness   01229 823708

Dovey Marine Aberdovey 01654 767581

Down Marine Co Ltd
Belfast   028 9048 0247

Douglas Marine Preston 01772 812462

Dubois Phillips & McCallum Ltd
Liverpool   0151 236 2776

Duncan Ltd, JS Wick   01955 602689

Duncan Yacht Chandlers
Glasgow   0141 429 6044

East Anglian Sea School
Ipswich   01473 659992

Eccles Marine Co
Middlesbrough   01642 230123

Emsworth Chandlery
Emsworth   01243 375500

Exe Leisure Exeter   01392 879055

Fairways Chandlery
Burnham-on-Crouch   01621 782659

Fathom Marine Bridport 01308 420988

Ferrypoint Boat Co
Youghal   00353 24 94232

Findhorn Marina & Boatyard
Findhorn   01309 690099

Firmhelm Ltd Pwllheli 01758 612244

**Fisherman's Mutual Asssociation
(Eyemouth) Ltd**
Eyemouth   01890 750373

**Fleetwood Trawlers' Supply Co Ltd,
The** Fleetwood   01253 873476

Floetree Ltd (Loch Lomond Marina)
Balloch   01389 752069

Foc'sle, The Exeter   01392 874105

Freeport Marine Jersey 01534 888100

French Marine Motors Ltd
Brightlingsea   01206 302133

Gallichan Marine Ltd
Jersey   01534 746387

Galway Marine Chandlers Ltd
Galway   00353 91 566568

GB Attfield & Company
Dursley   01453 547185

Gibbons Ship Chandlers Ltd
Sunderland   0191 567 2101

Gibbs Chandlery
Shepperton   01932 242977

Glaslyn Marine Supplies Ltd
Porthmadog   01766 513545

Goodwick Marine
Fishguard   01348 873955

Gorleston Marine Ltd
Great Yarmouth   01493 661883

GP Barnes Ltd
Shoreham   01273 591705/596680

Green Marine, Jimmy
Fore St Beer   01297 20744

Greenham Marine
Emsworth   01243 378314

Gunn Navigation Services, Thomas
Aberdeen   01224 595045

Hale Marine, Ron
Portsmouth   023 92732985

Harbour Marine Services Ltd (HMS)
Southwold   01502 724721

Hardware & Marine Supplies
Wexford   00353 53 29791

Hardway Marine Store
Gosport   023 92580420

Harris Marine (1984) Ltd, Ray
Barry   01446 740924

Hartlepool Marine Supplies
Hartlepool   01429 862932

Harwoods Yarmouth   01983 760258

Hawkins Marine Shipstores, John
Rochester   01634 840812

Hayles, Harold Yarmouth 01983 760373

Herm Seaway Marine Ltd
St Peter Port   01481 726829

Hornsey (Chandlery) Ltd, Chris
Southsea   023 9273 4728

Hunter & Combes
Cowes   01983 299599

Inverness Boat Centre
North Kessock   01463 731383

Iron Stores Marine
St Helier   01534 877755

Isles of Scilly Steamship Co
St Mary's   01720 422710

Jackson Yacht Services
Jersey   01534 743819

Jamison and Green Ltd
Belfast   028 90322444

Jeckells and Son Ltd
Lowestoft   01502 565007

JF Marine Chandlery
Rhu   01436 820584

JNW Services Peterhead 01779 477346

Johnston Brothers
Mallaig   01687 462215

Johnstons Marine Stores
Lamlash   01770 600333

Jones & Teague
Saundersfoot   01834 813429

Kearon Ltd, George
Arklow   00353 402 32319

Kelpie Boats
Pembroke Dock   01646 683661

Kelvin Hughes Ltd
Southampton   023 80634911

Kildale Marine Hull   01482 227464

Kingfisher Marine
Weymouth   01305 766595

Kip Chandlery Inverkip
Greenock   01475 521485

Kirkcudbright Scallop Gear Ltd
Kirkcudbright   01557 330399

Kyle Chandlers Troon   01292 311880

Lamb & Sons Ltd, JP Liverpool	0151 709 4861
Landon Marine, Reg Truro	01872 272668
Largs Chandlers Largs	01475 686026
Lencraft Boats Ltd Dungarvan	00353 58 68220
Lincoln Marina Lincoln	01522 526896
Looe Chandlery West Looe	01503 264355
Lynch Ltd, PA Morpeth	01670 512291
Mackay Boatbuilders (Arbroath) Ltd Aberdeen	01241 872879
Mailspeed Marine Warrington	01925 838858
Manx Marine Ltd Douglas	01624 674842
Marine & Leisure Europe Ltd Plymouth	01752 268826
Marine Connections Bitterne	023 803 36200
Marine Instruments Falmouth	01326 312414
Marine Scene Cardiff	029 2070 5780
Marine Services Jersey	01534 626930
Marine Store Maldon	01621 854380
Marine Store Walton on the Naze	01255 679028
Marine Superstore Port Solent Chandlery Portsmouth	023 9221 9843
MarineCo Looe	01503 265444

Marquand Brothers St Peter Port	01481 720962
Martello Yacht Services Canvey Island	01268 681970
Maryport Harbour and Marina Maryport	01900 818447/4431
Matthews Ltd, D Cork	00353 214 277633
Mayflower Chandlery Plymouth	01752 500121
McCready Sailboats Ltd Holywood	028 9042 1821
Mengham Marine Hayling Island	023 92464333
Moore & Son, J Mevagissey	01726 842964
Morgan & Sons Marine, LH Brightlingsea	01206 302003
Mount Batten Boathouse Plymouth	01752 482666
Murphy, Nicholas Dunmore East	00353 51 383259
Mylor Chandlery & Rigging Falmouth	01326 375482
Nancy Black Oban	01631 562550
Nautical World Bangor	028 91460330
New World Yacht Care Helensburgh	01436 820586
Norfolk Marine Great Yarmouth	01692 670272
Norfolk Marine Chandlery Shop Norwich	01603 783150

North Quay Marine St Sampson's	01481 246561
Northshore King's Lynn	01485 210236
Ocean Blue Penzance	01736 364004
Ocean Leisure Ltd London	020 7930 5050
Ocean World Ltd Cowes	01983 291744
One Stop Chandlery Chelmsford	01245 380680
O'Sullivans Marine Ltd Tralee	00353 66 7124524

OUTRIGGERS/UPPER DECK MARINE
Albert Quay, Fowey, Cornwall
PL23 1AQ
Tel: 01726 833233
Fax: 01726 833265
www.fowey.com
'Outriggers' casual and marine clothing, footwear, nautical gifts. Admiralty chart agent and marine books.

Partington Marine Ltd, William Pwllheli	01758 612808
Pascall Atkey & Sons Ltd Isle of Wight	01983 292381
Paterson, A Macduff	01261 832784
Pennine Marine Ltd Skipton	01756 792335
Penrhos Marine Aberdovey	01654 767478
Penzance Marine Services Penzance	01736 361081
Perry Marine, Rob Axminster	01297 631314
Peterhead Watersports Centre Peterhead	01779 480888
Peters PLC Chichester	01243 511033
Piplers of Poole Poole	01202 673056

PIRATES CAVE LTD
Unit 14, Northpoint Business Estate, Enterprise Close, Medway City Estate, Frindsbury, Rochester ME2 4LX
Tel: (01634) 295233
Fax: (01634) 722326
e-mail: piratescaveuk@yahoo.co.uk
We hold a very large stock of general chandlery as well as being main dealers for XM, Silva, Raymarine, Whale, Jabsco, Barton, Spincock and ECS products. Staffed by people with boating experience.

Powersail and Island Chandlers Ltd East Cowes Marina	01983 299800
Preston Marine Services Ltd Preston	01772 733595
Price & Co Ltd, WF Bristol	0117 929 2229
Pumpkin Marine Supplies Hayling Island	023 9246 8794
Purple Sails & Marine Walsall	01922 614787
Quay West Chandlers Poole	01202 742488

Tel: 01485 210236   Email: info@northshoresport.co.uk
NORFOLK'S LEADING SAILING SCHOOL
- Shorebased navigation & VHF/GMOSS radio courses.
- Wide range of practical sailing courses
- All skills / ages catered for.
- Chandlery / Workshop
- Stockists of Barton and Harken & Holt

The Boatyard, Brancaster Staithe, Kings Lynn, Norfolk

2004/M&WC6/d

PURPLE SAILS & MARINE

Specialist Suppliers of Sailboat Gear

Chandlery & Sailing Equipment Suppliers
137-138 Stafford Street, Walsall, West Midlands WS2 8EA
Tel: (01922) 614787   Fax: (01922) 630766
E-mail: purple.marine@virgin.net
Website: www.teampurple.co.uk

2004/M&WM32/d

Quayside Marine
Salcombe 01548 844300

Racecourse Yacht Basin (Windsor) Ltd Windsor 01753 851501

Rat Rigs Water Sports
Cardiff 029 2062 1309

Reliance Marine Wirral 0151 625 5219

Reynolds, Cliff Hartlepool
01429 272049

RHP Marine Cowes 01983 290421

Rhu Chandlery Rhu 01436 820584

RNS Marine Northam 01237 474167

Sail Loft Bideford 01271 860001

Sailaway St Anthony 01326 231357

Sailcraft Sea School
Norfolk 01485 210236

Salcombe Boatstore
Salcombe 01548 843708

Salterns Chandlery
Poole 01202 701556

Sandrock Marine Rye 01797 222679

Schull Watersports Centre
Schull 00353 28 28554

Sea & Shore Ship Chandler
Dundee 01382 202666

Sea Cruisers of Rye Rye 01797 222070

Sea Span Edinburgh 0131 552 2224

Sea Teach Ltd Emsworth 01243 375774

Seafare Tobermory 01688 302277

Seahog Boats Preston 01772 633016

Seamark-Nunn & Co
Felixstowe 01394 275327

Seaquest Marine Ltd
St Peter Port 01481 721773

Seaware Ltd Penryn 01326 377948

Seaway Marine Macduff 01261 832877

Severn Valley Boat Centre
Stourport-on-Severn 01299 871165

Shamrock Chandlery
Southampton 023 8063 2725

Sharp & Enright Dover 01304 206295

Shearwater Engineering Services Ltd
Dunoon 01369 706666

Shell Bay Marine & Watersports Centre Studland Bay 01202 450340

Shipmates Chandlery
Dartmouth 01803 839292

Shipmates Chandlery
Salcombe 01548 844555

Ship 'N Shore
Hayling Island 023 9243 7373

Shipshape Marine
King's Lynn 01553 764058

Shipsides Marine Ltd
Preston 01772 797079

Shorewater Sports
Chichester 01243 672315

Simpson Marine Ltd
Newhaven 01273 612612

Simpson Marine Ltd, WA
Dundee 01382 566670

Sketrick Marine Centre
Killinchy 028 9754 1400

Smith & Gibbs
Eastbourne 01323 734656

Smith AM (Marine) Ltd
London 020 8529 6988

Solent Marine Chandlery Ltd
Gosport 023 9258 4622

South Coast Marine
Christchurch 01202 482695

South Pier Shipyard
St Helier 01534 519700

Southampton Yacht Services Ltd
Southampton 023 803 35266

Southern Masts & Rigging
Brighton 01273 818189

Spinnaker Yacht Chandlery Bembridge
01983 874324

Standard House Chandlery Wells-next-the-Sea 01328 710593

Stornoway Fishermen's Co-op
Stornoway 01851 702563

Storrar Marine Store Newcastle upon Tyne 0191 266 1037

Sunset Marine & Watersports Sligo
00353 71 62792

Sussex Marine St Leonards on Sea
01424 425882

Sussex Marine Centre Shoreham
01273 454737

Sutton Marine (Dublin) Sutton
00353 1 832 2312

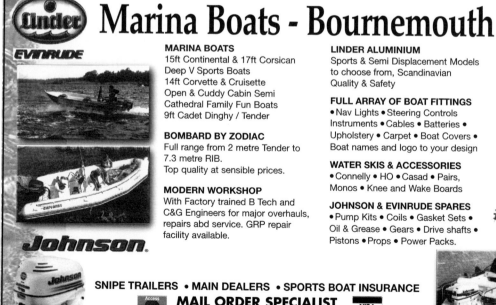

SW Nets Newlyn	01736 360254	
Tarbert Ltd, JSB Tarbert	01880 820180	
TCS Chandlery Grays	01375 374702	
TCS Chandlery Southend	01702 444423	
Thulecraft Ltd Lerwick	01595 693192	
Torbay Boating Centre Paignton	01803 558760	
Torquay Chandlers Torquay	01803 211854	
Tradewinds Marine Conwy	01492 572777	
Trafalgar Yacht Services Fareham	01329 823577	
Trident UK N Shields	0191 259 6797	
Union Chandlery Cork	00353 21 4554334	
Upper Deck Marine and Outriggers Fowey	01726 832287	
V Ships (Isle of Man) Douglas	01624 688886	

Viking Marine Ltd
Dun Laoghaire   00353 1 280 6654

Waterfront Marine
Bangor   01248 352513

Western Marine
Dalkey   00353 1280 0321

Whitstable Marine
Whitstable   01227 262525/274168

Williams Ltd, TJ Cardiff   029 20 487676

Worcester Yacht Chandlers Ltd
Barbourne   01905 22522

Wyatts Chandlery Ltd
Colchester   01206 384745

XM Yachting Ltd
Polegate   01323 870092

Yacht & Sports Gear Ltd
Chichester   01243 784572

Yacht Parts Plymouth   01752 252489

Yachtmail Ltd Lymington   01590 672784

Yare Boatique Norwich   01603 715289

Crewsaver Gosport   023 9252 8621
Douglas Gill Nottingham 0115 9460844
Fat Face Havant   02392 485555
Gul International Ltd
Bodmin   01208 262400
Guy Cotten UK Ltd
Liskeard   01579 347115
Harwoods Yarmouth   01983 760258
Helly Hansen
Nottingham   0115 9608797
Henri Lloyd Manchester 0161 799 1212
Joules
Market Harborough   01858 461156
Mad Cowes Clothing Co
Cowes   01983 293710
Matthews Ltd, D
Cork   00353 214 277633
Musto Ltd Laindon   01268 491555
Ocean World Ltd Cowes 01983 291744
OUTRIGGERS/UPPER DECK MARINE
Albert Quay, Fowey, Cornwall PL23 1AQ
Tel: 01726 833233
Fax: 01726 833265
www.fowey.com
'Outriggers' casual and marine clothing, footwear, nautical gifts. Admiralty chart agent and marine books.

Purple Sails & Marine Walsall
01922 614787
Quba Sails Salcombe   01548 844026
Ravenspring Ltd Totnes 01803 867092
Shorewater Sports
Chichester   01243 672315
Splashdown Leeds   0113 270 7000
T & G Clothing
Stockbridge   01264 811000
Yacht Parts
Plymouth 01752 252489

Booth Marine Surveys, Graham
Birchington-on-Sea   01843 843793
Cannell & Associates, David M
Wivenhoe   01206 823337

BPSC Marine Services
Southampton   023 8023 0045
Cleghorn Waring Ltd
Letchworth   01462 480380
Plastimo (UK) Ltd
Eastleigh   023 8026 2211
Rule – ITT Industries
Hoddesdon   01992 450145
Seath Instruments (1992) Ltd
Lowestoft   01502 573811
Yachting Instruments Ltd
Sturminster Newton   01258 817662

407 RACING
- Yacht Charter -
Where the best yachts just get better
Fleet of Race-prepared
Beneteau 40.7 Firsts
* RORC and Regatta Racing * Team-building with experts
* Cruising (bareboat or skippered) * Corporate Events
www.407yachtcharter.co.uk
Charter Our RIBS 20' to 30'   Extensive Fleet of Sunseekers from 34' to 68'
Luxury Swans from 48' to 60'
Tel. +44 (0)1590 688407 Fax. +44 (0)1590 610407
407racing@407yachtcharter.co.uk

2004/M&WM28/d

C-map Ltd Fareham   01329 517777
Dolphin Maritime Software
White Cross   01524 841946
Forum Software Ltd
Nr Haverfordwest   01646 636363
Kelvin Hughes Ltd
Southampton   023 8063 4911
Mariteck Ltd Glasgow   0141 571 9164
PC Maritime Plymouth   01752 254205
Sea Information Systems Ltd
Aberdeen   01224 621326
Square Mile Marlow   0870 1202536

Indulgence Charters
Wendover   01296 696006
407 Racing (Yacht Charter)
Lymington   01590 688407

407 Racing (Yacht Charter)
Lymington   01590 688407

Arklow Customs   00353 402 32553
Bantry Customs   00353 27 50061
Carlingford Lough Customs
00353 42 34248
Cork Customs   00353 21 311024
Dingle Customs   00353 66 7121480
Dublin Customs   00353 1 679 2777
Dun Laoghaire Customs
00353 1 280 3992
Dunmore East Customs
00353 51 875391
Fenit Harbour Customs
00353 66 36115

Galway Customs   00353 91 567191
Killybegs Customs   00353 73 31070
Kilmore Customs   00353 53 33741
Kilrush Customs   00353 61 415366
Kinsale Customs   00353 21 311044
Lough Swilly Customs
00353 74 21611
Malahide Customs 00353 1 874 6571
Prest Customs   00353 94 21131
Rathmullan Customs 00353 74 26324
Rosslare Customs   00353 53 33116
Schull Customs   00353 27 51562
Shannon Customs   00353 61 471076
Shannon Estuary Customs
00353 69 415366
Sligo Customs   00353 71 61064
UK Customs Nationwide
0845 0109000
Waterford Customs 00353 51 875391
Wexford Customs   00353 532 2889
Wicklow Customs   00353 404 67222

ANCHORWATCH UK
67 Morningside Park, Edinburgh EH10 5EZ
Tel: 0131 447 5057
e-mail: anchorwatch@aol.com
www.anchorwatch.co.uk
Electronic anchor monitoring equipment. Anchorwatch measures the loading on an anchor cable up to 1000kg. Records peak loading and includes alarm facility.

Aries Van Gear Spares
Penryn   01326 377467
Frederiksen Boat Fittings (UK) Ltd
Gosport   023 9252 5377
Harken UK Lymington   01590 689122
Kearon Ltd George   00353 402 32319
Marine Maintenance
Tollesbury   01621 860441
Nauquip Warsash   01489 885336
Pro-Boat Ltd
Burnham-on-Crouch   01621 785455

Ryland, Kenneth
Stanton   01386 584270

Smith, EC & Son Ltd
Luton   01582 729721

Timage & Co Ltd
Braintree   01376 343087

VETUS DEN OUDEN LTD
39 South Hants Ind. Park, Totton,
Southampton SO40 3SA
Tel: 023 8086 1033
Fax: 023 8066 3142
e-mail: sales@vetus.co.uk
www.vetus.co.uk
Wholesalers of diesel engines,
generators, exhaust systems, propellers,
shafts, bow thrusters, hatches, portlights,
windlasses, ventilators, fuel and water
tanks, hydraulics systems, air
conditioning, wipers, pumps, seats, hoses
and much much more.

DIESEL MARINE/ FUEL ADDITIVES

Corralls Poole   01202 674551

Cotters Marine & General Supplies
Baltimore   00353 28 20106

Gorey Marine Fuel Supplies
Gorey   07797 742384

Hammond, George
Dover   01304 206809

Iron Wharf Boatyard
Faversham   01795 537122

Lallow, Clare Cowes   01983 760707

Marine Support & Towage
Cowes   01983 200716/07860 297633

Quayside Fuel
Weymouth   07747 182181

Rossiter Yachts
Christchurch   01202 483250

Sleeman & Hawken
Shaldon   01626 872750

DIVERS

Abco Divers Belfast   028 90610492

Andark Diving
Southampton   01489 581755

Aquatech Diving Services
Port of St Mary   01624 833037

Argonaut Marine
Aberdeen   01224 706526

**Baltimore Diving and Watersports
Centre** West Cork   00353 28 20300

C & C Marine Services
Largs   01475 687180

**Cardiff Commercial Boat Operators
Ltd** Cardiff   029 2037 7872

C I Diving Services Ltd
Invergordon   01349 852500

Divesafe Sunderland   0191 567 8423

Divetech UK King's Lynn 01485 572323

Diving & Marine Engineering
Barry   01446 721553

Donnelly, R South Shields 07973 119455

DV Diving   028 91 464671

Falmouth Divers Ltd
Penryn   01326 374736

Fathom Diving (Chislehurst)
Chislehurst   020 8289 8237

Fathoms Ltd Wick   01955 605956

Felixarc Marine Ltd
Felixstowe   01394 676497

Grampian Diving Services
New Deer   01771 644206

Higgins, Noel
Southern Ireland   00353 872027650

Hudson, Dave
Trearddur Bay   01407 860628

Hunt, Kevin Tralee   00353 6671 25979

Inverkip Diving Services
Inverkip   01475 521281

Kaymac Diving Services
Swansea   01792 793316

Keller, Hilary
Buncrana   00353 77 62146

Kilkee Diving Centre
Kilkee   00353 6590 56707

Leask Marine Kirkwall   01856 874725

Looe Divers Hannafore 01503 262727

MacDonald, D Nairn   01667 455661

Medway Diving Contractors Ltd
Gillingham   01634 851902

Mojo Maritime Penzance 01736 762771

Murray, Alex Stornoway 01851 704978

New Dawn Dive Centre
Lymington   01590 675656

New Tec Diving Services
Blackpool   01253 691665

Northern Divers (Engineering) Ltd
Hull   01482 227276

Offshore Marine Services Ltd
Bembridge   01983 873125

Old Harbour Dive School
Portland   01305 861000

**Parkinson (Sinbad Marine Services),
J** Killybegs   00353 73 31417

Port of London Authority
Gravesend   01474 560311

Purcell, D – Crouch Sailing School
Burnham   01621 784140/0585 33

Salvesen UK Ltd
Liverpool   0151 933 6038

Sea Technical Services Ltd
Denmead   023 92255200

Seaguard Marine Engineering Ltd
Goodwick   01348 872976

Sea-Lift Ltd Dover   01304 201112

Southern Cylinder Services
Fareham   01329 221125

Stealaway Diving Oban 01631 566349

Sub Aqua Services
North Ormesby   01642 230209

Teign Diving Centre
Teignmouth   01626 773965

Thorpe, Norman Portree 01478 612274

Tuskar Rock Marine
Rosslare   00353 53 33376

Underwater Services
Dyffryn Arbwy   01341 247702

Wilson Alan c/o Portrush Yacht Club
Portrush   028 2076 2225

Woolford, William
Bridlington   01262 671710

ELECTRICAL AND ELECTRONIC ENGINEERS

Allworth Riverside Services, Adrian
Chelsea Harbour Marina 07831 574774

Belson Design Ltd, Nick
Southampton   077 6835 1330

Biggs, John Weymouth Marina,
Weymouth   01305 778445

BJ Marine Ltd Bangor 028 9127 1434

Calibra Marine
Dartmouth   01803 833094

Campbell & McHardy Lossiemouth
Marina, Lossiemouth   01343 812137

CES Sandown Sparkes Marina,
Hayling Island   023 9246 6005

DDZ Marine Clyde Marina,
Ardossan   01294 607077

Energy Solutions
Rochester   01634 290772

**Enterprise Marine Electronic &
Technical Services Ltd**
Aberdeen   01224 593281

Eurotex Marine Brighton Marina,
Brighton   01273 818990

Floetree Ltd (Loch Lomond Marina)
Balloch   01389 752069

HNP Engineers (Lerwick) Ltd
Lerwick   01595 692493

Index Marine
Bournemouth   01202 470149

Jackson Yacht Services
Jersey   01534 743819

Jedynak, A Salcombe   01548 843321

Kippford Slipway Ltd
Dalbeattie   01556 620249

Kiss Marine Yacht Services Hythe
Marina, Southampton   023 8084 0100

Land & Sea Electronics
Aberdeen   01224 593281

Langley Marine Services Ltd
Eastbourne   01323 470244

Lifeline Marine Services
Dolphin Haven, Poole   01202 669676

Lynch Ltd, PA Morpeth 01670 512291

Mackay Boatbuilders (Arbroath) Ltd
Aberdeen   01241 872879

Marine, AW Gosport   023 9250 1207

Marine Electrical Repair Service
London   020 7228 1336

MES Falmouth Marina,
Falmouth   01326 378497

Mount Batten Boathouse
Plymouth   01752 482666

New World Yacht Care
Rhu   01436 820586

Neyland Marine Services Ltd
Milford Haven   01646 698968

Powell, Martin Shamrock Quay,
Southampton   023 8033 2123

R & J Marine Electricians Suffolk Yacht
Harbour Ltd, Ipswich   01473 659737

Radio & Electronic Services Beaucette
Marina, Guernsey   01481 728837

Redcar Fish Company
Stockton-on-Tees   01642 633638

RHP Marine Cowes   01983 290421

Rothwell, Chris
Torquay Marina   01803 850960

Rutherford, Jeff Largs   01475 568026

Sea Electric Hamble   023 8045 6255

SM International
Plymouth   01752 662129

South Pier Shipyard
St Helier   01534 519700

SP Engineering
Helensburgh   01436 820260

Sussex Fishing Services
Rye   01797 223895

Ultra Marine Systems
Mayflower International Marina, Plymouth
    07989 941020

Upham, Roger
Chichester   01243 528299

Volspec Woolverstone Marina,
Ipswich   01473 780144

Western Marine Power Ltd
Plymouth   01752 408804

WESTERN MARINE POWER LTD
Western Hangar, Mount Batten,
Plymouth, Devon PL9 9SJ.
TEL: (01752) 408804 FAX: (01752) 408807
e-mail: info@wmp.co.uk

Suppliers and installers of:-
Watermakers, Air Conditioning,
Generators, Electrical Systems,
Prim tabs, Electronic Engine Controls,
Bow and Stern Thrusters, Teak Decks,
Davits, Passarelles and Cranes,
Galley and Sanitation Equipment.
ISO 9002 Quality Assurance.
Website: www.wmp.co.uk/
2004/M&WMD36/d

Wroath, DG Cowes   01983 281467

Yoldings Marine
Eastbourne   01323 470882

ELECTRONIC DEVICES AND EQUIPMENT

Anchorwatch UK
Edinburgh   0131 447 5057

Aquascan International Ltd
Newport   01633 841117

Atkinson Marine
Lymington   01590 688389

Atlantis Marine Power Ltd
Plymouth   01752 225679

Autosound Marine
Bradford   01274 688990

AW Marine Gosport   023 9250 1207

Brookes & Gatehouse
Maylandsea   01621 743546

Brookes & Gatehouse
Romsey   01794 518448

Boat Electrics & Electronics Ltd
Troon   01292 315355

**Cactus Navigation & Communication
Ltd** London   020 7493 1115

CDL Aberdeen   01224 706655

Charity & Taylor Ltd
Lowestoft   01502 581529

Devtech Plymouth   01752 223388

Diverse Yacht Services
Hamble   023 8045 3399

Dyfed Electronics Ltd
Milford Haven   01646 694572

Echopilot Marine Electronics Ltd
Ringwood   01425 476211

Euro Tek Marine
Brighton   01273 687790

Euronav Ltd Portsmouth 023 9237 3855

Furuno (UK) Ltd
Denmead   023 9223 0303

Garmin (Europe) Ltd
Romsey   01794 579944

Golden Arrow Marine Ltd
Southampton   023 8071 0371

Greenham Regis Marine Electronics
Cowes   01983 293996

Greenham Regis Marine Electronics
Emsworth   01243 378314

Greenham Regis Marine Electronics
Lymington   01590 671144

Greenham Regis Marine Electronics
Southampton   023 8063 6555

ICS Electronics Arundel 01903 731101

JG Technologies Ltd
Weymouth   0845 458 9616

Kongsberg Simrad Ltd
Aberdeen   01224 226500

Kongsberg Simrad Ltd
Wick   01955 603606

Landau UK Ltd Hamble 01489 881588

Land & Sea Electronics
Aberdeen   01224 593281

Marathon Leisure
Hayling Island   023 9263 7711

Marconi Marine
Aberdeen   01224 585334

Marconi Marine
Brixham   01803 851993

Marconi Marine
Fraserburgh   01346 518187

Marconi Marine
Lowestoft   01502 572365

Marconi Marine Newlyn 01736 361320

Marconi Marine Penryn 01326 378031

Marconi Marine
Peterhead   01779 480921

Marconi Marine
Southampton   023 8051 1868

Marine Instruments
Falmouth   01326 312414

Marinetrack Ltd
Shoreham-by-Sea   01273 265425

Maritek Ltd Glasgow   0141 571 9164

Microcustom Ltd Ipswich 01473 780724

Nasa Marine Instruments
Stevenage   01438 354033

Navcom Chichester   01243 776625

Navionics UK Plymouth 01752 204735

Navtronics Lowestoft   01502 587696

Ocean Leisure Ltd
London   020 7930 5050

Plymouth Marine Electronics
Plymouth   01752 227711

Radio & Electronic Services Ltd
St Peter Port   01481 728837

Raymarine Ltd
Portsmouth   023 9269 3611

Redfish Car Company
Stockton-on-Tees   01642 633638

Robertson, MK Oban   01631 563836

Safe Marine Ltd
Aberdeen   01224 338338

Satcom Distribution Ltd
Salisbury   01722 410800

Sea Information Systems Ltd
Aberdeen   01224 621326

Seaquest Marine Ltd
Guernsey   01481 721773

Seatronics Aberdeen   01224 853100

Silva Ltd Livingston   01506 419555

Simrad Ltd Gosport   01329 245100

SM International
Plymouth   01752 662129

Sperry Marine Ltd
Peterhead   01779 473475

Sperry Marine Ltd
Ullapool   01854 612024

Stenmar Ltd Aberdeen   01224 827288

STN Atlas Marine UK Ltd
Peterhead   01779 478233

Tacktick Ltd Emsworth   01243 379331

Transas Nautic
Portsmouth   023 9267 4016

Veripos Precise Navigation
Fraserburgh   01346 511411

Wema (UK) Bristol   01454 316103

Western Battery Service
Mallaig   01687 462044

Wilson & Co Ltd, DB
Glasgow   0141 647 0161

Woodsons of Aberdeen Ltd
Aberdeen   01224 722884

Yachtbits.co.uk
Lowestoft   01502 569079

Yeoman Romsey   01794 521079

ENGINES AND ACCESSORIES

Airylea Motors
Aberdeen   01224 872891

Amble Boat Co Ltd
Amble   01665 710267

Anchor Marine Products
Benfleet 01268 566666

Aquafac Ltd Luton 01582 568700

Attfield & Company, GB
Dursley 01453 547185

Barrus Ltd, EP Bicester 01869 363636

BHG MARINE
Bucklers Hard, Beaulieu,
Hampshire SO42 7XB
Tel: 0845 644 6645
Fax: 0845 644 6635
e-mail: info@bng-marine.co.uk
Stockist of Yamaha outboards, Avon
inflatables and R.I.B.s. Sports boats and
fishing boats.

Brigantine
Teignmouth 01626 872400

British Polar Engines Ltd
Glasgow 0141 445 2455

Bukh Diesel UK Ltd
Poole 01202 668840

CJ Marine Mechanical
Troon 01292 313400

Cleghorn Waring Ltd
Letchworth 01462 480380

Cook's Diesel Service Ltd
Faversham 01795 538553

Felton Marine Engineering
Brighton 01273 601779

Felton Marine Engineering
Eastbourne 01323 470211

Fender-Fix Maidstone 01622 751518

Fettes & Rankine Engineering
Aberdeen 01224 573343

Fleetwood & Sons Ltd, Henry
Lossiemouth 01343 813015

Gorleston Marine Ltd
Great Yarmouth 01493 661883

Halyard Salisbury 01722 710922

Interseals (Guernsey) Ltd
Guernsey 01481 246364

Kelpie Boats
Pembroke Dock 01646 683661

Keypart Watford 01923 330570

Lancing Marine Brighton 01273 410025

Lencraft Boats Ltd
Dungarvan 00353 58 68220

Lewmar Ltd Havant 023 9247 1841

Liverpool Power Boats
Bootle 0151 944 1163

Lynch Ltd, PA Morpeth 01670 512291

MacDonald & Co Ltd, JN
Glasgow 0141 334 6171

Marine Maintenance
Tollesbury 01621 860441

Mariners Weigh
Shaldon 01626 873698

Maritime International Ltd
Guernsey 01481 723716

Mooring Mate Ltd
Bournemouth 01202 421199

Mount Batten Boathouse
Plymouth 01752 482666

Nauquip Warsash 01489 885336

Newens Marine, Chas
Putney 020 8788 4587

Ocean Safety
Southampton 023 8072 0800

Outboard Centre
Fareham 01329 234277

Plastimo (UK) Ltd
Eastleigh 023 8026 2211

Riley Marine Dover 01304 214544

RK Marine Ltd Hamble 01489 583585

RK Marine Ltd Swanwick 01489 583572

Rule - ITT Industries
Hoddesdon 01992 450145

Sillette Sonic Ltd
Sutton 020 8715 0100

Smith & Son Ltd, EC
Luton 01582 729721

Sowester Simpson-Lawrence Ltd
Poole 01202 667700

Timage & Co Ltd
Braintree 01376 343087

Trident UK Gateshead 0191 259 6797

Troop & Co, James
Liverpool 0151 709 0581

Vetus Den Ouden Ltd
Totton 023 8086 1033

Western Marine
Dublin 00353 1 280 0321

Whitstable Marine
Whitstable 01227 262525

Yates Marine, Martin
Galgate 01524 751750

Ynys Marine Cardigan 01239 613179

FABRICATION

Sailspar Ltd
Brightlingsea 01206 302679

FIRST AID

Bisham Abbey Sailing & Navigation
School Bisham 01628 474960

Coastal Sea School
Weymouth 0870 321 3271

East Coast Offshore Yachting - Les
Rant Perry 01480 861381

Hamble School of Yachting
Hamble 023 8045 6687

Hoylake Sailing School
Wirral 0151 632 4664

LYMINGTON CRUISING SCHOOL
24 Waterloo Road, Lymington,
Hampshire SO41 9DB
Tel: (01590) 677478
Fax: (01590) 689210
e-mail: lymingtoncruisin@aol.com
www.lymingtoncruising.co.uk
All RYA practical and shorebased courses
including: Yachtmaster preparation,
Coastal Skipper, Day Skipper, Competent
Crew, SRC and First Aid. Relaxed,
friendly, caring service. Courses
structured to suit the individuals needs.
Adventure and fun but safety paramount.

Plymouth Sailing School
Plymouth 01752 667170

Sail North Wales
Conwy 01492 584208

Southern Sailing
Swanwick 01489 575511

Start Point Sailing
Kingsbridge 01548 810917

Warsash Maritime Centre
Warsash 01489 576161

FOUL-WEATHER GEAR

Century Finchampstead 0118 9731616

Compass Devizes 01380 813100

Crewsaver Gosport 023 9252 8621

Douglas Gill Nottingham 0115 9460844

Gul International Ltd
Bodmin 01208 262400

Helly Hansen
Nottingham 0115 9608797

Henri Lloyd Manchester 0161 799 1212

Marinepool Cowes 01983 282490

Musto Ltd Laindon 01268 491555

Pro Rainer Windsor 01753 868300

Splashdown Leeds 0113 270 7000

GENERAL MARINE EQUIPMENT & SPARES

Ampair Ringwood 01425 480780

Aries Vane Gear Spares
Penryn 01326 377467

Arthurs Chandlery, R
Gosport 023 9252 6522

Barden UK Ltd Fareham 01489 570770

Calibra Marine International Ltd
Southampton 08702 400358

CH Marine (Cork)
Cork 00353 21 4315700

Chris Hornsey (Chandlery) Ltd
Southsea 023 9273 4728

Compass Marine (Dartmouth)
Dartmouth 01803 835915

Cox Yacht Charter Ltd, Nick
Lymington 01590 673489

CTC Marine & Leisure
Middlesbrough 01642 230123

DEEVY & CO LTD, C. J.
48 Pomoell St, Waterford,
Ireland.
Tel: 00 353 (51) 855717
Fax: 00 353 (51) 855710
e-mail: sales@deevys.com
www.deevys.com
Motor & marine supplies for the South
East region of Ireland. Est 1935. Offering
a comprehensive range of products to
both marine enthusiasts and motor
enthusiasts. Branches in Waterford and
Clonmell.

Docksafe Ltd
Bangor 028 9147 0453

Frederiksen Boat Fittings (UK) Ltd
Gosport 023 9252 5377

Furneaux Riddall & Co Ltd
Portsmouth   023 9266 8624

Hardware & Marine Supplies
Co Wexford   00353 (53) 29791

Index Marine
Bournemouth   01202 470149

Kearon Ltd, George
Arklow   00353 402 32319

Marathon Leisure
Hayling Island   023 9263 7711

PIRATES CAVE LTD
Unit 14, Northpoint Business Estate, Enterprise Close, Medway City Estate, Frindsbury, Rochester ME2 4LX
Tel: (01634) 295233
Fax: (01634) 722326
e-mail:
piratescaveuk@yahoo.co.uk
We hold a very large stock of general chandlery as well as being main dealers for XM, Silva, Raymarine, Whale, Jabsco, Barton, Spincock and ECS products. Staffed by people with boating experience.

Pro-Boat Ltd
Burnham-on-Crouch   01621 785455

Pump International Ltd
Cornwall   01209 831937

Quay West Chandlers
Poole   01202 742488

Rogers, Angie Bristol   0117 973 8276

Ryland, Kenneth
Stanton   01386 584270

SHERATON MARINE CABINET
White Oak Green, Hailey, Witney, Oxfordshire OX8 5XP
Tel/Fax: (01993) 868275
Manufacturers of quality teak and mahogany marine fittings, louvre doors, grating and tables. Special fitting-out items to customer specification. Colour catalogue available on request.

Tiflex Liskeard   01579 320808

Vetus Boating Equipment
Southampton   023 8086 1033

Western Marine Power Ltd
Plymouth   01752 408804

Whitstable Marine
Whitstable   01227 262525

Yacht Parts Plymouth   01752 252489

GENERATORS

Fischer Panda UK Ltd
Verwood   01202 820840

Genacis Poole   01202 624356

Sigma Supplies Ltd
Luton   01582 488110

WESTERN MARINE POWER LTD
Western Hangar, Mount Batten, Plymouth, Devon PL9 9SJ.
Tel: (01752) 408804
Fax: (01752) 408807
e-mail: info@wmp.co.uk
www.wmp.co.uk

Suppliers and installers of:- Watermakers, Air Conditioning, Generators, Electrical Systems, Electronic Engine Controls, Bow and Stern Thrusters, Teak Decks, Davits, Passarelles and Cranes, Galley and Sanitation Equipment. ISO 9002 Quality Assurance.

Wyko Industrial Services
Inverness   01463 224747

HARBOUR MASTERS

Aberaeron HM	01545 571645
Aberdeen HM	01224 597000
Aberdovey HM	01654 767626
Aberystwyth HM	01970 611433
Alderney & Burhou HM	01481 822620
Amble HM	01665 710306
Anstruther HM	01333 310836
Appledore HM	01237 474569
Arbroath HM	01241 872166
Ardglass HM	028 4484 1291
Ardrossan Control Tower HM	01294 463972
Arinagour Piermaster	01879 230347
Arklow HM	00353 402 32466
Baltimore HM	00353 28 22145
Banff HM	01261 815544
Bantry Bay HM	00353 27 53277
Barmouth HM	01341 280671
Barry HM	01446 732665
Beaucette HM	01481 245000
Beaulieu River HM	01590 616200
Belfast Lough HM	028 90 553012
Belfast River Manager	028 90 328507
Bembridge HM	01983 872828
Berwick-upon-Tweed HM	01289 307404
Bideford HM	01237 346131
Blyth HM	01670 352678
Boston HM	01205 362328
Bridlington HM	01262 670148/9
Bridport HM	01308 423222
Brighton HM	01273 819919
Bristol HM	0117 926 4797
Brixham HM	01803 853321
Buckie HM	01542 831700
Bude HM	01288 353111
Burghead HM	01343 835337
Burnham-on-Crouch HM	01621 783602
Burnham-on-Sea HM	01278 782180
Burtonport HM	00353 075 42155
Caernarfon HM	01286 672118
Camber Berthing Offices – Portsmouth	023 92297395
Campbeltown HM	01586 552552

Canal Office (Inverness) HM	01463 233140
Cardiff HM	029 20400500
Carnlough Harbour HM	07703 606763
Castletown Bay HM	01624 823549
Charlestown HM	01726 67526
Chichester Harbour HM	01243 512301
Christchurch HM	01202 495061
Conwy HM	01492 596253
Cork HM	00353 21 4273125
Corpach Canal Sea Lock HM	01397 772249
Courtmacsherry HM	00353 23 46311/46600
Coverack HM	01326 280545
Cowes HM	01983 293952
Crail HM	01333 450820
Craobh Haven HM	01852 502222
Crinan Canal Office HM	01546 603210
Cromarty Firth HM	01381 600479
Crookhaven HM	00353 28 35319
Cullen HM	01261 842477
Dingle HM	00353 66 9151629
Douglas HM	01624 686628
Dover HM	01304 240400 Ext 4520
Dublin HM	00353 1 874871
Dun Laoghaire HM	00353 1 280 1130/8074
Dunbar HM	01368 863206
Dundee HM	01382 224121
Dunmore East HM	00353 51 383166
East Loch Tarbert HM	01859 502444
Eastbourne HM	01323 470099
Eigg Harbour HM	01687 482428
Elie HM	01333 330051
Estuary Control - Dumbarton HM	01389 726211
Eyemouth HM	01890 750223
Falmouth HM	01326 312285
Findochty HM	01542 831466
Fisherrow HM	0131 665 5900
Fishguard (Lower Harbour) HM	01348 874726
Fishguard HM	01348 404425
Fleetwood HM	01253 872323
Flotta HM	01856 701411
Folkestone HM	01303 715354
Fowey HM	01726 832471/2.
Fraserburgh HM	01346 515858
Galway Bay HM	00353 91 561874
Garlieston HM	01988 600274
Glasson Dock HM	01524 751724
Gorey HM	01534 853616
Gourdon HM	01569 762741
Great Yarmouth HM	01493 335501
Grimsby Dockmaster	01472 359181
Groomsport Bay HM	028 91 278040

Hamble River HM	01489 576387	Plockton HM	01599 534589	St Ives HM	01736 795018
Hayle HM	01736 754043	Poole HM	01202 440233	St Margaret's Hope HM	01856 831454
Helford River HM	01326 250749	Port St Mary HM	01624 833205	St Mary's HM	01720 422768
Helmsdale HM	01431 821692	Porth Dinllaen HM	01758 720276	St Monans HM	01333 350055
Holy Island HM	01289 389217	Porthleven HM	01326 574207	St Peter Port HM	01481 720229
Holyhead HM	01407 763071	Porthmadog HM	01766 512927	Stonehaven HM	01569 762741
Hopeman HM	01343 835337	Portknockie HM	01542 840833	Stornoway HM	01851 702688
Howth HM	00353 1 832 2252	Portland HM	01305 824044	Strangford Lough HM	028 44 881637
Ilfracombe HM	01271 862108	Portpatrick HM	01776 810355	Stromness HM	01856 850744
Inverness HM	01463 715715	Portree HM	01478 612926	Stronsay HM	01857 616317
Irvine HM	01294 487286	Portrush HM	028 70822307	Sullom Voe HM	01806 242551
Johnshaven HM	01561 362262	Portsmouth Harbour Commercial Docks HM	023 92297395	Sunderland HM	0191 567 2626
Kettletoft Bay HM	01857 600227	Portsmouth Harbour Control	023 92723694	Swale HM	01795 561234
Killybegs HM	00353 73 31032			Swansea HM	01792 653787
Kilmore Quay HM	00353 53 29955	Portsmouth Harbour HM	023 92723124	Tees & Hartlepool Port Authority	01429 277205
Kinlochbervie HM	01971 521235	Preston HM	01772 726711	Teignmouth HM	01626 773165
Kinsale HM	00353 21 4772503	Pwllheli HM	01758 704081	Tenby HM	01834 842717
Kirkcudbright HM	01557 331135	Queenborough HM	01795 662051	Thames Estuary HM	01474 562200
Kirkwall HM	01856 872292	Queens Gareloch/Rhu HM	01436 674321	Tobermory Port Manager HM	01688 302017
Langstone Harbour HM	023 9246 3419	Ramsey HM	01624 812245	Torquay HM	01803 292429
Larne HM	02828 872100	Ramsgate HM	01843 572100	Troon HM	01292 281687
Lerwick HM	01595 692991	River Bann & Coleraine HM	028 7034 2012	Ullapool HM	01854 612091
Littlehampton HM	01903 721215	River Blackwater HM	01621 856487	Walton-on-the-Naze HM	01255 851899
Liverpool HM	0151 949 6134/5	River Colne (Brightlingsea) HM	01206 302200	Watchet HM	01984 631264
Loch Gairloch HM	01445 712140	River Dart HM	01803 832337	Waterford HM	00353 51 874907
Loch Inver HM	01571 844265	River Deben HM	01394 270106	Wells-next-the-Sea HM	01328 711646
Looe HM	01503 262839	River Exe Dockmaster	01392 274306	Weymouth HM	01305 206423
Lossiemouth HM	01343 813066	River Humber HM	01482 327171	Whitby HM	01947 602354
Lough Foyle HM	028 7186 0555	River Medway HM	01795 596593	Whitehaven HM	01946 692435
Lowestoft HM	01502 572286	River Orwell HM	01473 231010	Whitehills HM	01261 861291
Lyme Regis HM	01297 442137	River Roach HM	01621 783602	Whitstable HM	01227 274086
Lymington HM	01590 672014	River Stour HM	01255 243000	Wick HM	01955 602030
Lyness HM	01856 791387	River Tyne/North Shields HM	0191 257 2080	Wicklow HM	00353 404 67455
Macduff HM	01261 832236	River Yealm HM	01752 872533	Workington HM	01900 602301
Maryport HM	01900 814431	Rivers Alde & Ore HM	01473 450481	Yarmouth HM	01983 760321
Menai Strait HM	01248 712312	Rosslare Harbour HM	00353 53 57921	Youghal HM	00353 24 92626
Methil HM	01333 462725	Rothesay HM	01700 503842		
Mevagissey HM	01726 843305	Ryde HM	01983 613879		
Milford Haven HM	01646 696100	Salcombe HM	01548 843791		
Minehead HM	01643 702566	Sark HM	01481 832323		
Montrose HM	01674 672302	Scalloway HM	01595 880574		
Mousehole HM	01736 731511	Scarborough HM	01723 373530		
Mullion Cove HM	01326 240222	Scrabster HM	01847 892779		
Newhaven HM	01273 612868	Seaham HM	0191 581 3246		
Newlyn HM	01736 362523	Sharpness HM	01453 811862/64		
Newquay HM	01637 872809	Shoreham HM	01273 598100		
Newtown Creek HM	01983 525994	Silloth HM	016973 31358		
Oban HM	01631 562892	Sligo HM	00353 71 61197		
Padstow HM	01841 532239	Southampton HM	023 8033 9733		
Par HM	01726 818337	Southend-on-Sea HM	01702 611889		
Peel HM	01624 842338	Southwold HM	01502 724712		
Penrhyn Bangor HM	01248 352525	St Helier HM	01534 885588		
Penzance HM	01736 366113				
Peterhead HM	01779 483630				
Pierowall HM	01857 677216				
Pittenweem HM	01333 312591				

HARBOURS

Bristol Harbour Bristol 0117 922 2000

Serviced berths available throughout Bristol Harbour for all types of leisure craft
Harbour Office
Underfall Yard, Cumberland Road, Bristol BS1 6XG
Website
www.bristol-city.gov.uk

2004/M&WMDT8/d

Clyde Marina – Ardrossan
01294 607077

Hafan Pwllheli
Pwllheli 01758 701219

Jersey Harbours
St Helier   01534 885588

Maryport Harbour and Marina
Maryport   01900 818447/4431

**PADSTOW HARBOUR
COMMISSIONERS**
Harbour House, Padstow,
Cornwall PL28 8AQ
Tel: (01841) 532239
Fax: (01841) 533346
e-mail:
padstowharbour@compuserve.com
www.padstow-harbour.co.uk
Inner harbour controlled by tidal gate -
opens HW±2 hours. Minimum depth 3
metres at all times. Yachtsmen must be
friendly as vessels raft together. Services
include showers, toilets, diesel, water and
ice. Security by CCTV.

Peterhead Bay Authority
Peterhead   01779 474020

Sark Moorings – Channel Islands
                    01481 832260

INSTRUMENTATION & POSITION FIXING

Belson Design Ltd, Nick
Southampton   077 6835 1330

Cooke & Son Ltd, B
Hull   01482 223454

Diverse Yacht Services Hamble
                    023 8045 3399

Dolphin Maritime Software Ltd
Lancaster   01624 673965

Garmin Romsey   01794 519944

Geonav UK Ltd Poole   0870 240 4575

Lilley & Gillie Ltd, John
North Shields   0191 257 2217

Smith AM (Marine) Ltd
London   020 8529 6988

Yachting Instruments Ltd
Sturminster Newton   01258 817662

Yeoman Romsey   01794 521079

INSURANCE/FINANCE

Admiral Marine Ltd
Salisbury   01722 416106

Bigfish London   020 8651 4096

Bishop Skinner Boat Insurance
London   0800 7838057

Bristol Channel Marine
Cardiff   029 2063 1163

Carter Boat Insurance, RA
                    0800 174061

Castlemain Ltd
St Peter Port   01481 721319

Clark Insurance, Graham
Tyneside   0191 455 8089

Craftinsure.com
Orpington   01689 889507

Craven Hodgson Associates
Leeds   0113 243 8443

Curtis & Partners, Colin
Plymouth   01752 664649

Giles Insurance Brokers
Irvine   01294 315481

GJW Direct Liverpool   0151 473 8000

Haven Knox-Johnston
West Malling   01732 223600

Lombard Southampton   023 8051 5050

Mardon Insurance
Shrewsbury   0800 515629

**Marine & General Insurance Services
Ltd** Maidstone   01622 201106

Mercia Marine Malvern 01684 564457

Nautical Insurance Services Ltd
Leigh-on-Sea   01702 470811

Navigators & General
Brighton   01273 863400

Pantaenius UK Ltd
Plymouth   01752 223656

Porthcawl Insurance Consultants
Porthcawl   01656 784866

Saga Boat Insurance Folkestone
                    01303 771135

St Margarets Insurances
London   020 8778 6161

Weysure Ltd Weymouth 07000 939787

LIFERAFTS & INFLATABLES

AB Marine Ltd Guernsey 01481 722378

Adec Marine Ltd
Croydon   020 8686 9717

Avon Inflatables Llanelli 01554 882000

Cosalt International Ltd
Aberdeen   01224 588327

Glaslyn Marine Supplies Ltd
Porthmadog   01766 513545

Hale Marine, Ron
Portsmouth   023 9273 2985

Herm Seaway Marine Ltd
St Peter Port   01481 722838

IBS Boats South Woodham Ferrers
                    01245 323211/425551

KTS Seasafety Kilkeel 028 918 28405

Nationwide Marine Hire
Warrington   01925 245788

Norwest Marine Ltd
Liverpool   0151 207 2860

Ocean Safety
Southampton   023 8072 0800

Polymarine Ltd Conwy   01492 583322

Premium Liferaft Services
Burnham-on-Crouch   0800 243673

Ribeye Dartmouth   01803 832060

Ribs UK Ltd
Southampton   023 8022 2262

Secumar Swansea   01792 280545

South Eastern Marine Services Ltd
Basildon   01268 534427

Suffolk Sailing Ipswich 01473 833010

Whitstable Marine
Whitstable   01227 262525

MAIL ORDER

**ASAP Supplies – Equipment &
Spares Worldwide**
Suffolk   0845 1300 870

Bridger Marine, John
Exeter   01392 216420

Compass Watersports
Devizes   01380 813100

Duncan Yacht Chandlers
Glasgow   0141 429 6044

Inspirations Everything
Clacton-on-Sea   01255 428113

Mailspeed Marine
Warrington   01925 838858

Marinestore Chandlers
Maldon   01621 854380

Purple Sails & Marine
Walsall   01922 614787

Reed's Nautical
Bradford-on-Avon   01225 868821

MARINA DEVELOPMENT CONSULTANTS

Crest Nicholson Marinas Ltd
Bristol   01179 236466

MARINAS

Aberystwyth Marina
Aberystwyth   01970 611422

Albert Dock Liverpool 0151 709 6558

Allington Marina
Maidstone   01622 752057

Amble Marina Amble   01665 712168

Ardfern Yacht Centre Ltd
Argyll   01852 500247

Ardglass Marina   028 4484 2332

Ardminish Port
Port Ellen   01583 505254

ARDORAN MARINE
Lerags, Oban, Argyll,
Scotland PA34 4SE
Tel: 01631 566123
Fax: 01631 566611
e-mail: colin@ardoran.co.uk
www.ardoran.co.uk
West coast Scotland. All marine facilities.

Arisaig Marine
Mallaig   01687 450224

Arklow Marina
Arklow   00353 402 39901

Ballycastle Marina
Ballycastle — 028 2076 8525

Bangor Marina Bangor — 028 91 453297

Beaucette Marina Vale — 01481 245000

Bellanoch Marina Ardrishaig — 01546 603210

Bembridge Marina
Bembridge — 01983 872828

Birdham Shipyard Ltd
Birdham — 01243 512310

Blackwater Marina
Maylandsea — 01621 740264

Blyth Marina Blyth — 01679 353636

Boston Marina Boston — 01205 364420

Bowling Basin (Dumbarton)
Dumbarton — 01389 877969

Bradwell Marina
Bradwell-on-Sea — 01621 776235

Bray Marina Bray — 01628 623654

Brentford Dock Marina
Brentford — 020 8298 8941

Bridge Marsh Marina
Althorpe — 01621 740414

Brighton Marina
Brighton — 01273 819919

Bristol Marina Bristol — 0117 9213198

British Waterways
Aedrishaig — 01546 603210

Brixham Marina
Brixham — 01803 882929

Bucklers Hard Marina
Brockenhurst — 01590 616200

Burgh Castle Marina
Norfolk — 01493 780331

Burnham Yacht Harbour Marina Ltd
Burnham-on-Crouch — 01621 782150

Caernarfon Dock (Menai Strait)
Caernarfon — 01286 672346

Cahersiveen Marina
Cahersiveen — 00353 669 473214

Caley Marina Inverness — 01463 233437

Carlingford Marina – Ireland
— 00353 42 9373073

Carrickfergus Marina
Carrickfergus — 028 93 366666

Castlepark Marina
Kinsale — 00353 21 4774959

Challenger Marine
Penryn — 01326 377222

Chatham Maritime Marina
Medway — 01634 899200

Chelsea Harbour Ltd
London — 020 7225 9108

Chichester Marina
Chichester — 01243 512731

Chiswick Quay Marina
London — 020 8994 8743

Clyde Marina
Ardrossan — 01294 607077

Cobb's Quay Marina
Poole — 01202 674299

Coleraine Marina
Coleraine — 028 7034 4768

Conwy Marina Conwy — 01492 593000

Cowes Yacht Haven
Cowes — 01983 299975

Craobh Marina
Argyll — 01852 500222

CREST NICHOLSON MARINAS LTD
Avon House, Newbrick Road,
Stokegifford, Bristol BS34 8RA
Tel: (01179) 236466
Fax: (01179) 236508
e-mail:
sriggs@crestnicholson.com
A wholly owned subsidiary of Crest Nicholson plc, operate comprehensive yachting facilities at 5 locations in the UK and are marketing agents for Malahide Marina in Dublin Bay.

Crosshaven Boatyard Marina – Ireland Cork — 00353 21 48 31161

Cuxton Marina Ltd
Rochester — 01634 721941

Dart Marina Dartmouth — 01803 833351

Darthaven Marina Ltd
Kingswear — 01803 752242

Dartside Quay Brixham — 01803 845445

Dingle Marina – Ireland
Dingle — 00353 66 915 1629

Dolphin Haven Poole — 01202 649488

Doune Marine
Loch Alsh — 01687 462667

Dove Marina
London — 020 8748 9474

Dover Marina Dover — 01304 241663

Dun Laoghaire Marina
Dun Laogharie — 00353 1 202 0040

Dunstaffnage Marina Ltd
By Oban — 01631 566555

East Cowes Marina
Isle of Wight — 01983 293983

East Ferry Marina
Cobh — 00353 21 481 1342

Elizabeth Marina
St Helier — 01534 885530

Elmhaven Marina
Halling — 01634 240489

Emsworth Yacht Harbour Ltd
Emsworth — 01243 377727

Essex Marina Rochford — 01702 258531

Fairlie Quay
Inverkip — 01475 568267

Falmouth Marina
Falmouth — 01326 316620

Falmouth Visitors' Yacht Haven
Falmouth — 01326 312285

Fareham Marina
Fareham — 01329 822445

Fenit Marina
Fenit — 00353 66 7136231

Fleetwood Harbour Village Marina
Fleetwood — 01253 872323

Fox's Marina Ipswich Ltd
Ipswich — 01473 689111

Gallions Point Marina
London — 020 7476 7054

18 marinas
in prime boating
locations

  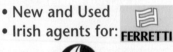

Gillingham Marina
Gillingham 01634 280022

Glasson Dock Marina
Lancaster 01524 751491

Gosport Marina Ltd
Gosport 023 9252 4811

Hafan Pwllheli
Pwllheli 01758 701219

Hamble Point Marina
Hamble 023 8045 2464

Hartlepool Marina
Hartlepool 01429 865744

Haslar Marina Gosport 023 9260 1201

Heybridge Basin
Maldon 01621 853506

Holy Loch Marina
Dunoon 01369 701800

Holyhead Marina & Trinity Marine Ltd
Holyhead 01407 764242

Hoo Marina
Rochester 01634 250311

Howth Marina – Ireland
Howth 00353 1 839 2777

Hull Marina Hull 01482 330505

Humber Cruising Association Marina
Grimsby 01472 268424

Hythe Marina Village
Southampton 023 8020 7073

Ipswich Haven Marina
Ipswich 01473 236644

Island Harbour Marina
Newport 01983 822999

Itchen Marina
Southampton 023 8063 1500

Jersey Harbours
St Helier 01534 885588

Kilmore Quay Marina – Ireland
Co Wexford 00353 53 29955

Kilrush Marina & Boatyard – Ireland
Co Clare 00353 65 9052072

Kinsale Yacht Club Marina
Kinsale 00353 21 4772196

Kip Marina 01475 521485

Kirkwall Marina Kirkwall 01856 872292

La Collette Yacht Basin
St Helier 01534 885588

Lady Bee Marina
Brighton 01273 593801

Lake Yard Poole 01202 674531

Largs Yacht Haven
Largs 01475 675333

Lawrence Cove Marina – Ireland
Co Cork 00353 27 75044

Limehouse Basin Marina
London 020 7537 2828

Littlehampton Marina
Littlehampton 01903 713553

Liverpool Marina
Liverpool 0151 708 5228

Longmans Yacht Haven
Inverness 01463 715715

Lossiemouth Marina
Lossiemouth 01343 813066

Lowestoft Haven Marina
Lowestoft 01502 580300

Lymington Marina
Lymington 01590 673312

Lymington Yacht Haven
Lymington 01590 677071

Malahide Marina – Ireland
Co Dublin 00353 1 845 4129

Maryport Harbour and Marina
Maryport 01900 814431

Mayflower International Marina
Plymouth 01752 556633

Medway Bridge Marina
Rochester 01634 843576

Medway Pier Marina
Gillingham 01634 851113

Melfort Pier & Harbour
Kilmelford 01852 200333

Mercury Yacht Harbour
Hamble (023) 8045 5994

Meridian Quay Marina
Grimsby 01472 268424

Milford Marina
Milford Haven 01646 696312/3

Mill Bay Village Marina
Plymouth 01752 226785

Mylor Yacht Harbour Ltd
Falmouth 01326 372121

Naburn Marina 01904 621021

Nairn Marina 01667 454330

NEPTUNE MARINA LTD
Neptune Quay, Ipswich, Suffolk
IP4 1AX
Tel: (01473) 215204
Fax: (01473) 215206
e-mail: enquiries@neptune-marina.com
www.neptune-marina.com
Accessible through continuously operating lockgates (VHF Channel 68) Neptune Marina (VHF Channels 80 or 37) is located on the north side of Ipswich wet dock immediately adjacent to the town centre and integrated into the rapidly regenerating northern quays.

NEWHAVEN MARINA
The Yacht Harbour, Fort Road, Newhaven, East Sussex BN9 9BY
Tel: 01273 513881
Fax: 01273 510493
Situated in Newhaven Harbour on the western bank of the Ouse. The marina offers good shelter and is accessible in all weathers. Water, electricity, diesel, toilets, workshops, restaurant and parking.

Neyland Yacht Haven Ltd
Neyland 01646 601601

Northney Marina
Hayling Island 023 9246 6321

Noss-on-Dart Marina
Dartmouth 01803 834582

Ocean Marine (Mayflower Marina)
Plymouth 01752 500121

Ocean Village Marina
Southampton 023 8022 9385

Orkney Marinas Ltd
Kirkwall 01856 879600

Padstow Harbour Commissioners
Padstow 01841 532239

Parkstone YC (Haven) Ltd
Poole 01202 743610

Penarth Marina Penarth 029 20705021

Penton Hook Marina
Chertsey 01932 568681

Peter Georgeson Marina - Vaila Sound
(Walls) Lerwick 01595 809273

Peterhead Bay Authority
Peterhead 01779 474020

Phennick Cove Marina
Ardglass 028 44842332

Plymouth Yacht Haven
Plymouth 01752 404231

Poplar Dock Marina
London 020 7515 1046

Port Dinorwic Marina
Y Felinheli 01248 671500

Port Edgar Marina & Sailing School
South Queensferry 0131 331 3330

Port Hamble Marina
Hamble (023) 8045 2741

Port Medway Marina
Rochester 01634 720033

Port Pendennis Marina
Falmouth 01326 211211

Port Solent Marina
Portsmouth 023 9221 0765

Portaferry Marina
Portaferry 028 427 29598

Portavon Marina
Keynsham 0117 9861626

Portishead Quays Marina
Bristol 01275 841941

Premier Marinas Ltd
Port Solent 023 9221 4145

Preston Marina
Preston 01772 733595

Queen Anne's Battery
Plymouth 01752 671142

Queenborough Harbour
Isle of Sheppey 01795 662051

Racecourse Yacht Basin (Windsor)
Ltd Windsor 01753 851501

Ramsgate Royal Harbour Marina
Ramsgate 01843 572100

Rhu Marina Ltd Rhu 01436 820238

Ridge Wharf Yacht Centre
Wareham 01929 552650

Royal Cork Yacht Club Marina
Crosshaven 00353 21 4831023

Royal Harbour Marina
Ramsgate 01843 592277

Royal Norfolk and Suffolk Yacht Club
Lowestoft 01502 566726

Royal Quays Marina
North Shields 0191 272 8282

Ryde Leisure Harbour
Ryde 01983 613879

Salterns Marina Boatyard & Hotel
Poole 01202 707321

Salve Marine Ltd – Ireland
Co Cork   00353 21 483 1145

Sandpoint Marina (Dumbarton)
Dumbarton   01389 762396

Saxon Wharf
Southampton   023 8033 9490

Seaport Marina
Inverness   01463 233140

Seatons Marina
Coleraine   028 703 832086

Shamrock Quay
Southampton   023 8022 9461

Sharpness Marine
Berkeley   01453 811476

Shepards Wharf Boatyard Ltd
Cowes   01983 297821

Shepperton Marina
London   01932 247427

Shotley Marina Ltd
Ipswich   01473 788982

South Dock Marina
London   020 7252 2244

South Ferriby Marina
Barton on Humber   01652 635620

Southdown Marina
Millbrook   01752 823084

Southsea Marina
Southsea   023 9282 2719

Sovereign Harbour Marina
Eastbourne   01323 470099

Sparkes Marina
Hayling Island   023 92463572

St Helier Marina
St Helier   01534 885588

St Katharine Haven
London   020 7481 8350

St Peter Port Marinas
St Peter Port   01481 720229

St Peters Marina
Newcastle upon Tyne   0191 265 4472

Strangford Lough Marina
Portaferry   00353 1247 729598

Stromness Marina
Stromness   01856 850744

Suffolk Yacht Harbour Ltd
Ipswich   01473 659240

Sunderland Marina
Sunderland   0191 5144721

Sutton Harbour Marina
Plymouth   01752 204186

Swale Marina Ltd
Teynham   01795 521562

Swansea Marina
Swansea   01792 470310

Swanwick Marina
Southampton   01489 885000

Tarquin Marina
Emsworth   01243 377727

Tayport Harbour   01382 553679

Thornham Marina
Emsworth   01243 375335

Tide Mill Yacht Harbour
Woodbridge   01394 38574

Titchmarsh Marina
Walton-on-the-Naze   01255 672185

Tollesbury Marina
Tollesbury   01621 869202

Torpoint Yacht Harbour
Plymouth   01752 813658

Torquay Marina
Torquay   01803 200210

Town Quay Marina
Southampton   023 8023 4397

Troon Yacht Haven
Troon   01292 315553

Victoria Marina
St Peter Port   01481 725987

Walton and Frinton Yacht Trust
Walton-on-the-Naze   01255 675873

Walton Yacht Basin
Walton-on-the-Naze   01255 675526

Waterford City Marina – Ireland
Waterford City   00353 51 309900

West Wick Marina Ltd
Nr Chelmsford   01245 741268

Weymouth Marina
Weymouth   01305 767576

Whitby Marina Whitby   01947 602354

Whitehaven Harbour Marina
Whitehaven   01946 692435

Whitehills Marina   01261 861291

Windsor Marina
Windsor   01753 853911

Wisbech Yacht Harbour
Wisbech   01945 588059

Woolverstone Marina
Ipswich   01473 780206

Yarmouth Harbour
Yarmouth   01983 760321

MARINE ACTIVITY CENTRES

Cowes Yacht Haven
Cowes   01983 299975

Doune Marine
Mallaig   01687 462667

Tollesbury Marina
Tollesbury   01621 869202

MARINE ARTISTS

Farrow Marine Artist, Steve
Cleethorpes   01472 311994

Lynch, Mari Godalming 01483 201085

Taylor Marine Artist, Neil
Newcastle   01782 251194

Wright Marine Artist, Colin
Poole   01202 687947

MARINE CONSULTANTS AND SURVEYORS

Amble Boat Company Ltd
Amble   01665 710267

Ark Surveys East Anglia/South Coast
                01621 857065/01794 521957

Atkin and Associates
Lymington   01590 688633

Barbican Yacht Agency Ltd
Plymouth   01752 228855

Booth Marine Surveys, Graham
Birchington-on-Sea   01843 843793

Bureau Maritime Ltd
Maldon   01621 859181

Byrde & Associates
Kimmeridge   01929 480064

Cannell & Associates, David M
Wivenhoe   01206 823337

Cardiff Commercial Boat Operators Ltd Cardiff   029 2037 7872

Clarke Designs LLP, Owen
Dartmouth   01803 770495

Davies, Peter N
Wivenhoe   01206 823289

Down Marine Co Ltd
Belfast   028 90480247

Green, James Plymouth 01752 660516

Greening Yacht Design Ltd, David
Chichester   023 9263 1806

Hansing & Associates
North Wales/Midlands   01248 671291

JP Services – Marine Safety & Training Chichester   01243 537552

Marintec Lymington   01590 683414

Norwood Marine
Margate   01843 835711

Quay Consultants Ltd
West Wittering   01243 673056

Scott Marine Surveyors & Consultants Conwy   01248 680759

Staton-Bevan, Tony
Lymington   01590 645755

Swanwick Yacht Surveyors
Southampton   01489 564822

Thomas, Stephen
Southampton   023 8048 6273

Victoria Yacht Surveys
Cornwall   0800 093 2113

Ward & McKenzie
Ipswich   01473 255200

Ward & McKenzie (North East)
Pocklington   01759 304322

Yacht Designers & Surveyors Association Bordon   0845 0900 162

MARINE ENGINEERS

Allerton Engineering
Lowestoft   01502 537870

APAS Engineering Ltd
Southampton   023 8063 2558

Ardmair Boat Centre
Ullapool   01854 612054

Arfon Oceaneering
Caernarfon   01286 676055

Arisaig Marine
Inverness-shire   01687 450224

Arun Craft Littlehampton 01903 723667

Attrill & Sons, H
Bembridge   01983 872319

Auto & Marine Services
Botley   01489 785009

Auto Marine Southsea 023 9282 5601

BJ Marine Ltd
Bangor, Ireland 028 9127 1434

Bristol Boat Ltd Bristol 01225 872032

Buzzard Marine Engineering
Yarmouth 01983 760707

C & B Marine Ltd
Chichester Marina 01243 511273

Caddy, Simon Falmouth Marina,
Falmouth 01326 372682

Caledonian Marine
Rhu Marina 01436 821184

Cambrian Engineering (Cymru) Ltd
Bangor 01248 370248

Cardigan Outboards
Cardigan 01239 613966

Channel Islands Marine Ltd
Guernsey 01481 716880

Channel Islands Marine Ltd
Jersey 01534 767595

Clarence Marine Engineering
Gosport 023 9251 1555

Cook's Diesel Service Ltd
Faversham 01795 538553

Cragie Engineering
Kirkwall 01856 874680

Crane Marine, John
Havant 023 9240 0121

Crinan Boatyard Ltd
Crinan 01546 830232

Cutler Marine Engineering, John
Emsworth 01243 375014

Dale Sailing Co Ltd
Milford Haven 01646 603110

Davis Marine Services
Ramsgate 01843 586172

Denney & Son, EL
Redcar 01642 483507

DH Marine (Shetland) Ltd
Shetland 01595 690618

Emark Marine Ltd
Emsworth 01243 375383

Evans Marine Engineering, Tony
Pwllheli 01758 613219

Fairways Marine Engineers
Maldon 01621 852866

Felton Marine Engineering
Brighton 01273 601779

Felton Marine Engineering
Eastbourne 01323 470211

Ferrypoint Boat Co
Youghal 00353 24 94232

Fettes & Rankine Engineering
Aberdeen 01224 573343

Fleetwood & Sons Ltd, Henry
Lossiemouth 01343 813015

Fleming Engineering, J
Stornoway 01851 703488

Floetree Ltd (Loch Lomond Marina)
Balloch 01389 752069

Fowey Harbour Marine Engineers
Fowey 01726 832806

Fox Marine Services Ltd
Jersey 01534 721312

Freeport Marine Jersey 01534 888100

French Marine Motors Ltd
Colchester 01206 302133

GH Douglas Marine Services
Fleetwood Harbour Village Marina,
Fleetwood 01253 877200

Golden Arrow Marine
Poole 01202 661190

Golden Arrow Marine
Southampton 023 8071 0371

Goodchild Marine Services
Great Yarmouth 01493 782301

Goodwick Marine
Fishguard 01348 873955

Gosport Boat Yard
Gosport 023 9258 6216

Griffins Garage Dingle Marina,
Co Kerry 00353 66 91 51178

Hale Marine, Ron
Portsmouth 023 9273 2985

Hamnavoe Engineering
Stromness 01856 850576

Hampshire Marine Ltd
Stubbington 01329 665561

Harbour Engineering
Itchenor 01243 513454

Hardway Marine Store
Gosport 023 9258 0420

Hartlepool Marine Engineering
Hartlepool 01429 867883

Hayles, Harold
Yarmouth 01983 760373

Herm Seaway Marine Ltd
St Peter Port 01481 726829

HNP Engineers (Lerwick Ltd)
Lerwick 01595 692493

Home Marine Emsworth Yacht Harbour,
Emsworth 01243 374125

Hook Marine Ltd
Troon 01292 679500

Hooper Marine
Littlehampton 01903 731195

Humphrey, Chris
Teignmouth 01626 772324

Instow Marine Services
Bideford 01271 861081

Jones (Boatbuilders), David
Chester 01244 390363

Keating Marine Engineering Ltd, Bill
Jersey 01534 733977

Kippford Slipway Ltd
Dalbeattie 01556 620249

Kiss Marine Yacht Services Hythe
Marina, Southampton 023 8084 0100

Langley Marine Services Ltd
Eastbourne 01323 470244

Lansdale Pannell Marine
Chichester 01243 512374

Lencraft Boats Ltd
Dungarvan +353 58 68220

Lifeline Marine Services
Dolphin Haven, Poole 01202 669676

Llyn Marine Services
Pwllheli 01758 612606

Lynx Engineering
St Helens, Isle of Wight 01983 873711

M&G Marine Services
Mayflower International Marina, Plymouth
  01752 563345

MacDonald & Co Ltd, JN
Glasgow 0141 334 6171

Mainbrayce Marine
Alderney 01481 822772

Malakoff and Moore
Lerwick 01595 695544

Mallaig Boat Building and
Engineering Mallaig 01687 462304

Marindus Engineering
Kilmore Quay 00353 53 29794

Marine Engineering Looe
Brixham 01803 844777

Marine Engineering Looe
Looe 01503 263009

Marine General Engineers Beaucette
Marina, Guernsey 01481 245808

Marine Maintenance
Portsmouth 023 9260 2344

Marine Maintenance
Tollesbury 01621 860441

Marine Propulsion
Hayling Island 023 9246 1694

Marine-Trak Engineering Mylor Yacht
Harbour, Falmouth 01326 376588

Marlec Marine
Ramsgate 01843 592176

MARINE SUPPLIES AND SERVICES GUIDE

MARINAS – MARINE ENGINEERS

Martin (Marine) Ltd, Alec
Birkenhead   0151 652 1663

Medusa Marine Ipswich 01473 780090

Mobile Marine Engineering Liverpool
Marina, Liverpool   01565 733553

Motortech Marine Engineering
Portsmouth   023 9251 3200

Mount's Bay Engineering
Newlyn   01736 363014

MP Marine Maryport   01900 810299

New World Yacht Care
Helensburgh   01436 820586

North Western Automarine Engineers
Largs   01475 687139

Noss Marine Services
Dart Marina, Dartmouth   01803 833343

Owen Marine, Robert
Porthmadog   01766 513435

Pace, Andy Newhaven   01273 516010

Parkin, Mo Wellington Dock,
Dover   01304 219658

**Penzance Dry Dock and Engineering
Co Ltd** Penzance   01736 363838

Pirie & Co, John S
Fraserburgh   01346 513314

Portavon Marine
Keynsham   0117 986 1626

Power Afloat, Elkins Boatyard
Christchurch   01202 489555

Powerplus Marine Cowes Yacht Haven,
Cowes   01983 200036

Pro-Marine Queen Anne's Battery
Marina, Plymouth   01752 267984

PT Marine Engineering
Hayling Island   023 9246 9332

R & M Marine
Portsmouth   023 9265 1355

R & S Engineering Dingle Marina,
Ireland   00353 66 915 1189

Reddish Marine
Salcombe   01548 844094

Reynolds, Cliff
Hartlepool   01429 272049

RHP Marine
Cowes   01983 290421

River Tees Engineering & Welding Ltd
Middlesbrough   01642 226226

RK Marine Ltd Hamble   01489 583585

RK Marine Ltd
Swanwick   01489 583572

Rossiter Yachts Ltd
Christchurch   01202 483250

Ryan & Roberts Marine Services
Askeaton   00353 61 392198

Salve Marine Ltd
Crosshaven   00353 21 4831145

Scarborough Marine Engineering Ltd
Scarborough   01723 375199

**SEA START LIMITED
Unit 13, Hamble Point Marina,
Hamble, Southampton SO31 4JD
Tel: (023) 8045 8000
Fax: (023) 8045 2666
e-mail: sales@seastart.co.uk**

www.seastart.co.uk
24 hours a day, 365 days a year - marine
breakdown assistance.

Seaguard Marine Engineering Ltd
Goodwick   01348 872976

Seamark-Nunn & Co
Felixstowe   01394 275327

Seaward Engineering
Glasgow   0141 632 4910

Seaway Marine
Gosport   023 9260 2722

Shearwater Engineering Services Ltd
Dunoon   01369 706666

Silvers Marina Ltd
Helensburgh   01436 831222

Starey Marine
Salcombe   01548 843655

Stratton Boatyard, Ken
Bembridge   01983 873185

Strickland Marine Engineering, Brian
Chichester   01243 513454

Tollesbury Marine Engineering
Tollesbury Marina,
Tollesbury   01621 869919

Troon Marine Services Ltd
Troon   01292 316180

Troop & Co, James
Liverpool   0151 709 0581

Vasey Marine Engineering, Gordon
Fareham   07798 638625

Volspec Ltd Ipswich Marina,
Ipswich   01473 219651

Wallis, Peter Torquay Marina,
Torquay   01803 844777

WB Marine Chichester   01243 512857

West Point Marine Services
Fareham   01329 232881

Western Marine Power Ltd
Plymouth   01752 408804

**Weymouth Marina Mechanical
Services** Weymouth   01305 779379

Whittington, G Lady Bee Marine,
Shoreham   01273 593801

Wigmore Wright Marine Services
Penarth Marina   029 2070 9983

Williams Ltd, TJ
Cardiff   029 2048 7676

Wright, M Manaccan   01326 231502

Wyko Industrial Services
Inverness   01463 224747

Yates Marine, Martin
Galgate   01524 751750

Ynys Marine
Cardigan   01239 613179

Yoldings Marine
Eastbourne   01323 470882

Youngboats
Faversham   01795 536176

1° West Marine Ltd
Portsmouth   023 9283 8335

MASTS, SPARS & RIGGING

Allspars Plymouth   01752 266766

Amble Boat Co Ltd
Morpeth   01665 710267

Arun Canvas & Rigging
Littlehampton   1903 732561

Atlantis Spars Ltd
Brixham   01803 843322

**BOATWORKS + LTD
Castle Emplacement,
St Peter Port,
Guernsey, Channel Islands
GY1 1AU.
Tel: (01481) 726071
Fax: (01481) 714224**
Boatworks + provides a comprehensive
range of services including boatbuilding
and repairs, chandlery, clothing and fuel
supplies.

Buchanan, Keith
St Mary's   01720 422037

Bussell & Co, WL
Weymouth   01305 785633

Carbospars Ltd Hamble 023 8045 6736

Coates Marine Ltd
Whitby   01947 604486

Dauntless Boatyard Ltd
Canvey Island   01268 793782

Davies Marine Services
Ramsgate   01843 586172

Eurospars Ltd Plymouth 01752 550550

Exe Leisure Exeter 01392 879055

Fox's Marine Ipswich Ltd
Ipswich 01473 689111

Freeland Yacht Spars Ltd
Dorchester on Thames 01865 341277

Gordon, AD Portland 01305 821569

Harris Rigging
Totnes 01803 840160

Heyn Engineering
Belfast 028 9035 0022

HOLMAN RIGGING
Chichester Marina, Chichester,
West Sussex PO20 7EJ.
Tel/Fax: (01243) 514000
e-mail:
enquiries@holmanrigging.co.uk
www.holmanrigging.co.uk
Agent for major suppliers in this field we
offer a specialist mast and rigging service.
Purpose designed mast trailer for quick
and safe transportation. Installation for
roller headsail and mainsail reefing
systems. Insurance reports and
quotations.

Lowestoft Yacht Services
Lowestoft 01502 585535

Marine Resource Centre
Oban 01631 720291

MP Marine Maryport 01900 810299

Ocean Rigging
Lymington 01590 676292

Owen Sails Oban 01631 720485

Pro Rig S Ireland 00353 87 298 3333

Rig Magic Ipswich 01473 655089

Rig Shop, The Poole 01202 677717

Rig Shop, The
Southampton 023 8033 8341

Roberts Marine Ltd, S
Liverpool 0151 707 8300

Sailspar Ltd
Brightlingsea 01206 302679

Salcombe Boatstore
Salcombe 01548 843708

Seldén Mast Ltd
Southampton 01489 484000

Silvers Marina Ltd
Helensburgh 01436 831222

Silverwood Yacht Services Ltd
Portsmouth 023 9232 7067

Southern Spar Services
Northam 023 8033 1714

Spencer Rigging Ltd
Cowes 01983 292022/292144

Storrar Marine Store
Newcastle-upon-Tyne 0191 266 1037

Tedfords Rigging & Rafts
Belfast 028 9032 6763

TJ Rigging Conwy 07780 972411

TS Rigging Malden 01621 874861

Windjammer Marine
Milford Marina 01646 699070

Yacht Rigging Services
Plymouth 01752 226609

Yacht Solutions Ltd
Portsmouth 023 9220 0670

XW Rigging Gosport 023 9251 3553

Z Spars UK Hadleigh 01473 822130

1° West Marine Ltd
Portsmouth 023 9283 8335

NAVIGATION EQUIPMENT – GENERAL

Belson Design Ltd, Nick
Southampton 077 6835 1330

Brown Son & Ferguson Ltd
Glasgow 0141 429 1234

Chattan Security Ltd
Edinburgh 0131 555 3155

Cooke & Son Ltd, B Hull 01482 223454

Diverse Yacht Services
Hamble 023 8045 3399

Dolphin Maritime Software Ltd
Lancaster 01524 841946

Dubois Phillips & McCallum Ltd
Liverpool 0151 236 2776

Eland Exeter 01392 255788

Garmin Romsey 01794 519944

Geonav UK Ltd Poole 0870 240 4575

Imray Laurie Norie and Wilson Ltd
Edinburgh 01480 462114

Kelvin Hughes
Southampton 023 8063 4911

Lilley & Gillie Ltd, John
North Shields 0191 257 2217

Maptech UK Ltd
Westbourne 01243 389352

Marine Chart Services
Wellingborough 01933 441629

PC Maritime Plymouth 01752 254205

Plastimo (UK) Ltd
Eastleigh 023 8026 2211

Price & Co, WF Bristol 0117 929 2229

Raymarine Ltd
Portsmouth 023 9269 3611

Robbins Marine Electronics
Liverpool 0151 709 5431

Royal Institute of Navigation
London 020 7591 3130

Sea Chest Nautical Bookshop
Plymouth 01752 222012

Seath Instruments (1992) Ltd
Lowestoft 01502 573811

Smith (Marine) Ltd, AM
London 020 8529 6988

South Bank Marine Charts Ltd
Grimsby 01472 361137

Southcoasting Navigators
Devon 01626 335626

Stanford Charts
West Mersea 01206 381580

Todd Chart Agency Ltd
County Down 028 9146 6640

UK Hydrographic Office
Taunton 01823 337900

Warsash Nautical Bookshop
Warsash 01489 572384

Yachting Instruments Ltd
Sturminster Newton 01258 817662

Yeoman Romsey 01794 521079

OVERSEAS

D.C.G. BANBURY
1 Longfellow Road
Banbury, Oxon OX16 9LB
Tel: 01295 257707
Fax: 01295 257707
e-mail: info@subrella.co.uk
www.subrella.co.uk
Makers of 'SUBRELLA' the only proven,
fast, effective, reliable, yet incredibly
simple device available anywhere in the
world for rapidly closing off holes in the
hull below the waterline from the
complete safety of the inside of the
vessel. Carrying 'SUBRELLA' makes
saving the sanctuary of the parent vessel
more than just a possibility.

PAINT & OSMOSIS

Advanced Blast Cleaning Paint
Tavistock 01822 617192/07970 407911

Blakes Paints
Southampton 01489 864440

Herm Seaway Marine Ltd
St Peter Port 01481 726829

International Coatings Ltd
Southampton 023 8022 6722

Marineware Ltd
Southampton 023 8033 0208

New Guard Coatings Ltd
Wetherby 01937 568311

NLB Marine Ardrossan 01563 521509

Pro-Boat Ltd
Burnham on Crouch 01621 785455

Rustbuster Ltd
Peterborough 0870 9090093

Smith & Son Ltd, EC
Luton 01582 729721

SP Systems
Isle of Wight 01983 828000

Stone Pier Yacht Services
Warsash 01489 885400

Teal & Mackrill Ltd Hull 01482 320194

Troon Marine Services Ltd
Troon 01292 316180

POLICE

Aberdeen Police 01224 386000

Aberdovey Police 01286 673333

Abersoch Police 01286 673333

Aberystwyth Police 01970 612791

Alderney and Burhou Police
01481 725111

Anstruther Police 01333 592100

Appledore Police 08705 777444

Arbroath Police 01241 872222

Ardglass Police 028 4461501

Ardrishaig Police 01546 603233

Ardrossan Police 01294 468236

Arklow Police	00353 402 32304/5	
Baltimore Police	00353 28 20102	
Bantry Bay Police	00353 27 50045	
Barmouth Police	01286 673333	
Barry Police	01446 734451	
Beaulieu River Police	023 80335444	
Belfast Lough Police	028 91 454444	
Berwick-upon-Tweed Police		
	01289 307111	
Blyth Police	01661 872555	
Boston Police	01205 366222	
Bridlington Police	01262 672222	
Bridport Police	01308 422266	
Brighton Police	01273 606744	
Bristol Police	0117 9277777	
Brixham Police	0990 777444	
Buckie Police	01542 832222	
Burnham-on-Crouch Police		
	01621 782121	
Burnham-on-Sea Police		
	01823 337911	
Burry Port Police	01554 772222	
Caernarfon Police	01286 673333	
Campbeltown Police	01586 552253	
Cardiff Police	01446 734451	
Carlingford Lough Police		
	042 9373102	
Castle Haven Police	00353 28 36144	
Christchurch Police	01202 486333	
Colchester Police	01206 762212	
Conwy Police	01492 517171	
Corpach Police	01397 702361	
Courtmacsherry Police		
	00353 23 46122	
Crinan Canal Police	01546 602222	
Dartmouth Police	0990 777444	
Dingle Police	00353 66 9151522	
Douglas Police	01624 631212	
Dover Police	01304 216084	
Dover Police	01304 240055	
Dublin Police	00353 1 6665000	
Dunbar Police	01368 862718	
Dunmore East Police		
	00353 51 383112	
East Loch Tarbert Police		
	01880 820200	
Eastbourne Police	01323 722522	
Eyemouth Police	01890 750217	
Findhorn Police	01309 672224	
Fishguard Police	01437 763355	
Fleetwood Police	01524 63333	
Folkestone Police	01303 850055	
Fowey Police	0990 777444	
Fraserburgh Police	01346 513121	
Galway Bay Police	00353 91 538000	
Glandore Police	00353 23 48162	
Great Yarmouth Police	01493 336200	
Grimsby Police	01482 210031	

Guernsey Police	01481 725111
Hamble River Police	023 80335444
Hartlepool Police	01429 221151
Helmsdale Police	01431 821222
Holyhead Police	01286 673333
Hopeman Police	01343 830222
Howth Police	00353 1 6664900
Hull Police	01482 210031
Ilfracombe Police	08705 777444
Inverkip Police	01475 521222
Inverness Police	01463 715555
Isles of Scilly Police	01721 422444
Kenmare River Police	00353 64 41177
Keyhaven Police	01590 615101
Killybegs Police	00353 73 31002
Kilmore Quay Police	00353 53 29642
Kilrush Police	00353 65 51057
Kinlochbervie Police	01971 521222
Kinsale Police	00353 21 4772302
Kirkcudbright Police	01557 330600
Kirkwall Police	01856 872241
Lamlash Police	01770 302573
Largs Police	01475 674651
Larne Police	02828 272266
Lerwick Police	01595 692110
Littlehampton Police	01903 731733
Liverpool Police	0151 709 6010
Loch Melfort Police	01852 562213
Looe Police	01503 262233
Lossiemouth Police	01343 812022
Lough Foyle Police	028 77766797
Lough Swilly Police	00353 72 51102
Lowestoft Police	01986 855321
Lyme Regis Police	01297 442603
Macduff and Banff Police	01261 812555
Malahide Police	00353 1 6664600
Mallaig Police	01687 462177
Maryport Police	01900 602422
Medway Police	01634 811281
Menai Strait Police	01286 673333
Methil Police	01592 418888
Mevagissey Police	0990 777444
Milford Haven Police	01437 763355
Minehead Police	01823 337911
Montrose Police	01674 672222
Nairn Police	01667 452222
Newhaven Police	01273 515801
Newtown Creek Police	01983 528000
Oban Police	01631 562213
Padstow Police	08705 777444
Peel Police	01624 631212
Penzance Police	01736 362395
Peterhead Police	01779 472571
Plymouth Police	01752 701188
Poole Harbour Police	01202 223954

Port St Mary Police	01624 631212
Porthmadog Police	01286 673333
Portishead Police	01934 638272
Portland Police	01305 821205
Portpatrick Police	01776 702112
Portree Police	01478 612888
Portrush Police	028 70344122
Preston Police	01772 203203
Pwllheli Police	01286 673333
Queenborough Police	01795 477055
Ramsey Police	01624 631212
Ramsgate Police	01843 231055
Rhu Police	01436 672141
River Bann and Coleraine Police	028 70344122
River Colne Police	01255 221312
River Deben Police	01394 383377
River Humber Police	01482 359171
River Stour Police	01255 241312
River Tyne Police	0191 232 3451
River Yealm Police	0990 777444
Rivers Alde and Ore Police	01394 613500
Rothesay Police	01700 502121
Rye Police	01797 222112
S Queensferry Police	0131 331 1798
Salcombe Police	01548 842107
Scarborough Police	01723 500300
Schull Police	00353 28 28111
Scrabster Police	01847 893222
Seaham Police	0191 581 2255
Sharpness Police	01452 521201
Shoreham Police	01273 454521
Sligo Police	00353 71 57000
Southampton Police	023 80845511
Southend-on-Sea Police	01702 341212
Southwold Police	01986 855321
St Helier Police	01534 612612
Stonehaven Police	01569 762963
Stornoway Police	01851 702222
Strangford Lough Police	028 44615011
Stromness Police	01856 850222
Stronsay Police	01857 872241
Sunderland Police	0191 4547555
Swanage Police	01929 422004
Swansea Police	01792 456999
Teignmouth Police	01626 772433
Tenby Police	01834 842303
Thames Estuary Police	020 7 754421
The Swale Police	01795 536639
Tobermory Police	01688 302016
Torquay Police	0990 777444
Troon Police	01292 313100
Ullapool Police	01854 612017
Walton Backwaters Police	01255 241312

Wells-next-the-Sea Police	01493 336200
West Mersea Police	01206 382930
Westport Police	00353 98 25555
Wexford Police	00353 404 67107
Weymouth Police	01305 250512
Whitby Police	01947 603443
Whitehaven Police	01946 692616
Whitstable Police	01227 770055
Wick Police	01955 603551
Wicklow Police	00353 404 67107
Workington Police	01900 602422
Yarmouth Police	01983 528000
Youghal Police	00353 24 92200

PROPELLERS & STERNGEAR/REPAIRS

CJR Propulsion Ltd
Southampton 023 8063 9366

Darglow Engineering Ltd
Wareham 01929 556512

Gori Propellers Poole 01202 621631

Propeller Revolutions
Poole 01202 671226

ProProtector LTD
74 Abingdon Road, Maidstone,
Kent ME16 9EE
Tel: (01622) 728738
Fax: (01622) 727973
e-mail:
sails@prop-protector.co.uk
www.prop-protector.co.uk
Prevention is better than cure when it
comes to fouled propellers. ProProtectors
are now welcome and used worldwide as
the most economical and simplest way to
combat stray rope, netting, weed and
plastic bags. Fit one before it is too late.

Sillette – Sonic Ltd
Sutton 020 8715 0100

Vetus Den Ouden Ltd
Southampton 023 8086 1033

RADIO COURSES/SCHOOLS

**Bisham Abbey Sailing & Navigation
School** Bisham 01628 474960

Dart Sailing School
Dartmouth 01803 833973

**East Coast Offshore Yachting – Les
Rant** Perry 01480 861381

Fowey Cruising School
Fowey 01726 832129

Hamble School of Yachting
Hamble 023 8045 6687

Pembrokeshire Cruising
Neyland 01646 602500

Plymouth Sailing School
Plymouth 01752 667170

Sail East Ipswich 01206 734319

Sail North Wales
Conwy 01492 584208

Southern Sailing
Swanwick 01489 575511

Start Point Sailing
Kingsbridge 01548 810917

REEFING SYSTEMS

Atlantic Spars Ltd
Brixham 01803 843322

Calibra Marine International Ltd
Southampton 08702 400358

Eurospars Ltd Plymouth 01752 550550

Holman Rigging
Chichester 01243 514000

Plastimo (UK) Ltd
023 8026 2211

Rotomarine Ltd Bosham 01243 573131

Sea Teach Ltd Emsworth 01243 375774

Southern Spar Services
Northam 023 8033 1714

Wragg, Chris Lymington 01590 677052

Z Spars UK Hadleigh 01473 822130

REPAIR MATERIALS AND ACCESSORIES

Akeron Ltd
Southend on Sea 01702 297101

Howells & Son, KJ
Poole 01202 665724

JB Timber Ltd
North Ferriby 01482 631765

Robbins Timber Bristol 0117 9633136

Sika Ltd
Welwyn Garden City 01707 394444

SP Systems Newport,
Isle of Wight 01983 828000

Technix Rubber & Plastics Ltd
Southampton 023 8063 5523

Tiflex Liskeard 01579 320808

Timage & Co Ltd
Braintree 01376 343087

Trade Grade Products Ltd
Poole 01202 820177

Wessex Resins & Adhesives Ltd
Romsey 01794 521111

ROPE AND WIRE

Euro Rope Ltd
Scunthorpe 01724 280480

Malow Ropes
Hailsham 01323 847234

Mr Splice Leicester 0800 1697178

Spinlock Ltd Cowes 01983 295555

TJ Rigging Conwy 07780 972411

SAFETY EQUIPMENT

AB Marine Ltd
St Peter Port 01481 722378

Adec Marine Ltd
Croydon 020 8686 9717

Anchorwatch UK
Edinburgh 0131 447 5057

ADEC Marine Limited
Approved liferaft service station for South East.
Buy or hire new rafts. Complete range of safety
equipment for yachts including pyrotechnics.
Fire extinguishers – Lifejackets – Buoyancy aids
4 Masons Avenue, Croydon,
Surrey CR0 9XS
Tel: 020 8686 9717
Fax: 020 8680 9912
E-mail: sales@adecmarine.co.uk
Website: www.adecmarine.co.uk

Avon Inflatables
Llanelli 01554 882000

Cosalt International Ltd
Aberdeen 01224 588327

Crewsaver Gosport 023 9252 8621

Glaslyn Marine Supplies Ltd
Porthmadog 01766 513545

Guardian Fire Ltd
Norwich 01603 787679

Hale Marine, Ron
Portsmouth 023 9273 2985

Herm Seaway Marine Ltd
St Peter Port 01481 722838

IBS Boats South Woodham Ferrers
01245 323211/425551

KTS Seasafety Kilkeel 028 41762655

McMurdo Pains Wessex
Portsmouth 023 9262 3900

Met Office Bracknell 0845 300 0300

Nationwide Marine Hire
Warrington 01925 245788

Norwest Marine Ltd
Liverpool 0151 207 2860

Ocean Safety
Southampton 023 8072 0800

Plastimo (UK) Ltd
Eastleigh 023 8026 2211

Polymarine Ltd Conwy 01492 583322

Premium Liferaft Services
Burnham-on-Crouch 0800 243673

Ribs UK Ltd
Southampton 023 8022 2262

Ribeye Dartmouth 01803 832060

Secumar Swansea 01792 280545

South Eastern Marine Services Ltd
Basildon 01268 534427

Suffolk Sailing
Ipswich 01473 833010

Whitstable Marine
Whitstable 01227 262525

Winters Marine Ltd
Salcombe 01548 843580

SAILMAKERS & REPAIRS

Allison-Gray Dundee 01382 505888

Alsop Sailmakers, John
Salcombe 01548 843702

Arun Canvas & Rigging
Littlehampton 01903 732561

Arun Sails Chichester	01243 573185	
Bank Sails, Bruce Southampton	01489 582444	
Bissett and Ross Aberdeen	01224 580659	
Breaksea Sails Barry	01446 730785	
Bristol Sails Bristol	0117 922 5080	
Buchanan, Keith St Mary's	01720 422037	
C&J Marine Textiles Chichester	01243 782629	
Calibra Sails Dartmouth	01803 833094	
Canard Sails Swansea	01792 367838	
Covercare Fareham	01329 311878	
Crawford, Margaret Kirkwall	01856 875692	
Crusader Sails Poole	01202 670580	
Cullen Sailmakers Galway	00353 91 771991	
Dawson (Sails), J Port Dinorwic	01248 670103	
Dolphin Sails Harwich	01255 243366	
Doyle Sails Southampton	023 8033 2622	
Downer International Sails & Chandlery Dun Laoghaire	00353 1 280 0231	
Duthie Marine Safety, Arthur Glasgow	0141 429 4553	
East Coast Sails Walton-on-the-Naze	01255 678353	
Eurotech Marine Products Ltd London	020 7235 8273	
Flew Sailmakers Portchester	01329 822676	
Fylde Coast Sailmaking Co Fleetwood	01253 873476	
Garland Sails Bristol	0117 935 3233	
Gaw, EA Belfast	028 90451905	
Goldfinch Sails Whitstable	01227 272295	
Gowen Ocean Sailmakers West Mersea	01206 384412	
Green Sailmakers, Paul Plymouth	01752 660317	
Halsey Lidgard Sailmakers Chichester	01243 545410	
Halsey Lidgard Sailmakers Southsea	023 9229 4700	
Hood Sailmakers Lymington	01590 675011	
Hooper, A Plymouth	01752 830411	
Hyde Sails (Benfleet) Benfleet	01268 756254	
Irish Sea Yachts Maryport	01900 816881	
Island Yachts St Helier	01534 725048	
Jackson Yacht Services Jersey	01534 743819	
Jeckells and Son Ltd (Wroxham) Wroxham	01603 782223	
Jessail Ardrossan	01294 467311	

JKA Sailmakers Pwllheli	01758 613266
Kemp Sails Ltd Wareham	01929 554308/554378
Lawrence Sailmakers, J Brightlingsea	01206 302863
Lodey Sails Newlyn	01736 331557
Lucas Sails Portchester	023 9237 3699
Malakoff and Moore Lerwick	01595 695544
Malcolm Sails Fairlie	01475 568500
Mathew Sail Loft (Ocean Blue Chandlery), A Penzance	01736 364004
McCready and Co Ltd, J Belfast	028 90232842
McKillop Sails (Sail Locker) Ipswich	01473 780007
McNamara Sails, Michael Great Yarmouth	01692 584186
McWilliam Sailmaker (Crosshaven) Crosshaven	00353 21 4831505
McWilliam Sailmaker (Killinchy) Killinchy	028 97542345
Mitchell Sails Fowey	01726 833731
Montrose Rope and Sails Montrose	01674 672657
Mountfield Sails Hayling Island	023 9246 3720
Mouse Sails Holyhead	01407 763636
Nicholson Hughes Sails Rosneath	01436 831356
North Sea Sails Tollesbury	01621 869367
North West Sails Keighley	01535 652949
Northrop Sails Ramsgate	01843 851665
Ocean Sails Plymouth	01752 563666
Ösen Sails Ltd Plymouth	01752 563666
Owen Sails (Gourock) Gourock	01475 636196
Owen Sails By Oban	01631 720485
Parker & Kay Sailmakers – East Ipswich	01473 659878
Parker & Kay Sailmakers – South Hamble	023 8045 8213

Penrose Sailmakers Falmouth	01326 312705
Pollard Marine Port St Mary	01624 835831
Quantum Sails Ipswich Haven Marina	01473 659878
Quantum-Parker & Kay Sailmakers Hamble	023 8045 8213
Quay Sails (Poole) Ltd Poole	01202 681128
Ratsey & Lapthorn Isle of Wight	01983 294051
Ratsey Sailmakers, Stephen Milford Haven	01646 601561
Relling One Design Portland	01305 826555
Richardson Sails Southampton	023 8040 3914
Rig Shop, The Poole	01202 677717
Rig Shop, The Southampton	023 8033 8341
Rockall Sails Chichester	01243 573185
Sail Locker Woolverstone Marina	01473 780206
Sails & Canvas Exeter	01392 877527
Saltern Sail Co West Cowes	01983 280014
Saltern Sail Company Yarmouth	01983 760120
Saturn Sails Largs	01475 689933
Scott & Co, Graham St Peter Port	01481 728989
Shore Sailmakers Swanwick	01489 589450
Sketrick Sailmakers Ltd Killinchy	028 9754 1400
South West Sails Penryn	01326 375291
Southern Sails Poole	01202 677000
Stanley Sail & Cover Makers, G Hull	01482 225590
Stephen Ratsey Sailmakers Milford Haven	01646 601561
Suffolk Sails Woodbridge	01394 386323
Sunset Sails Sligo	00353 71 62792

Teltale Sails Prestwick	01292 475125	
Torquay Marina Sails and Canvas		
Exeter	01392 877527	
Trident UK Gateshead	0191 490 1736	
UK McWilliam Cowes	01983 281100	
Underwood Sails Queen Anne's		
Battery, Plymouth	01752 229661	
W Sails Leigh-on-Sea	01702 714550	
Watson Sails		
Dublin 13	00353 1 832 6466	
WB Leitch and Son		
Tarbert	01880 820287	
Westaway Sails		
Plymouth Yacht Haven	01752 892560	
Wilkinson, Ursula		
Brighton	01273 677758	
Wilkinson Sails		
Teynham	01795 521503	
William Leith		
Berwick on Tweed	01289 307264	

SEA DELIVERIES

PETERS & MAY LTD
18 Canuse Road, Ocean Village,
Southampton SO14 3FJ
Tel: 023 8048 0480
Fax: 023 8048 0400
e-mail: sales@petersandmay.com
www.petersandmay.com
Peters and May move marine equipment and 900+ sailboats and motoryachts each year worldwide. Weekly sailings to Australasia, Far and Middle East; shipping monthly to Mediterranean and Caribbean; daily airfreight shipments of urgent spares/equipment.

SLIPWAYS

Aberystwyth Marina	
Aberystwyth	01970 611422
Amble Marina Amble	01665 712168
Ardfern Yacht Centre Ltd	
by Lochgilphead	01852 500247
Arklow Marina	
Arklow	00353 402 39901
Bangor Marina	
Bangor, Ireland	028 91 453297
Beaucette Marina	
Vale, Guernsey	01481 245000
Birdham Pool Marina	
Chichester	01243 512310
Blackwater Marina	
Maylandsea	01621 740264
Bradwell Marina	
Bradwell-on-Sea	01621 776235
Bristol Marina Bristol	0117 9213198
Buckler's Hard Marina	
Beaulieu	01590 616200
Cahersiveen Marina	
Cahersiveen	00353 669 473214
Caley Marina	
Inverness	01463 233437
Carlingford Marina – Ireland	
Carlingford	00353 42 9373073

Carrickfergus Marina	
Carrickfergus	028 93 366666
Castlepark Marina	
Kinsale	00353 21 4774959
Chichester Marina	
Chichester	01243 512731
Coleraine Marina	
Coleraine	028 7034 4768
Craobh Marina	
By Lochgilphead	01852 500222
Crosshaven Boatyard Marina –	
Ireland Crosshaven 00353 21 48 31161	
Darthaven Marina	
Kingswear	01803 752242
Dingle Marina – Ireland	
Co Kerry	00353 66 91 51629
Dover Marina Dover	01304 241663
Dunstaffnage Marina Ltd	
By Oban	01631 566555
Duver Boatyard	
St Helens, Isle of Wight	01983 873711
East Ferry Marina	
Cobh	00353 21 481 1342
Emsworth Yacht Harbour	
	01243 377727
Falmouth Yacht Haven	
Falmouth	01326 312285
Fleetwood Harbour Village Marina	
Fleetwood	01253 872323
Glasson Dock Marina	
Lancaster	01524 751491
Gosport Marina	
Gosport	023 9252 4811
Hafan Pwllheli Pwllheli	01758 701219
Hamble Point Marina	
Hamble	023 8045 2464
Hartlepool Marina	
Hartlepool	01429 865744
Haslar Marina	
Gosport	023 9260 1201
Holy Loch Marina	
Dunoon	01369 701800
Holyhead Marina	
Holyhead	01407 764242
Howth Marina – Ireland	
Howth	00353 1 839 2777
Hythe Marina Village	
Southampton	023 8020 7073
Island Harbour Marina	
Newport, Isle of Wight	01983 822999
Kilmore Quay Marina – Ireland	
Co Wexford	00353 53 29 955
Kilrush Marina & Boatyard – Ireland	
Co Clare	00353 65 9052072
Kinsale Yacht Club Marina	
Kinsale	00353 21 4772196
Lady Bee Marina	
Shoreham	01273 593801
Largs Yacht Haven	
Largs	01475 675333
Lawrence Cove Marina – Ireland	
Bantry Bay	00353 27 75 044
Littlehampton Marina	
Littlehampton	01903 713553

Liverpool Marina	
Liverpool	0151 708 5228
Lossiemouth Marina	
Lossiemouth	01343 813066
Lymington Marina	
Lymington	01590 673312
Malahide Marina – Ireland	
Malahide	00353 1 8454129
Maryport Harbour and Marina	
Maryport	01900 814431
Mayflower International Marina	
Plymouth	01752 556633
Melfort Pier & Harbour	
Kilmelford	01852 200333
Mercury Yacht Harbour	
Hamble	023 8045 5994
Milford Marina	
Milford Haven	01646 696312/3
Mylor Yacht Harbour Ltd	
Falmouth	01326 372121
Newhaven Marina Ltd	
Newhaven	01273 513881
Northney Marina	
Hayling Island	023 9246 6321
Noss-on-Dart Marina	
Dartmouth	01803 834582
Ocean Village Marina	
Southampton	023 8022 9385
Parkstone YC (Haven) Ltd	
Poole	01202 743610
Penarth Marina	
Penarth	029 2070 5021
Penton Hook Marina	
Chertsey	01932 568681
Peterhead Bay Marina	
Peterhead	01779 474020
Phennick Cove Marina	
Ardglass	028 448 42332
Plymouth Yacht Haven	
Plymouth	01752 404231
Port Edgar Marina & Sailing School	
South Queensferry	0131 331 3330
Portaferry Marina	
Portaferry	028 427 29598
Portishead Quays Marina	
Bristol	01275 841941
Queen Anne's Battery	
Plymouth	01752 671142
Ramsgate Royal Harbour Marina	
Ramsgate	01843 592277
Ridge Wharf Yacht Centre	
Wareham	01929 552650
Royal Cork Yacht Club Marina	
Crosshaven	00353 21 4831023
Royal Norfolk and Suffolk Yacht Club	
Lowestoft	01502 566726
Ryde Leisure Harbour	
Ryde	01983 613879
Salterns Marina Boatyard & Hotel	
Poole	01202 707321
Sandpoint Marina (Dumbarton)	
Dumbarton	01389 762396
Saxon Wharf Marina	
Southampton	023 8033 9490

Seaport Marina
Inverness 01463 233140

Seatons Marina
Coleraine 028 703 832086

Shamrock Quay Marina
Southampton 023 8022 9461

Shepards Wharf Boatyard Ltd
Cowes 01983 297821

St Helier Marina (La Collette)
St Helier 01534 885588

St Peter Port Marinas
St Peter Port 01481 720229

Stromness Marina
Stromness 01856 850744

Suffolk Yacht Harbour
Ipswich 01473 659240

Sunderland Marina
Sunderland 0191 5144721

Sutton Harbour Marina
Sutton 01752 204186

Swanwick Marina
Hamble 01489 885000

Titchmarsh Marina
Walton-on-the-Naze 01255 672185

Tollesbury Marina
Maldon 01621 869202

Torpoint Yacht Harbour
Plymouth 01752 813658

Torquay Marina (Paignton Harbour
Master) 01803 557812

Town Quay Marina
Southampton 023 8023 4397

Troon Yacht Haven
Troon 01292 315553

Victoria Marina
St Peter Port 01481 725987

West Wick Marina Ltd
Nr Chelmsford 01245 741268

Weymouth Marina
Weymouth 01305 767576

Whitby Marina
Whitby 01947 602354

Whitehaven Harbour Marina
Whitehaven 01946 692435

Windsor Marina
Windsor 01753 853911

Winters Marine Ltd
Salcombe 01548 843580

Wisbech Yacht Harbour
Wisbech 01945 588059

Woolverstone Marina
Ipswich 01473 780206

SOLAR POWER

Ampair Ringwood 01425 480780

Barden UK Ltd Fareham 01489 570770

Marlec Engineering Co Ltd
Corby 01536 201588

SPRAYHOODS & DODGERS

A & B Textiles
Gillingham 01634 579686

Allison–Gray Dundee 01382 505888

Arton, Charles
Milford-on-Sea 01590 644682

Arun Canvas and Rigging Ltd
Littlehampton 01903 732561

Buchanan, Keith
St Mary's 01720 422037

C & J Marine Textiles
Chichester 01243 785485

Covercare Fareham 01329 311878

Covercraft Southampton 023 8033 8286

Crawford, Margaret
Kirkwall 01856 875692

Dex-Tamar Marine
Plymouth 01752 491454

Eurotech Marine Products Ltd
London 020 7235 8273

Flexicovers Poole 01202 721309

Jasper Covers Fareham 01329 845353

JB Yacht Services
Southampton 01489 572487

Jeckells and Son Ltd
Lowestoft 01502 565007

Jeckells and Son Ltd
Wroxham 01603 782223

Jessail Ardrossan 01294 467311

Lomond Boat Covers
Alexandria 01389 602734

Lucas Sails
Portchester 023 9237 3699

Poole Canvas Co Ltd
Poole 01202 677477

Saundersfoot Auto Marine
Saundersfoot 01834 812115

Teltale Sails Prestwick 01292 475125

Trident UK Gateshead 0191 490 1736

SURVEYORS AND NAVAL ARCHITECTS

Amble Boat Company Ltd
Amble 01665 710267

Ark Surveys East Anglia/South Coast
01621 857065/01794 521957

Atkin & Associates
Lymington 01590 688633

AYERS MARINE SURVEY
5A Church Street, Modbury,
Ivybridge, Devon PL21 0QW
Tel: 01548 830496
Mob: 07831 118056
Fax: 01548 830917
West Country YBDSA Surveyor, prompt
service.

Barbican Yacht Agency Ltd
Plymouth 01752 228855

Battick, Lee
St Helier 01534 611143

Booth Marine Surveys, Graham
Birchington-on-Sea 01843 843793

Byrde & Associates
Kimmeridge 01929 480064

Bureau Maritime Ltd
Maldon 01621 859181

Cannell & Associates, David M
Wivenhoe 01206 823337

**Cardiff Commercial Boat Operators
Ltd** Cardiff 029 2037 7872

CE Proof
Hamble 023 8045 3245

Clarke Designs LLP, Owen
Dartmouth 01803 770495

Cox, David Penryn 01326 340808

Davies, Peter N
Wivenhoe 01206 823289

Down Marine Co Ltd
Belfast 028 90480247

Evans, Martin
Kirby le Soken 01255 677883

Giles Naval Architects, Laurent
Lymington 01590 641777

Goodall, JL
Whitby 01947 604791

Green, James
Plymouth 01752 660516

Greening Yacht Design Ltd, David
Chichester 023 9263 1806

Hansing & Associates
North Wales/Midlands 01248 671291

**JP Services – Marine Safety &
Training** Chichester 01243 537552

Levy, Derek
Brighton 01273 721095

MacGregor, WA
Felixstowe 01394 676034

Mahoney & Co, KPO
Co Cork 00353 21 477 6150

Marintec
Lymington 01590 683414

McGarry, Mark
Port Dinorwic 01248 671023

Norwood Marine
Margate 01843 835711

Pritchard, Jim
Southampton 023 8045 5544

Quay Consultants Ltd
West Wittering 01243 673056

**Scott Marine Surveyors &
Consultants** Conwy 01248 680759

Stapley & Associates, Anthony
Southampton 023 8040 7407

Staton-Bevan, Tony
Lymington 01590 645755

Swanwick Yacht Surveyors
Southampton 01489 564822

Temple, Chris
Yarmouth 01983 760947

Thomas, Stephen
Southampton 023 8048 6273

Victoria Yacht Surveys
Cornwall 0800 093 2113

Ward & McKenzie
Ipswich 01473 255200

Ward & McKenzie (North East)
Pocklington 01759 304322

**YDSA Yacht Designers & Surveyors
Association** Bordon 0845 0900162

TAPE TECHNOLOGY

Adhesive Technologies
Braintree   01376 346511

CC Marine (Rubbaweld) Ltd
Chichester   01243 672606

Trade Grade Products Ltd
Poole   01202 820177

UK Epoxy Resins
Burscough   01704 892364

3M United Kingdom plc
Bracknell   01344 858315

TRANSPORT/YACHT DELIVERIES

Anglo European Boat Transport
Devon   01803 868691

Boat Shifters
        07733 344018/01326 210548

Convoi Exceptionnel Ltd
Hamble   023 8045 3045

East Coast Offshore Yachting
                         01480 861381

Forrest Marine Ltd
Exeter   01392 833504

Hainsworth's UK and Continental
Bingley   01274 565925

Houghton Boat Transport
Tewkesbury   07831 486710

Moonfleet Sailing
Poole   01202 682269

Ocean Yacht Deliveries
Mold   01352 740962

Performance Yachting
Plymouth   01752 565023

Peters & May Ltd
Southampton   023 8048 0480

Reeder School of Seamanship, Mike
Lymington   01590 674560

Sail North Wales
Conwy   01492 584208

Seafix Boat Transfer
North Wales   01766 514507

Sealand Boat Deliveries Ltd
Liverpool   01254 705225

Shearwater Sailing
Southampton   01962 775213

Southcoasting Navigators
Devon   01626 335626

West Country Boat Transport
                         01566 785651

Wolff, David   07659 550131

Yacht Care Ltd
Lymington   01590 688856

TUITION/SAILING SCHOOLS

Association of Scottish Yacht Charterers Argyll   01880 820012

Bisham Abbey Sailing & Navigation School Bisham   01628 474960

Blue Baker Yachts
Ipswich   01473 780008

Britannia Sailing (East Coast)
Ipswich   01473 787019

British Offshore Sailing School
Hamble   023 8045 7733

Coastal Sea School
Weymouth   0870 321 3271

Conwy School of Yachting
Conwy   01492 572999

Corsair Sailing
Banstead   01737 211466

Dart Sailing School
Dartmouth   01803 833973

Dartmouth Sailing
Dartmouth   01803 833399

Drake Sailing School
Plymouth   01635 253009

East Anglian Sea School
Ipswich   01473 659992

East Coast Offshore Yachting – Les Rant Perry   01480 861381

Five Star Sailing
Southampton   01489 885599

Fowey Cruising School
Fowey   01726 832129

Gibraltar Sailing Centre
Gibraltar   00350 78554

Go Sail Ltd East
Cowes   01983 280220

Hamble School of Yachting
Hamble   023 8045 6687

Haslar Marina & Victory Yacht Charters Gosport   023 9252 0099

Hobo Yachting
Southampton   023 8033 4574

Hoylake Sailing School
Wirral   0151 632 4664

Ibiza Sailing School   07092 235 853

International Yachtmaster Academy
Southampton   0800 515439

Island Sea School
Menai Strait   01977 680860

JP Services – Marine Safety & Training Chichester   01243 537552

LONGSCAR POWERBOATING
Lock Office, Hartlepool Marina,
Slake Terrace, Hartlepool
TS24 0RU
Tel: (01429) 292877
Fax: (01429) 292877
e-mail:
longscar@rya-online.net
www.longscarpowerboating.co.uk
RYA training centre and member of the
National Federation of Sea Schools. ICCs
and CEVNI tests at reasonable rates. All
levels of the RYA Powerboat scheme
taught in our boat or your own.
Recognised to teach all RYA shorebased
courses. BMF Basic Maintenance
courses available this winter.

Lymington Cruising School
Lymington 01590 677478

Menorca Cruising School
                         01995 679240

Moncur Sailing School, Bob
Newcastle upon Tyne   0191 265 4472

Moonfleet Sailing Poole 01202 682269

National Federation of Sea Schools,
The Woodlands   023 8029 3822

National Marine Correspondence
School Birkenhead   0151 647 6777

Northshore King's Lynn   01485 210236

On Deck Sailing
Southampton   023 8033 3887

Pembrokeshire Cruising
Neyland   01646 602500

Performance Yachting
Plymouth   01752 565023

Plain Sailing
Dartmouth   01803 853843

PLAS MENAI NATIONAL
WATERSPORTS CENTRE
Caernarfon, Gwynedd LL55 1UE
Tel: (01248) 670964
Fax: (01248) 670964
e-mail: plas.menai@scw.co.uk
www.plasmenai.co.uk
Practical and shore-based RYA sailing
courses, refresher & flotilla cruising
weekends around the North Wales coast,
Ireland, Isle of Man and southern Scotland
Competent Crew to Yachtmaster and
one-day shore-based safety and
navigation skills courses.

Plymouth Sailing School
Plymouth   01752 667170

Port Edgar Marina & Sailing School
Port Edgar   0131 331 3330

Portsmouth Outdoor Centre
Portsmouth   023 9266 3873

Portugal Sail & Power   01473 833001

Rainbow Sailing School
Swansea   01792 467813

Reeder School of Seamanship, Mike
Lymington   01590 674560

Safe Water Training Sea School Ltd
Wirral   0151 630 0466

Sail East Ipswich   01206 734319

Sally Water Training
East Cowes   01983 299033

Sea 'N' Ski Portsmouth   023 9246 6041

Seafever   01342 316293

Solaris Mediterranean Sea School
   01925 642909

Solent School of Yachting
Southampton   01489 577383

Southcoasting Navigators
Devon   01626 335626

Southern Sailing
Southampton   01489 575511

Start Point Sailing
Dartmouth   01548 810917

Sunsail
Port Solent/Largs   0870 770 6314

Team Sailing Gosport   023 9273 5199

The Dream Or Two Experience of
Yachting Portsmouth   0800 970 7845

Tiller School of Navigation
Banstead   01737 211466

Workman Marine School
Gloucester   01452 381157

Wride School of Sailing, Bob
North Ferriby   01482 635623

WATERSIDE ACCOMMODATION & RESTAURANTS

Abbey, The Penzance   01736 330680

Arun View Inn, The
Littlehampton   01903 722335

Baywatch on the Beach
Bembridge   01983 873259

Baywatch on the Harbour
Yarmouth   01983 760054

Beaucette Marina restaurant
Guernsey   01481 247066

Bella Napoli
Brighton Marina   01273 818577

Bembridge Coast Hotel
Bembridge   01983 873931

Budock Vean Hotel
Porth Navas Creek   01326 252100

Café Mozart Cowes   01983 293681

Caffé Uno Port Solent   023 9237 5227

Chandlers Bar & Bistro Queen Anne's
Battery Marina, Plymouth   01752 257772

Chiquito Port Solent   023 9220 1181

Critchards Seafood Restaurant
Porthleven   01326 562407

Cruzzo Malahide Marina, Co Dublin
   00353 1 845 0599

Cullins Yard Bistro
Dover   01304 211666

Custom House, The
Poole   01202 676767

Dart Marina River Lounge
Dartmouth   01803 832580

Deer Leap, The Exmouth 01395 265030

Doghouse Swanwick Marina,
Hamble   01489 571602

Dolphin Restaurant
Gorey   01534 853370

Doune Knoydart   01687 462667

El Puertos
Penarth Marina   029 2070 5551

Falmouth Marina Marine Bar and
Restaurant Falmouth   01326 313481

Ferry Boat Inn West Wick Marina,
Nr Chelmsford   01621 740208

Ferry Inn, The (restaurant)
Pembroke Dock   01646 682947

First and Last, The Braye,
Alderney   01481 823162

Fisherman's Wharf
Sandwich   01304 613636

Folly Inn Cowes   01983 297171

Gaffs Restaurant Fenit Harbour Marina,
County Kerry   00353 66 71 36666

Godleys Hotel Fenit,
County Kerry   00353 66 71 36108

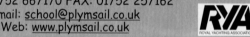

Harbour Lights Restaurant
Walton on the Naze   01255 851887

Haven Bar and Bistro, The
Lymington Yacht Haven   01590 679971

Haven Hotel Poole   01202 707333

HMS Ganges Restaurant
Mylor Yacht Harbour   01326 374320

Jolly Sailor, The
Bursledon   023 8040 5557

Kames Hotel Argyll   01700 811489

Ketch Rigger, The Hamble Point Marina
Hamble   023 8045 5601

La Cala Lady Bee Marina,
Shoreham   01273 597422

Las Margaritas Poole   01202 670066

Le Nautique
St Peter Port   01481 721714

Lighter Inn, The
Topsham   01392 875439

Mariners Bistro Sparkes Marina,
Hayling Island   023 9246 9459

Mary Mouse II Haslar Marina,
Gosport   023 9258 8810

Martha's Vineyard
Milford Haven   01646 697083

Master Builder's House Hotel
Buckler's Hard   01590 616253

Millstream Hotel
Bosham   01243 573234

Montagu Arms Hotel
Beaulieu   01590 612324

Olivo Port Solent   023 9220 1473

Oyster Quay Mercury Yacht Harbour,
Hamble   023 8045 7220

Paris Hotel Coverack   01326 280258

Pebble Beach, The
Gosport   023 9251 0789

Petit Champ Sark   01481 832046

Philip Leisure Group
Dartmouth   01803 833351

Priory Bay Hotel Seaview,
Isle of Wight   01983 613146

Quayside Hotel Brixham 01803 855751

Queen's Hotel Kirkwall 01856 872200

Sails Dartmouth   01803 839281

Sea View Hotel Braye,
Alderney   01481 822738

Sharksfin Waterside
Mevagissey   01726 843241

Shell Bay Seafood Restaurant
Poole Harbour   01929 450363

Simply Italian Sovereign Harbour,
Eastbourne   01323 470911

Slackwater Jacques
Port Solent   023 9278 0777

Spinnaker, The
Chichester Marina   01243 511032

Spit Sand Fort
The Solent   023 9250 4207

Smugglers, The Newlyn 01736 331501

Square Rigger, The Port Hamble Marina
Hamble   023 8045 3446

Steamboat Inn Lossiemouth Marina,
Lossiemouth   01343 812066

Sundeck, The
Mevagissey   01726 843051

Taps Shamrock Quay,
Southampton   023 8022 8621

Tayvallich Inn, The
Argyll   01546 870282

Thai Marina Sovereign Harbour,
Eastbourne   01323 470414

Top Deck Restaurant & Bar Southsea
Marina, Southsea   023 9287 4500

Villa Adriana Newhaven Marina
Newhaven   01903 722335

Warehouse Brasserie, The
Poole   01202 677238

Windrose Bar & Restaurant
Carrickfergus Marina,
Carrickfergus   028 9335 1164

36 on the Quay
Emsworth   01243 375592

WEATHER INFORMATION/ METEOROLOGICAL

MARINECALL
iTouch (UK) Ltd, Avalon House,
57-63 Scrutton Street, London
EC2A 4PF
Tel: (0870) 600 4219
Fax: (0870) 600 4229
e-mail: marinecall@itouch.co.uk
www.marinecall.co.uk
Marinecall - weather at sea. Specialist
weather forecasts for UK inshore /
coastal and offshore areas. 5 day reports
call 09068 505 200 (60p/min).

Met Office Bracknell   0845 300 0300

WIND POWER

Ampair Ringwood   01425 480780

LVM Limited Arlesey   01462 733336

MARLEC ENGINEERING CO LTD
Rutland House, Trevithick Road,
Corby, Northamptonshire
NN17 5XY
Tel: (01536) 201588
Fax: (01536) 400211
e-mail: sales@marlec.co.uk
www.marlec.co.uk
For wind and solar powered battery
charging on the board talk to Marlec. We
manufacture the Rutland Marine range of
wind windchargers, and import and
distribute BP Solar photovoltaic modules.
Manufacturer of Leisurelights - low energy
high efficiency 12v lamps.

WOOD FITTINGS

Howells & Son, KJ
Poole   01202 665724

Onward Trading Co Ltd
Southampton   023 8063 7810

Robbins Timber
Bristol   0117 963 3136

Sheraton Marine Cabinet
Witney   01993 868275

YACHT BROKERS

ABC Powermarine
Beaumaris   01248 811413

ABYA Association of Brokers & Yacht
Agents Bordon   0845 0900162

Adur Boat Sales
Southwick   01273 596680

Ancasta International Boat Sales
Southampton   023 8045 0000

Anglia Yacht Brokerage Bury St
Edmunds   01359 271747

ARDFERN YACHT CENTRE LTD
Ardfern by Lochgilphead,
Argyll, PA31 8QN
Tel: (01852) 500247/636
Fax: (01852) 500624
e-mail: office@ardfernyacht.co.uk
www.ardfernyacht.co.uk
Boatyard with full repairs and
maintenance facilities. Timber and GRP
repairs, painting and engineering.
Sheltered moorings and pontoon
berthing. Winter storage, chandlery,
showers, fuel, Calor, 20-ton boat hoist,
rigging. Hotel, bars and restaurant.

Ardmair Boat Centre
Ullapool   01854 612054

Assured Boating Egham 01784 473300

Barbican Yacht Agency, The
Plymouth   01752 228855

Bates Wharf Marine Sales Ltd
                                      01932 571141

BJ Marine
Bangor   028 9127 1434

BLUE BAKER YACHTS
Charter & Brokerage
Management.
Woolverstone Marina,
Woolverstone, Ipswich, Suffolk
IP9 1AS
Tel: (01473) 780111 / 780008
Fax: (01473) 780911
e-mail:
brokerage@bluebakeryachts.com
www.bluebakeryachts.com
Blue Baker Yacht Management, East
Coast Brokerage and Charter
Management for bareboat, skippered and
corporate yacht charters. Sales of new
and used yachts.

Bluewater Horizons
Weymouth   01305 782080

Boatworks + Ltd
St Peter Port   01481 726071

Caley Marina Inverness 01463 236539

Calibra Marine International Ltd
Southampton   08702 400358

Carne (Sales) Ltd, David
Falmouth   01326 318314

Carne (Sales) Ltd, David
Penryn   01326 374177

Carrick Marine Projects
Co Antrim   02893 355884

Carroll's Ballyhack Boatyard
New Ross   00353 51 389164

Chichester Harbour Brokerage
Emsworth   0845 345 1473

CJ Marine Mechanical
Troon   01292 313400

Clarke & Carter Interyacht Ltd
Ipswich/Burnham on Crouch
01473 659681/01621 785600

Coastal Leisure Ltd
Southampton   023 8033 2222

Dale Sailing Brokerage
Neyland   01646 603105

Deacons
Southampton   023 8040 2253

Dex-Tamar Marine
Plymouth   01752 491454

DICKIES OF BANGOR
36 Garth Road, Bangor,
Gwynedd LL57 2SE
Tel: (01248) 363400
Fax: (01248) 354169
e-mail: info@dickies.co.uk
www.dickies.co.uk
Full yard services, chandlery, brokerage
and new boat dealers for Beneteau Sail
and power boats and Lagoon power
catamarans.

Exe Leisure
Essex Marina   01702 258190

Ferrypoint Boat Co
Youghal   00353 24 94232

Gweek Quay Boatyard
Helston   01326 221657

International Barge & Yacht Brokers
Southampton   023 8045 5205

Iron Wharf Boatyard
Faversham   01795 537122

Jackson Yacht Services
Jersey   01534 743819

Kings Yacht Agency
Beaulieu/Southampton
01590 616316/023 8033 1533

Kippford Slipway Ltd
Dalbeattie   01556 620249

Knox-Johnston, Paul
Southsea   023 9286 4524

Lencraft Boats Ltd
Dungarvan   00353 58 68220

Liberty Yachts Ltd
Plymouth   01752 227911

Lucas Yachting, Mike
Torquay   01803 212840

Network Yacht Brokers
Dartmouth   01803 834864

Network Yacht Brokers
Plymouth   01752 605377

New Horizon Yacht Agency
Guernsey   01481 726335

Oyster Brokerage Ltd
Ipswich   01473 602263

Pearn and Co, Norman
(Looe Boatyard) Looe   01503 262244

Performance Boat Company
Maidenhead   07768 464717

Peters Chandlery
Chichester   01243 511033

Portavon Marina
Keynsham   0117 986 1626

Prosser Marine Sales Ltd
Glasgow   0141 552 2005

Retreat Boatyard
Topsham   01392 874720

Scanyachts
Southampton   023 8045 5608

SD Marine Ltd
Southampton   023 8045 7278

Sea & Shore Ship Chandler
Dundee   01382 202666

South Pier Shipyard
St Helier   01534 519700

South West Yacht Brokers Group
Plymouth   01752 551991

Sunbird Marine Services
Fareham   01329 842613

Trafalgar Yacht Services
Fareham   01329 823577

Transworld Yachts
Hamble   023 8045 7704

WA Simpson Marine Ltd
Dundee   01382 566670

Walton Marine Sales
Brighton   01273 670707

Walton Marine Sales
Portishead   01275 840132

Walton Marine Sales
Wroxham   01603 781178

Watson Marine, Charles
Hamble   023 8045 6505

Western Marine
Dublin   00353 1280 0321

Westways of Plymouth Ltd
Plymouth   01752 670770

Woodrolfe Brokerage
Maldon   01621 868494

Youngboats Faversham   01795 536176

YACHT CHARTERS & HOLIDAYS

Ardmair Boat Centre
Ullapool   01854 612054

Association of Scottish Yacht
Charterers Argyll   01880 820012

Blue Baker Yachts
Ipswich   01473 780111/780008

Coastal Leisure Ltd
Southampton   023 8033 2222

Crusader Yachting
Turkey   01732 867321

Dart Sailing Charters
Dartmouth   01803 833973

Dartmouth Sailing
Dartmouth   01803 833399

Dartmouth Yacht Charters
Dartmouth   01803 883718

Doune Marine Mallaig   01687 462667

Elizabethan Charters (Dartmouth)
Bristol   0117 9615739

Four Seasons Yacht Charter
Gosport   023 9251 1789

Golden Black Sailing
Cornwall   01209 715757

Hamble Point Yacht Charters
Hamble   023 8045 7110

Haslar Marina & Victory Yacht
Charters Gosport   023 9252 0099

Indulgence Charters
Wendover   01296 696006

ISLE OF SKYE YACHTS
Ardvasar, Isle of Skye IV45 8RS
Tel: 01471 844216
Fax: 01471 844387
e-mail:
enquiries@isleofskyeyachts.co.uk
www.isleofskyeyachts.co.uk
Bareboat and Skippered Yacht Charter,
boat repairs, servicing, moorings,
supplies.

Liberty Yachts West Country, Greece,
Mallorca & Italy   01752 227911

Nautilus Yachting Mediterranean &
Caribbean   01732 867445

Patriot Charters & Sail School
Milford Haven   01437 741202

Plain Sailing Yacht Charters
Dartmouth   01803 853843

Portway Yacht Charters
Plymouth/Falmouth
01752 606999/01326 212320

PT Yacht Charters
Portsmouth   023 9252 1585

Puffin Yachts
Port Solent 01483 420728

Rainbow Sailing School
Swansea 01792 467813

Sailing Holidays Ltd
Mediterranean 020 8459 8787

Sailing Holidays in Ireland
Kinsale 00353 21 477 2927

Setsail Holidays Greece, Turkey,
Croatia, Majorca 01787 310445

Shannon Sailing Ltd
Tipperary 00353 67 24499

Sleat Marine Services
Isle of Skye 01471 844216

Smart Yachts
Mediterranean 01425 614804

Sunsail Worldwide 0870 770 0102

Templecraft Yacht Charters
Lewes 01273 812333

Top Yacht Charter Ltd
Worldwide 01243 520950

West Wales Yacht Charter
Pwllheli 07748 634869

Westward Ho Sailing Ltd
UK and Greece 01633 760970

Westways of Plymouth Ltd
Plymouth 01752 481200

39 North (Mediterranean)
Kingskerswell 07071 393939

407 Racing (Yacht Charter)
Lymington 01590 688407

YACHT CLUBS

Aberaeron YC
Aberdovey 01545 570077

Aberdeen and Stonehaven SC
Nr Inverurie 01569 764006

Aberdour BC Aberdour 01383 860632

Abersoch Power BC
Abersoch 01758 712027

Aberystwyth BC
Aberystwyth 01970 624575

Aldeburgh YC Aldeburgh 01728 452562

Alderney SC Alderney 01481 822959

Alexandra YC
Southend-on-Sea 01702 340363

Arklow SC Arklow 00353 402 33100

Arun YC Littlehampton 01903 716016

Axe YC Axemouth 01297 20043

Ayr Yacht and CC Ayr 01292 476034

Ballyholme YC Bangor 028 91271467

Baltimore SC
Baltimore 00353 28 20426

Banff SC Cults 01261 815296

Bantry Bay SC Bantry 00353 27 50081

Barry YC Barry 01446 735511

Beaulieu River SC
Brockenhurst 01590 616273

Bembridge SC
Isle of Wight 01983 872686

Benfleet YC
Canvey Island 01268 792278

**Blackpool and
Fleetwood YC** 01253 884205

Blackwater SC Maldon 01621 853923

Blundellsands SC 0151 929 2101

Bosham SC Chichester 01243 572341

Brading Haven YC
Isle of Wight 01983 872289

Bradwell CC Bradwell 01621 892970

Bradwell Quay YC
Wickford 01268 776539

Brancaster Staithe SC 01485 210249

Brandy Hole YC
Hullbridge 01702 230320

Brightlingsea SC
Colchester 01206 303275

Brighton Marina YC
Peacehaven 01273 818711

Bristol Avon SC Bristol 01225 873472

Bristol Channel YC
Swansea 01792 366000

Bristol Corinthian YC
Axbridge 01934 732033

Brixham YC Brixham 01803 853332

**Burnham Overy
Staithe SC** 01328 730961

Burnham-on-Crouch SC
Burnham-on-Crouch 01621 782812

Burnham-on-Sea SC
Bridgwater 01278 792911

Burry Port YC
Burry Port 01554 833635

Cabot CC 0117 9514389

Caernarfon SC (Menai Strait)
Caernarfon 01286 672861

Campbeltown SC
Campbeltown 01586 552488

Cardiff YC Cardiff 029 2046 3697

Cardiff Bay YC Cardiff 029 20226575

Carlingford Lough YC
Rostrevor 028 4173 8604

Carrickfergus SC
Whitehead 028 93 351402

Castle Cove SC
Weymouth 01305 783708

Castlegate Marine Club
Stockton on Tees 01642 583299

Chanonry SC Fortrose 01463 221415

Chichester Cruiser and Racing Club
01483 770391

Chichester YC
Chichester 01243 512918

Christchurch SC
Christchurch 01202 483150

Clyde CC Glasgow 0141 221 2774

Co Antrim YC
Carrickfergus 028 9337 2322

Cobnor Activities Centre Trust
01243 572791

Coleraine YC Coleraine 028 703 44503

Colne YC Brightlingsea 01206 302594

Conwy YC Deganwy 01492 583690

Coquet YC 01665 711179

Corrib Rowing & YC
Galway City 00353 91 564560

Cowes Combined Clubs
01983 295744

Cowes Corinthian YC
Isle of Wight 01983 296333

Cowes Yachting 01983 280770

Cramond BC 0131 336 1356

Creeksea SC
Burnham-on-Crouch 01245 320578

Crookhaven SC
Crookhaven 087 2379997 mobile

Crouch YC
Burnham-on-Sea 01278 782252

Dale YC Dale 01646 636362

Dartmouth YC
Dartmouth 01803 832305

Deben YC Woodbridge 01394 385400

Dell Quay SC Chichester 01243 785080

Dingle SC Dingle 00353 66 51984

Douglas Bay YC
Douglas 01624 673965

Dovey YC Aberdovey 01654 767607

Dun Laoghaire MYC 00353 1 288 938

Dunbar SC
Cockburnspath 01368 86287

East Antrim BC Antrim 028 28 277204

East Belfast YC Belfast 028 9065 6283

East Cowes SC
Isle of Wight 01983 531687

East Dorset SC Poole 01202 706111

East Lothian YC 01620 892698

Eastney Cruising Association
Portsmouth 023 92734103

Eling SC 023 80863987

Emsworth SC Emsworth 01243 372850

Emsworth Slipper SC
Emsworth 01243 372523

Epic Ventures Ltd
Cowes 01983 291292

Essex YC Southend 01702 478404

Exe SC (River Exe)
Exemouth 01395 264607

Eyott SC Mayland 01245 320703

Fairlie YC 01294 213940

Falmouth Town SC
Falmouth 01326 373915

Falmouth Watersports Association
Falmouth 01326 211223

Fareham Sailing & Motor BC
Fareham 01329 233324

Felixstowe Ferry SC
Felixstowe 01394 283785

Findhorn YC Findhorn 01309 690247

Fishguard Bay YC
Lower Fishguard 01348 872866

Flushing SC Falmouth 01326 374043

Folkestone Yacht and Motor BC
Folkestone 01303 251574

Forth Corinthian YC
Haddington 0131 552 5939

Forth YCs Association
Edinburgh 0131 552 3006

Fowey Gallants SC
Fowey 01726 832335

Foynes YC Foynes 00353 69 91201

Galway Bay SC 00353 91 794527

Glasson SC Lancaster 01524 751089

Glenans Irish Sailing School
00353 1 6611481

Glenans Irish SC (Westport)
00353 98 26046

Gosport CC Gosport 02392 586838

Gravesend SC
Gravesend 01474 533974

Greenwich YC London 020 8858 7339

Grimsby and Cleethorpes YC
Grimsby 01472 356678

Guernsey YC
St Peter Port 01481 722838

Halfway YC 01702 582025

Hamble River SC
Southampton 023 80452070

Hampton Pier YC
Herne Bay 01227 364749

Hardway SC Gosport 02392 581875

Hartlepool YC
Hartlepool 01429 233423

Harwich Town SC
Harwich 01255 503200

Hastings and St Leonards YC
Hastings 01424 420656

Haven Ports YC
Woodbridge 01394 659658

Hayling Ferry SC; Locks SC
Hayling Island 023 80829833

Hayling Island SC
Hayling Island 023 92463768

Helensburgh SC Rhu 01436 672778

Helensburgh 01436 821234

Helford River SC
Helston 01326 231006

Herne Bay SC
Herne Bay 01227 375650

Highcliffe SC
Christchurch 01425 274874

Holyhead SC Holyhead 01407 762526

Holywood YC Holywood 028 90423355

Hoo Ness YC Sidcup 01634 250052

Hornet SC Gosport 02392 580403

Howth YC Howth 00353 1 832 2141

Hoylake SC Wirral 0151 632 2616

Hullbridge YC 01702 231797

Humber Yawl Club 01724 733458

Hurlingham YC London 020 8788 5547

Hythe SC Southampton 023 80846563

Ilfracombe YC
Ilfracombe 01271 863969

Iniscealtra SC
Limerick 00353 61 338347

Invergordon BC 01349 877612

Irish CC 00353 214870031

Island CC Salcombe 01548 531176

Island SC Isle of Wight 01983 296621

Island YC Canvey Island 01268 510360

Isle of Bute SC
Rothesay 01700 502819

Isle of Man YC
Port St Mary 01624 832088

Itchenor SC Chichester 01243 512400

Keyhaven YC Keyhaven 01590 642165

Killyleagh YC
Killyleagh 028 4482 8250

Kircubbin SC
Kirkcubbin 028 4273 8422

Kirkcudbright SC
Kirkcudbright 01557 331727

Langstone SC Havant 023 92484577

Largs SC Largs 01475 670000

Larne Rowing & SC
Larne 028 2827 4573

Lawrenny YC 01646 651212

Leigh-on-Sea SC 01702 476788

Lerwick BC Lerwick 01595 696954

Lilliput SC Poole 01202 740319

**Littlehampton Sailing and Motor
Club** Littlehampton 01903 715859

Loch Ryan SC Stranraer 01776 706322

Lochaber YC Fort William 01397 772361

Locks SC Portsmouth 023 92829833

Looe SC Looe 01503 262559

Lossiemouth CC
Fochabers 01348 812121

Lough Swilly YC Fahn 00353 74 22377

Lowestoft CC
Lowestoft 01502 574376

Lyme Regis Power BC
Lyme Regis 01297 443788

Lyme Regis SC
Lyme Regis 01297 442800

Lymington Town SC
Lymington 0159 674514

Lympstone SC Exeter 01395 264152

Madoc YC Porthmadog 01766 512976

Malahide YC
Malahide 00353 1 845 3372

Maldon Little Ship Club
01621 854139

Manx Sailing & CC
Ramsey 01624 813494

Marchwood YC
Marchwood 023 80666141

Margate YC Margate 01227 292602

Marina BC Pwllheli 01758 612271

Maryport YC 01228 560865

Mayflower SC Plymouth 01752 662526

Mayo SC (Rosmoney)
Rosmoney 00353 98 27772

Medway YC Rochester 01634 718399

Menai Bridge BC
Beaumaris 01248 810583

Mengham Rythe SC
Hayling Island 023 92463337

Merioneth YC
Barmouth 01341 280000

Monkstone Cruising and SC
Swansea 01792 812229

Montrose SC Montrose 01674 672554

Mumbles YC Swansea 01792 369321

Mylor YC Falmouth 01326 374391

Nairn SC Nairn 01667 453897

National YC
Dun Laoghaire 00353 1 280 5725

Netley SC Netley 023 80454272

New Quay YC
Aberdovey 01545 560516

Newhaven & Seaford SC
Seaford 01323 890077

Newport and Uskmouth SC
Cardiff 01633 271417

Newtownards SC
Newtownards 028 9181 3426

Neyland YC Neyland 01646 600267

North Devon YC
Bideford 01271 860367

North Fambridge Yacht Centre
01621 740370

North Haven YC Poole 01202 708830

**North of England Yachting
Association** Kirkwall 01856 872331

North Sunderland Marine Club
Sunderland 01665 721231

North Wales CC
Conwy 01492 593481

**North West Venturers YC
(Beaumaris)** Beaumaris 0161 2921943

Oban SC Ledaig by Oban
01631 563999

Orford SC Woodbridge 01394 450444

Orkney SC Kirkwall 01856 872331

Orwell YC Ipswich 01473 602288

Oulton Broad Yacht Station
01502 574946

Ouse Amateur SC
Kings Lynn 01553 772239

Paignton SC Paignton 01803 525817

Parkstone YC Poole 01202 743610

Peel Sailing and CC
Peel 01624 842390

Pembroke Haven YC 01646 684403

Pembrokeshire YC
Milford Haven 01646 692799

Penarth YC Penarth 029 20708196

Pentland Firth YC
Thurso 01847 891803

Penzance YC Penzance 01736 364989

Peterhead SC Ellon 01779 75527

Pin Mill SC Woodbridge 01394 780271

Plym YC Plymouth 01752 404991

Poolbeg YC 00353 1 660 4681

Poole YC Poole 01202 672687

Porlock Weir SC
Watchet 01643 862702

Port Edgar YC Penicuik 01968 674210

Port Navas YC
Falmouth 01326 340065

Port of Falmouth Sailing Association
Falmouth 01326 372927

Portchester SC
Portchester 01329 376375

Porthcawl Harbour BC
Swansea 01656 655935

Porthmadog & Trawsfynydd SC
Talsarnau 01766 513546

Portrush YC Portrush 028 70 823932

Portsmouth SC
Portsmouth 02392 820596

Prestwick SC Prestwick 01292 671117

Pwllheli SC Pwllheli 01758 613343

Queenborough YC
Queenborough 01795 663955

Quoile YC
Downpatrick 028 44 612266

R Towy BC Tenby 01267 241755

RAFYC 023 80452208

Redclyffe YC Poole 01929 557227

Restronguet SC
Falmouth 01326 374536

Ribble CC
Lytham St Anne's 01253 739983

River Wyre YC 01253 811948

RNSA (Plymouth)
Plymouth 01752 55123/83

Rochester CC
Rochester 01634 841350

Rock Sailing and Water Ski Club
Wadebridge 01208 862431

Royal Dart YC
Dartmouth 01803 752496

Royal Motor YC Poole 01202 707227

Royal Anglesey YC (Beaumaris)
Anglesey 01248 810295

Royal Burnham YC
Burnham-on-Crouch 01621 782044

Royal Channel Islands YC (Jersey)
St Aubin 01534 745783

Royal Cinque Ports YC
Dover 01304 206262

**Royal Corinthian YC
(Burnham-on-Crouch)**
Burnham-on-Crouch 01621 782105

Royal Corinthian YC (Cowes)
Cowes 01983 292608

Royal Cork YC
Crosshaven 00353 21 831023

Royal Cornwall YC (RCYC)
Falmouth 01326 312126

Royal Dorset YC
Weymouth 01305 786258

Royal Forth YC
Edinburgh 0131 552 3006

Royal Fowey YC Fowey 01726 833573

Royal Gourock YC
Gourock 01475 632983

ROYAL HARWICH YACHT CLUB
**Marina Road, Woolverstone,
Ipswich, Suffolk IP9 1AT
Tel: 01473 780319
Fax: 01473 780919
e-mail:
secretary@rhyc.demon.co.uk
www.rhyc.demon.co.uk**
40 berth members marina. Fully serviced
berths for visitors. Shower, toilet & laundry
facilities. Bar & restaurant. Car parking.
Visitors especially welcomed.

Royal Highland YC
Connel 01546 510261

Royal Irish YC
Dun Laoghaire 00353 1 280 9452

Royal London YC
Isle of Wight 019 83299727

Royal Lymington YC
Lymington 01590 672677

Royal Mersey YC
Birkenhead 0151 645 3204

Royal Motor YC Poole 01202 707227

ROYAL
HARWICH
YACHT CLUB

Visit the Club Marina on the River Orwell
and enjoy some of the best river views on the
East Coast.

There is a warm welcome for visitors – just
come alongside the hammer heads which are
kept free for visitors.

For further information, contact the Club on
01473 780319 during office hours
or contact Geoff Prentice, our Berth Master,
at weekends on 07742 145 994.

2004/M&WMD13/j

**Royal Naval Club and Royal Albert
YC** Portsmouth 023 9282 5924

Royal Naval Sailing Association
Gosport 023 9252 1100

Royal Norfolk & Suffolk YC
Lowestoft 01502 566726

Royal North of Ireland YC
028 90 428041

Royal Northern and Clyde YC
Rhu 01436 820322

Royal Northumberland YC
Blyth 01670 353636

Royal Plymouth Corinthian YC
Plymouth 01752 664327

Royal Scottish Motor YC
0141 881 1024

Royal Solent YC
Yarmouth 01983 760256

Royal Southampton YC
Southampton 023 8022 3352

Royal Southern YC
Southampton 023 8045 0300

Royal St George YC
Dun Laoghaire 00353 1 280 1811

Royal Tay YC Dundee 01382 477516

Royal Temple YC
Ramsgate 01843 591766

Royal Torbay YC
Torquay 01803 292006

Royal Ulster YC
Bangor 028 91 270568

Royal Victoria YC
Fishbourne 01983 882325

Royal Welsh YC (Caernarfon)
Caernarfon 01286 672599

Royal Welsh YC
Aernarfon 01286 672599

Royal Western YC
Plymouth 01752 660077

Royal Yacht Squadron
Isle of Wight 01983 292191

Royal Yorkshire YC
Bridlington 01262 672041

Rye Harbour SC Rye 01797 223136

Salcombe YC Salcombe 01548 842593

Saltash SC Saltash 01752 845988

Scalloway BC Lerwick 01595 880409

Scarborough YC
Scarborough 01723 373821

Schull SC Schull 00353 28 37352

Scillonian Sailing and BC
St Mary's 01720 277229

Seasalter SC
Whitstable 01227 264784

Seaview YC
Isle of Wight 01983 613268

Shoreham SC Henfield 01273 453078

Skerries SC
Carlingdford Lough 00353 1 849 1233

Slaughden SC Duxford 01223 835395

Sligo YC Sligo 00353 71 77168

Solva Boat Owners Association
Fishguard 01437 721538

Solway YC
Kirkdudbright 01556 620312

South Caernavonshire YC
Abersoch 01758 712338

South Cork SC 00353 28 36383

South Devon Sailing School
Newton Abbot 01626 52352

**South Gare Marine Club - Sail
Section** Middlesbrough 01642 453031

South Shields SC
South Shields 0191 456 5821

South Woodham Ferrers YC
Chelmsford 01245 325391

Southampton SC
Southampton 023 80446575

Southwold SC 01502 716776

Sovereign Harbour YC
Eastbourne 01323 470888

St Helier YC
St Helier 01534 721307/32229

St Mawes SC
St Mawes 01326 270686

Starcross Fishing & CC (River Exe)
Starcross 01626 891996

Starcross YC
Exeter 01626 890470

Stoke SC Ipswich 01473 780815

Stornoway SC
Stornoway 01851 705412

Stour SC 01206 393924

Strangford Lough YC
Newtownards 028 97 541883

Strangford SC
Downpatrick 028 4488 1404

Strood YC
Aylesford 01634 718261

Sunderland YC
Sunderland 0191 567 5133

Sunsail Portsmouth 023 92222224

Sussex YC
Shoreham-by-Sea 01273 464868

Swanage SC
Swanage 01929 422987

Swansea Yacht & Sub-Aqua Club
Swansea 01792 469096

Tamar River SC
Plymouth 01752 362741

Tarbert Lochfyne YC
Tarbert 01880 820376

Tay Corinthian BC
Dundee 01382 553534

Tay YCs Association 01738 621860

Tees & Hartlepool YC 01429 233423

Tees SC
Aycliffe Village 01429 265400

Teifi BC - Cardigan Bay
Fishguard 01239 613846

Teign Corinthian YC
Teignmouth 01626 772734

Tenby SC
Tenby 01834 842762

Tenby YC 01834 842762

Thames Estuary YC 01702 345967

Thorney Island SC
Thorney Island 01243 371731

Thorpe Bay YC 01702 587563

Thurrock YC
Grays 01375 373720

Tollesbury CC
Tollesbury 01621 869561

Topsham SC
Topsham 01392 877524

Torpoint Mosquito SC -
Plymouth 01752 812508

Tralee SC
Tralee 00353 66 36119

Troon CC
Troon 01292 311908

Troon YC
Troon 01292 315315

Tudor SC
Portsmouth 023 92662002

Tynemouth SC
Newcastle upon Tyne 0191 2572167

Up River YC
Hullbridge 01702 231654

Upnor SC
Upnor 01634 718043

Wakering YC
Rochford 01702 530926

Waldringfield SC
Wickham Market 01728 736633

Walls Regatta Club
Lerwick 01595 809273

Walton & Frinton YC
Walton-on-the-Naze 01255 675526

Warrenpoint BC
Warrenpoint 028 4175 2137

Warsash SC
Southampton 023 80583575

Watchet Boat Owner Association
Watchet 01984 633736

Waterford Harbour SC
Dunmore East 00353 51 383230

Watermouth YC
Watchet 01271 865048

Wear Boating Association
0191 567 5313

Wells SC
Wells-next-the-sea 01328 711190

West Kirby SC
West Kirby 0151 625 5579

West Mersea YC
Colchester 01206 382947

Western Isles YC 01688 302371

Western YC
Kilrush 00353 87 2262885

Weston Bay YC
Portishead 01275 620772

Weston CC
Southampton 07905 557298

Weston SC
Southampton 023 80452527

Wexford HBC
Wexford 00353 53 22039

Weymouth SC
Weymouth 01305 785481

Whitby YC
Whitby 01947 603623

Whitstable YC
Whitstable 01227 272343

Wicklow SC
Wicklow 00353 404 67526

Witham SC
Boston 01205 363598

Wivenhoe SC
Colchester 01206 822132

Woodbridge CC
Woodbridge 01394 386737

Wormit BC 01382 553878

Yarmouth SC
Yarmouth 01983 760270

Yealm YC
Newton Ferrers 01752 872291

Youghal Sailing Club
Youghal 00353 24 92447

YACHT DESIGNERS

Cannell & Associates, David M
Wivenhoe 01206 823337

Clarke Designs LLP, Owen
Dartmouth 01803 770495

Giles Naval Architects, Laurent
Lymington 01590 641777

Greening Yacht Design Ltd
Chichester 023 9263 1806

Harvey Design, Ray
Barton on Sea 01425 613492

Jones Yacht Design, Stephen
Warsash 01489 576439

Wharram Designs, James
Truro 01872 864792

Wolstenholme Yacht Design
Coltishall 01603 737024

YACHT MANAGEMENT

Barbican Yacht Agency Ltd
Plymouth 01752 228855

Coastal Leisure Ltd
Southampton 023 8033 2222

O'Sullivan Boat Management
Dun Laoghaire 00353 86 829 6625

Swanwick Yacht Surveyors
Swanwick 01489 564822

407 Racing (Yacht Charter)
Lymington 01590 688407

YACHT VALETING

Blackwell, Craig
Co Meath 00353 87 677 9605

Bright 'N' Clean
South Coast 07789 494430

BoatScrubber International
Haslar Marina, Gosport 023 9251 0567

Clean It All
Nr Brixham 01803 844564

Kip Marina Inverkip 01475 521485

Mainstay Yacht Maintenance
Dartmouth 01803 839076

Marine Gleam
Lymington 0800 074 4672

Mobile Yacht Maintenance
07900 148806

Smart Yachts
Bangor 028 9127 5932

Smith Boat Care, Paul
Isle of Wight 01983 754726

Yacht Care Ltd
Lymington 01590 688856

INDEX OF ADVERTISERS

MARINE SUPPLIES AND SERVICES GUIDE

YACHT CLUBS · YACHT VALETING

Leave the rest to us

GPS 72

GPSMAP 176c

GPSMAP 182c

GPS navigation - the ultimate crew member

GPSMAP 2010c

Brighter resolution screens & faster redraw rates

Whether you venture high open seas or secluded inland waters, GARMIN has a chartplotter or handheld unit for you. Our new range of GPS chartplotters have brighter 16-colour transflective screens. They are clearly visible in direct sunlight and have higher-speed processors with rapid redraw rates. Plus, with GARMIN's revolutionary new 'BlueChart™' marine cartography, your course is clearly mapped out.

GARMIN

GARMIN (Europe) Ltd, Unit 5, The Quadrangle, Abbey Park Industrial Estate, Romsey, Hampshire SO51 9DL UK. Tel: 0870 850 1241. Fax: 0870 850 1251. www.garmin.com

004/NC17/d

REEDS

Printed Products **2004**

Take a look at our latest range of updated products, complete with an easy to use order form for your convenience..

Almanacs

Handbooks

Cruising Companions

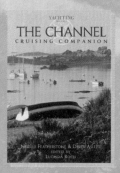
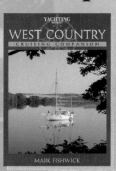
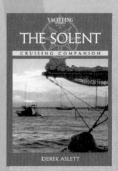
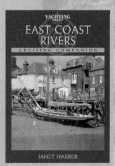

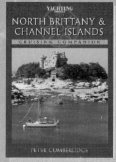

www.nauticaldata.com

THE 2004 REEDS REGIONAL ALMANACS

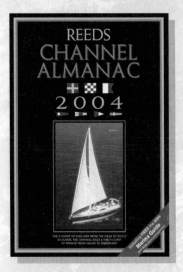

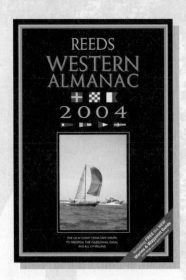

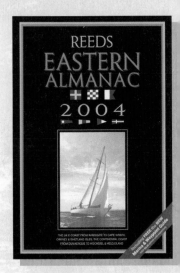

Reeds Channel Almanac 2004
The Reeds Channel Almanac offers essential data for the South coast of England from the Isles of Scilly to Dover, the Channel Islands and northern France from Calais to L'Aberildut.

Reeds Western Almanac 2004
including Ireland
The Western Almanac offers the cruising and racing yachtsman ready access to essential information by virtue of its clear layout and user friendly format.

Reeds Eastern Almanac 2004
including Orkney & Shetland Isles
The Eastern Almanac offers easy access to vital information on the UK East coast from Ramsgate to Cape Wrath and Helgoland to Gravelines.

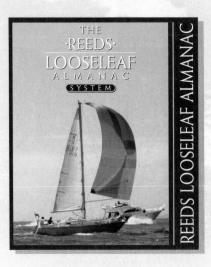

Reeds Looseleaf Almanac
• UK, Ireland, and Continental Europe
Update Packs
• UK, Ireland, and Continental Europe

• **Versatile**

• **Value for money**

• **Convenient**

• **Flexible**

• **Updateable**

PBO Small Craft Almanac 2004
In a practical, handy forma the PBO Small Craft Almanac contains many unique features and represents excellent value

Description	Price
Reeds Channel Alamanac	£23.95
Reeds Western Alamanac	£22.95
Reeds Eastern Alamanac	£21.95
Reeds Looseleaf Almanac (includes binder)	£34.95
Reeds Looseleaf Update Pack	£16.50
PBO Small Craft Alamanac	£12.95